DATE DUE

MAR 7 '77			
NOV 25 '81			
2-24-99			

MAN AND CULTURE IN THE LATE PLEISTOCENE

MAN AND CULTURE

Chandler Publications in
ANTHROPOLOGY *and* SOCIOLOGY
Leonard Broom, *General Editor*
L. L. Langness, *Editor*

RICHARD G. KLEIN
Northwestern University

With a Foreword by
F. CLARK HOWELL
University of Chicago

IN THE LATE PLEISTOCENE / A CASE STUDY

Chandler Publishing Company

124 Spear Street, San Francisco, California 94105

Distributed by Science Research Associates, Inc., A Subsidiary of IBM
259 East Erie Street, Chicago, Illinois 60611

Library of Congress Catalog Card No. 69–11254
Printed in the United States of America

To P. I. Boriskovskij,
P. P. Efimenko,
A. N. Rogachev,
S. N. Zamyatnin,
and the other Soviet scientists
upon whose splendid research
this book is based

CONTENTS

Preface xix

Foreword, by F. Clark Howell xxi

chapter 1. *Introduction* 1
THE PLEISTOCENE 1
THE PURPOSE OF THIS BOOK 4

chapter 2. *The Cultural Remains of Pleistocene Man* 7
FEATURES AND ARTIFACTS 7
STONE ARTIFACTS 8
NONSTONE ARTIFACTS 20
ARTIFACTS AND PLEISTOCENE PREHISTORY 22

chapter 3. *The History of Investigation of the Kostenki-Borshevo Sites* 25

INTRODUCTION 25
SITE, CULTURAL HORIZON, AND OCCUPATION HORIZON 26
THE HISTORY OF DISCOVERY OF THE KOSTENKI-BORSHEVO SITES 26

chapter 4. *The Geology of the Kostenki-Borshevo Sites* 33
INTRODUCTION 33
THE GEOLOGY OF THE KOSTENKI-BORSHEVO REGION 36
RADIOCARBON DATING OF KOSTENKI-BORSHEVO SITES 45
THE GEOLOGICAL AGE OF THE KOSTENKI-BORSHEVO SITES 47

chapter 5. *The Environment of Pleistocene Man in the Kostenki-Borshevo Region* 51
THE MODERN SETTING OF KOSTENKI AND BORSHEVO 51
FLORAL REMAINS AND PAST KOSTENKI-BORSHEVO ENVIRONMENT 52
FAUNAL REMAINS AND PAST KOSTENKI-BORSHEVO ENVIRONMENT 62
SUMMARY AND CONCLUSIONS 70

chapter 6. *Human Remains from the Kostenki-Borshevo Sites* 71

chapter 7. *Sites in the Lower Humic Bed on the Second Terrace* 75
KOSTENKI I-HORIZON 5, STRELETSKAYA II, KOSTENKI XII-HORIZON 3, AND ANOSOVKA II (= KOSTENKI XI)-HORIZON 5 76
KOSTENKI XVII-HORIZON 2 81
TEL'MANSKAYA-HORIZON 4, MARKINA GORA-HORIZON 4, KOSTENKI V-HORIZON 3, AND KOSTENKI XII-HORIZON 2 84
CONCLUSIONS 84

chapter 8. *Sites in the Upper Humic Bed on the Second Terrace* 87

MARKINA GORA-HORIZON 3 AND TEL'MANSKAYA-HORIZON 3 89
GORODTSOVSKAYA AND KOSTENKI XII-HORIZON 1B 92
TEL'MANSKAYA-HORIZON 2 99
KOSTENKI XVII-HORIZON 1 102
KOSTENKI XVI-HORIZONS 1 AND 2 102
MARKINA GORA-HORIZON 2 106
KOSTENKI XII-HORIZON 1A 107
ANOSOVKA II-HORIZON 4, KOSTENKI VII-HORIZONS 1 AND 2, AND KOSTENKI I-HORIZON 4 107
SUMMARY 108

chapter 9. *Sites Overlying the Upper Humic Bed on the Second Terrace* 109
KOSTENKI I-HORIZON 3 112
KOSTENKI I-HORIZON 2 112
KOSTENKI I-HORIZON 1, KOSTENKI XIII, AND KOSTENKI V-HORIZON 1 116
TEL'MANSKAYA-HORIZON 1 AND KOSTENKI V-HORIZON 2 141
KOSTENKI II AND ANOSOVKA II-HORIZON 1A 146
ANOSOVKA II-HORIZONS 3, 2, AND 1B 158
MARKINA GORA-HORIZON 1, KOSTENKI IX, AND BORSHEVO III 161
SUMMARY 163
KOSTENKI XVIII, AN APPENDIX 164

chapter 10. *Sites on the First Terrace* 167
KOSTENKI IV-HORIZON 2 167
KOSTENKI IV-HORIZON 1 180
KOSTENKI XIX AND KOSTENKI III 193
BORSHEVO I AND KOSTENKI XXI 200
BORSHEVO II-HORIZONS 1, 2, AND 3 204
STRELETSKAYA I AND RUDKINO 210
SUMMARY AND CONCLUSION 211

chapter 11. *Summary and Conclusions* 213
THE MEANING OF THE DIVERSITY AMONG THE KOSTENKI-BORSHEVO SITES 213
KOSTENKI-BORSHEVO AND THE REPLACEMENT OF THE MOUSTERIAN BY THE UPPER PALEOLITHIC 215

THE SUBSISTENCE BASE OF THE KOSTENKI-BORSHEVO PEOPLES 216
TECHNOLOGY IN THE KOSTENKI-BORSHEVO UPPER PALEOLITHIC 218
GROUP SIZE AND DURATION OF SETTLEMENT IN THE KOSTENKI-BORSHEVO UPPER PALEOLITHIC 220
LOCATION OF SITES 224
IDEOLOGY IN THE KOSTENKI-BORSHEVO UPPER PALEOLITHIC 226
FLINT, AND THE EXTERNAL RELATIONSHIPS OF THE KOSTENKI-BORSHEVO SITES 226

Appendix 231

Topical Bibliography 239

References Cited 243

Index 253

TABLES

1. *The Stratigraphic Subdivision of the Pleistocene* 3
2. *Modified Atterberg Scale* 34
3. *Radiocarbon Dates from Kostenki-Borshevo Sites* 46
4. *Provisional Sequence of Pleistocene Events in the Kostenki-Borshevo Area* 48
5. *Plants Represented by Charcoal in Cultural Horizons in the Kostenki-Borshevo Area* 60
6. *Pollen from Samples of the Buried Soil at Borshevo II* 61
7. *Seeds Identified in Samples of the Buried Soil at Borshevo II* 62
8. *Molluscan Species Represented by Shells in Deposits in the Kostenki-Borshevo Region* 63–64

9. *Major Game Animals Represented in the Kostenki-Borshevo Sites* 67
10. *Species of Rodents Represented by Bones in Different Major Stratigraphic Units in the Kostenki-Borshevo Region* 68
11. *Species Represented by Faunal Remains in Sites of the Lower Humic Bed* 77
12. *Typological Composition of the Artifact Assemblages from Kostenki I-Horizon 5, Streletskaya II, and Kostenki XII-Horizon 3* 80
13. *Artifact Inventory from Kostenki XVII-2* 83
14. *Species Represented by Remains in Sites of the Upper Humic Bed* 88
15. *Typological Composition of the Artifact Assemblages from Markina Gora-Horizon 3 and Tel'manskaya-Horizon 3* 92
16. *Typological Composition of the Artifact Assemblages from Gorodtsovskaya and Kostenki XII-1B* 97
17. *Typological Composition of the Artifact Assemblage from Tel'manskaya-Horizon 2* 101
18. *Typological Composition of the Artifact Assemblage from Kostenki XVII-Horizon 1* 104
19. *Typological Composition of the Artifact Assemblage from Kostenki XVI* 106
20. *Typological Composition of the Artifact Assemblage from Markina Gora-Horizon 2* 107
21. *Species Represented by Remains in Sites above the Upper Humic Bed on the Second Terrace* 110–111
22. *Typological Composition of the Artifact Assemblage from Kostenki I-Horizon 3* 116
23. *Typological Composition of the Artifact Assemblages from Kostenki I-Horizon 1 and Kostenki XIII* 123–124
24. *Typological Composition of the Artifact Assemblage from Tel'manskaya-Horizon 1* 144
25. *Typological Composition of the Artifact Assemblage from Kostenki II* 154–155

26. *Typological Composition of the Artifact Assemblage from Anosovka II-Horizon 1A* 158
27. *Typological Composition of the Artifact Assemblage from Anosovka II-Horizon 3* 159
28. *Typological Composition of the Artifact Assemblage from Anosovka II-Horizon 2* 160–161
29. *Species Represented by Bones in First Terrace Sites* 168–169
30. *Typological Composition of the Artifact Inventory of Kostenki IV-Horizon 2* 178–179
31. *Typological Composition of the Artifact Inventory of Kostenki IV-Horizon 1* 188–190
32. *Stone Artifact Assemblages from the Various Complexes of Kostenki XIX* 199
33. *Typological Composition of the Artifact Assemblage from Kostenki XIX* 200
34. *Typological Composition of the Artifact Assemblage from Kostenki III* 201
35. *Typological Composition of the Artifact Assemblages from Borshevo I and Kostenki XXI* 203
36. *Contents of Areas of Concentration of Cultural Materials in Borshevo II-Horizon 3* 206
37. *Typological Composition of the Artifacts from Borshevo II-Horizons 1, 2, and 3* 208–209
38. *Estimates of Maximum Duration of Occupation of Various Kostenki Sites by a Group of 50 People Requiring 114,000 Calories/Day* 222
39. *Estimates of Maximum Duration of Occupation of Some Mousterian Sites by a Group of 50 People Requiring 114,000 Calories/Day* 225
A-1. *The Chronology of Important Events in the History of Investigation of the Kostenki-Borshevo Sites* 231–232
A-2. *Comparison of Profiles through Deposits of the Second Terrace at Kostenki XVII (Don Valley) and at Kostenki XIV (Pokrovskij Ravine)* 233–234
A-3. *Comparison of Profiles through the First Terrace at Kostenki III and Borshevo II* 235

A-4. *General Description of the Human Remains from Kostenki-Borshevo Sites* 236–237
A-5. *Some Measurements on Fossil Human Crania from Kostenki Sites* 237

FIGURES

1. *Stone-Artifact Technology and Typology I* 10
2. *Stone-Artifact Technology and Typology II* 12
3. *The Manufacture of a Burin* 14
4. *Stone-Artifact Technology and Typology III* 16
5. *Stone-Artifact Technology and Typology IV* 19
6. *Bone-Artifact Typology* 22
7. *Section through the Western Slope of the Don Valley in the Kostenki-Borshevo Region* 37
8. *Comparative Stratigraphy of the Kostenki-Borshevo Sites* 43
9. *Profiles of Kostenki V* 44
10. *Pollen Diagram from Kostenki I* 54
11. *Pollen Diagram from Gorodtsovskaya* 55
12. *Pollen Diagram from Kostenki XVII* 56
13. *Pollen Diagram from Kostenki XIX* 57
14. *Human Skull from Kostenki XVIII* 73
15. *Human Skull from Markina Gora-Horizon 3* 73
16. *Human Skull from Gorodtsovskaya* 74

17. *Human Skull from Kostenki II* 74
18. *Plan of Kostenki I-Horizon 5* 78
19. *Artifacts from Kostenki I-Horizon 5* 79
20. *Artifacts from Streletskaya II* 79
21. *Plan of Kostenki XVII-Horizon 2* 82
22. *Plan of Markina Gora-Horizon 3* 89
23. *Plan and Profiles of the Grave from Markina Gora* 91
24. *Plan of Tel'manskaya-Horizons 2 and 3* 93
25. *Plan and Profile of the Cultural Level of Gorodtsovskaya* 94
26. *Plan of the Bottom of the Grave from Gorodtsovskaya* 95
27. *"Paddle-Shaped Shovels" from Gorodtsovskaya* 98
28. *Topographic Map of Kostenki XII* 99
29. *Flints per Square Meter in Tel'manskaya-Horizon 2* 100
30. *Plan of Kostenki XVII-Horizon 1* 103
31. *Plan of Kostenki XVI* 105
32. *Plan of Kostenki I-Horizon 3* 113
33. *Plan of Kostenki I-Horizon 1* 115
34. *Distribution of Chipped Flint over the Area of Kostenki I-Horizon 1* 117
35. *"Habitation Pit A" of Kostenki I-Horizon 1* 119
36. *"Flint Axe" from Kostenki I-Horizon 1* 125
37. *Stone Artifacts from Kostenki I-Horizon 1* 126
38. *Bone Artifacts from Kostenki I-Horizon 1* 127
39. *Sculpted and Incised Bone Artifacts from Kostenki I-Horizon 1* 128
40. *Sculpted Anthropomorphic Artifacts from Kostenki I-Horizon 1* 129
41. *Animal Figures, Engraving, and Polisherlike Artifacts from Kostenki I-Horizon 1* 130
42. *Female Statuettes from Kostenki I-Horizon 1* 131
43. *Female Statuettes from Kostenki I-Horizon 1* 132
44. *Female Statuettes from Kostenki I-Horizon 1* 133

45. *Figurine Heads and Fragments and Engraving from Kostenki I-Horizon 1* 134
46. *Fragments of Female Figurines from Kostenki I-Horizon 1* 135
47. *"Medallions" and "Pendants" from Kostenki I-Horizon 1* 136
48. *Animal Heads from Kostenki I-Horizon 1* 137
49. *Animal Heads from Kostenki I-Horizon 1* 138
50. *Plan and Profile of Tel'manskaya-Horizon 1* 142
51. *Leaf-Shaped Points from Tel'manskaya-Horizon 1* 145
52. *Plan of the Excavations at Kostenki II* 147
53. *Complex I of Kostenki II* 148–149
54. *Complex II of Kostenki II* 152
55. *Complex III of Kostenki II* 156
56. *Anthropomorphic Figure from Kostenki II* 157
57. *Art Objects from Anosovka II-Horizon 2* 162
58. *Plan of Kostenki IV-Horizons 1 and 2, Showing Locations of Profiles* 170
59. *Plan and Profiles of Kostenki IV-Horizon 2, Southern Excavation* 172–173
60. *Plan and Profiles of Kostenki IV-Horizon 2, Northern Excavation* 176–177
61. *Artifacts from Kostenki IV-Horizon 2* 180
62. *Plan and Profiles of Kostenki IV-Horizon 1* 182–183
63. *Hearths and Pits in the Habitation Depressions of Kostenki IV-Horizon 1* 184–185
64. *Artifacts from Kostenki IV-Horizon 1* 187
65. *Various Art Objects from Kostenki IV-Horizon 1* 191
66. *Anthropomorphic Figures and Fragments Thereof from Kostenki IV-Horizon 1* 192
67. *Plan of Kostenki XIX* 194–195
68. *Hearth Pit of Kostenki XIX, Complex I* 197
69. *"Nucleiform/Macrolithic Tools" from Kostenki XIX* 199
70. *Plan of Borshevo I* 202

71. *Horizontal Distributions of Cultural Remains in Borshevo II-Horizons 1, 2, and 3* 205
72. *Antler "Mattocks" from Borshevo II-Horizon 3* 207
73. *Pattern of Stone Slabs in Borshevo II-Horizon 1* 211

MAPS

1. *Vegetation Zones of European Russia at the Maximum of the Last Glacial* 27
2. *The Kostenki-Borshevo Region* 28
3. *Geomorphological Map of the Environs of the Village of Kostenki* 40
4. *Distribution of Different Varieties of Flint to the Southwest of Kostenki* 228

PREFACE

My primary goal in writing this book was to provide a self-contained archeological-site report which would be of use in college-level courses on prehistory. Because of the lack of such reports, students are generally restricted in their reading to broad syntheses which they are unable to evaluate critically. Archeology therefore all too often remains a kind of magic whose conclusions must be accepted or rejected on faith. In this book I have not avoided conclusions, but I have attempted to show how they were derived from the data. I have made a special effort to point out the limitations and potentialities of the data used in reaching conclusions. In order to make the data intelligible to the uninitiated, I have explained those technical terms and concepts which the average college student is not likely to know.

I have chosen as the central focus of the book a group of

spectacular Early Man sites located in the Don Valley of European Russia. These sites have been the subject of intensive, high-quality investigation by Russian prehistorians for several decades. However, language barriers have caused them to remain very little known in the Western world. This book will serve to correct this unhappy situation.

Professors K. W. Butzer, L. G. Freeman, Jr., and F. C. Howell (all of the University of Chicago), and Professor L. L. Langness (University of Washington) commented critically on the manuscript. They were responsible for a number of improvements and I owe them considerable thanks.

Evanston, Illinois R. G. K.
October 1968

FOREWORD

By F. Clark Howell

The closing phases of the Pleistocene witnessed in Europe and in the circum-Mediterranean lands of Asia and Africa a remarkable set of human cultural adaptations which prehistorians traditionally refer to as the Upper Paleolithic. Beginning some 35,000 years ago new peoples with new ideas and new designs for living displaced and eventually replaced antecedent Neanderthal peoples and their Mousterian way of life. The nature of this transformation is still ill-understood, but the adaptive successes of the ancient Europeans of the Upper Paleolithic are now well documented from cultural residues recovered from many hundreds of caves, shelters, and open-air encampments. More than a century of prehistoric research on these ancient peoples has cast a diversity of light on their distributions, their adjustments to particular environments and to specific locales—through time and at specific moments in time—their habitation and visitation places, their subsistence activities, their technology in varied organic and inorganic substances, their decorative and artistic capabilities and proclivities, their burial practices, and even some aspects of their intellectual life.

These adjustments were not everywhere similar either in space or in time; local problems frequently called for local solutions, and the diffusion of knowledge and of new ideas was intermittent and, as always, probably retarded by traditional values. Prolonged and intensive exploration and excavations in the numerous caves and rock shelters of southwestern France, especially the Périgord, have understandably made that region of primary importance for the study of successive late Pleistocene cultural adjustments in temperate latitudes. Consequently the paleocultural manifestations there have frequently been taken as a scale by which all other developments elsewhere should be judged and evaluated. And that has been unfortunate, for the varieties of past human experience merit elucidation, appraisal, and appreciation—a goal which has often been thwarted by premature application of an assumed systematics rather than of hypotheses to be tested against another set of data.

The history of the recovery of traces of human occupation, and their evaluation and interpretation, in the Kostenki-Borshevo sector of the Don River basin clearly demonstrates the inadequacy and futility of this approach. The very distinctive character of human cultural adjustment at the close of the Ice Ages is superbly documented in this intensively and repeatedly occupied locale of the vast east European plain. Professor Klein has thoughtfully and critically evaluated these discoveries on the basis of an unparalleled knowledge of Russian language sources, coupled with his examination of artifact collections in the course of several paleoanthropological study tours in the Soviet Union. His study exposes to students and professional colleagues alike the elaborate cultural adjustments of these hunting peoples. His characterization will hopefully temper the familiar, and misleading, characterization of the troglodytic Cro-Magnon peoples.

The Kostenki-Borshevo sector of the Don basin represents an area of only some 30–35 square kilometers. Some two dozen prehistoric localities, comprising over 50 distinct occupational occurrences, are now known from this limited area. These are open-air sites, situated for the most part in relation to various cover sediments, including fossil soils (paleosols), which mantle three terraces flanking the western margin of the Don River floodplain. Most of the localities are related to the Middle (or Second) Terrace cover sediments and paleosols. These sediments, and the associated human occupations, are all evidently of Main and Late Last Glacial (Würm = Valdaj) age, none dating back further than about 25,000 years. There is no direct evidence of Mousterian occupations in the area prior to these occupations, a rather curious matter, since open-air encampments of such peoples are well documented in the Dnestr basin. The Kostenki-Borshevo occupations appear to span a period of some 12,000–15,000 years, according to the few radiocarbon determinations now available; the youngest occupations are from the end of the late Glacial, dating to about 11,000 years ago. This area is now practically a part of the south Russian steppe, characterized by a seasonally extreme continental climate. However, during the closing phases of the Pleistocene it was doubtless part of an extensive open loessic-steppe zone, transected by lightly wooded stream courses. Conditions then were far more severe than now, climatically comparable at least to those obtaining now some 10° farther north, and with mean annual temperatures some 10° C. colder, a frost-free season of very brief duration, and substantially reduced precipitation. The results of a few palynological studies, coupled with the presence in occupation sites of cold-loving mammalian species, including reindeer, arctic fox, and even (rarely) the musk ox, would tend to support this conclusion. In this situation hardy Upper Paleolithic hunters and trappers made a remarkable series of cultural adjustments, utilizing as a subsistence base an abundance of gregarious mammals, principally woolly mammoth and wild horse, and fur-bearers like wolf, arctic fox, and hare. By contrast with occurrences elsewhere, in eastern as well as parts of western Europe, aurochs is definitely rare, and reindeer, when present, is never abundant. Strangely, game birds and fish do not seem to have played a role in the subsistence economy.

The origins of these cultural adjustments are literally unknown. The initial human occupations at Kostenki, of which seven or eight occurrences are now known, foreshadow what was subsequently to become increasingly intensified exploitation of local resources. The already distinctive Kostenki-Borshevo character of these occupations is evident in the lithic assemblages (referred to the Kostenki/Streletskaya group), which infrequently but nevertheless do reflect the use of some nonlocal stone; in the workmanship in bone (largely restricted to the Kostenki XVII occupation); in the extent of occupational occurrences, distributions, and suggestion of structural features (only horizon 5 of Kostenki I is very informative); in occurrence and distribution of hearths; and in evidences indicative of varied human activities. A subsequent set of occupations (upper humic bed of the Middle Terrace), known from over a dozen occurrences, indicates more substantial and perhaps prolonged visitations, best evidenced in the Kostenki VIII (two horizons) and Kostenki XV (Gorodtsovskaya) localities, which are most complete and have experienced minimal disturbance. There is a fuller representation of cultural life—exemplified in the extent of occupation areas, in concentrations indicative of habitation units, in the development of storage pits, in emplacement of human burials, in the elaboration of technology in bone and in stone (stone including substantial nonlocal flint evidently transported over a relatively great distance), and in artistic expression in relation to both utilitarian and decorative objects.

Very extensive, diversified, and artifactually rich occupations characterize the uppermost sediments of the Middle Terrace. These occupations are known from thirteen localities, of which Kostenki I, II, VIII, and XI are the largest, richest, and best known. Occupation areas are extensive. There is solid evidence for some half dozen elongate and ovate or circular structures, sometimes of very substantial size and in association with complexes of hearths and storage and other pits; large and selected accumulations of animal (especially mammoth) bone, much of which was doubtless related to constructional and support uses; a complex pattern of human interment; distributions of artifacts and associated features suggestive of varied sets of activities; a diversified stone-weapon and tool assemblage; extensive and complex workmanship in bone and in ivory for a diversity of heavy- and light-duty tools; and objects of adornment and of (perhaps) symbolic significance. These occupations rank among the most elaborate and complex known from terminal glacial times in Europe; and their uniqueness, which Professor Klein has rightfully stressed, merits more attention than has customarily been given them. Some younger sites, in sediments of the First Terrace, exhibit many, if not most, of these qualities; the largest and most thoroughly studied are Kostenki IV and XIX and Borshevo II. Such occurrences substantially antedate communities and patterns of settlement usually taken to herald and to accompany the establishment of village farming communities in relation to activities of agriculture and animal domestication. Their substantial size, complexity, and persistence through time surely indicate a pattern of cultural adjustment and elaboration in a harsh but potentially rewarding environment, which reflects human inventiveness and adaptability quite independent of and prior to the agricultural revolution.

The discovery and controlled excavation of such open-air occupation places, including some not fundamentally unlike them in central Europe, have confronted students of late Pleistocene prehistory with a new assortment of data and a related set of problems. Most of all they afford incomparable evidence of distributions and associations of cultural residues and occupational features; these have usually been absent from most past excavations in cave fronts and rock shelters, where the successional aspects of artifactual materials have traditionally received primary consideration. This emphasis has changed in recent years, with different excavation procedures in various cave and shelter situations, as well as with the discovery and meticulous excavation of some open-air occupation places (Pincevent is an outstanding example) the results of which do or will provide a measure of comparability. These results demonstrate the varied and culturally distinctive responses of paleo-European peoples in the course of the so-called Upper Paleolithic. They suggest strongly the need for caution in the application of terminologies and schemes of cultural development worked out elsewhere at comparable times, but under quite different circumstances, by peoples with different resources and very probably different goals and values. These distinctions, which become increasingly evident with altered procedures of excavation, recording, and recovery, now require analysis, comparison, and appreciation if human life in the Late Pleistocene is to be more adequately understood. Professor Klein has made a splendid effort here to present a set of data and the attendant problems which must be considered with regard to that eventual goal of understanding.

The University of Chicago F. Clark Howell

MAN AND CULTURE IN THE LATE PLEISTOCENE

chapter 1. Introduction

The Pleistocene

Present evidence suggests that the first important steps in cultural evolution and many of the most important, if not the earliest, ones in human biological evolution were taken in the geological epoch known as the Pleistocene. Artifacts which we can be certain were made by the hand of man are currently unknown from any time interval preceding the Pleistocene; they make their first appearance at or shortly after its beginning. As time progresses they become more numerous, widespread, and varied, providing us with direct evidence of the evolution of culture. It now seems quite possible that creatures of broadly human affinities, that is, members of the zoological family Hominidae, made their appearance before the beginning of the Pleistocene. But at the same time the fossil record indicates that much important evolution within the Hominidae, in particular the development of the brain to its present size and complexity, took place during the epoch. In sum, it is clear that the duration and nature of the Pleistocene must be of considerable interest to students of various aspects of human evolution.

Recent advances in absolute dating based on the decay of radioactive isotopes within rocks have led scientists to push back their estimate of the time of the beginning of the Pleistocene from the date of 1,000,000 B.P. (= Before Present), widely accepted just a few years ago, to an estimate of 2,000,000+ B.P. today. (In fact, data are becoming available which indicate that 3,000,000+ B.P. is not out of the question.) Several ways of defining the beginning of the Pleistocene are currently in use. Although it is hoped that all of these provide coincident results, some are clearly of wider applicability than others, and one in particular stands out for the variety of localities in which it can be used. This definition states that the Pleistocene began when one of the really important climatic changes in geological history took place—namely, when the generally rather warm, though gradually cooling climate of the preceding 65–70 million years was punctuated, at least in middle and upper latitudes, by a pronounced cold fluctuation. This cold interval was followed by a return to somewhat warmer conditions and this in turn by a second cold interval; similar major oscillations between warmer and colder phases continued throughout the Pleistocene, and although their exact number is unknown, the last major cold interval seems to have ended around 10,000 years ago (roughly 8,000 B.C.). This date is commonly regarded as marking the end of the Pleistocene, although there is no reason to suppose that the succeeding warm period, the Holocene or Recent, in which we are now living, is not simply the latest in the series of warm intervals between cold snaps.

The major warm and cold intervals which make up the Pleistocene were accompanied by a number of important events which undoubtedly affected human physical and cultural evolution. So, for example, the climatic shifts from one interval to another certainly led to important changes in the distribution of plants and animals. Further, at least the later cold and warm oscillations were marked by alternate waxing and waning of the great continental ice sheets. And as a result of the repeated growth and shrinkage of the glaciers, sea level fell and rose again, alternately exposing and inundating large tracts of land at the margins of the continents.

Students of the Pleistocene have long found it useful to subdivide the epoch into a series of constituent cold and warm units, each with its own name. This seemingly basic task has proved far from simple, however. A once widely accepted general sequence of four major cold intervals and

TABLE 1. Stratigraphic Subdivision of the Pleistocene (after Butzer 1964:22 and 28)

Climatic oscillation	*Absolute date (years* B.P.*)*	*Stratigraphic Unit*	*Stage*
Warm		Holocene	Holocene
	ca. 10,000		
Cold		Würm	Upper Pleistocene
Warm		Eem	
Cold		Riss	Middle Pleistocene
Warm		Holstein	
Cold		Elster	Lower Pleistocene
Warm		Cromerian	
Cold		Menapian	Basal Pleistocene
Warm		Waalian	
Cold		Eburonian	
Warm		Tiglian	
Cold		Villafranchian	
	2,000,000+		

three intervening warm ones has been completely discarded by all serious scholars, and more complex schemes have sprung up in its place. One of these schemes, recently constructed through the synthesis of a variety of data, is presented in Table 1. It is important to note that the number of cold and warm intervals suggested in the table is far from an established fact. For example, there is reason to believe that the Riss and the Elster intervals may each be a complex of two or more cold oscillations separated from one another by warm intervals of at least the duration and/or intensity of the one separating the Riss from the Würm. Also, the long-standing practice of calling the various cold intervals "glacials" and the intervening warm periods "interglacials" is an undesirable one, since at present we have no clear evidence for continental glaciation prior to the so-called Elster cold interval (that is, it is not known whether the earlier cold intervals were or were not accompanied by growth of continental ice sheets).

Another concern is absolute dating within the Pleistocene. Radioisotopic dating techniques identical or similar to those which have altered our conclusions about the over-all duration of the Pleistocene also promise ultimately to provide us with reliable estimates (in years) of when various Pleistocene events took place. A problem arises, however, in that before a date for a particular event can be accepted, one must be certain that the deposits dated do indeed record that event. All too frequently radioisotopic dating has demonstrated that sediments or geomorphic features found at different localities, but supposed to date from the same interval, for example the Elster, must actually date from different intervals. Which of these intervals is then to be regarded as Elster, and thus to provide the "correct" date, is seldom easily determinable. There is currently no series of absolute dates which can reliably be attached to the named units of Table 1, and insofar as the purposes of this book do not demand that even rough guesses be made, only figures for the beginning and end of the Pleistocene are presented.

A grouping of the named Pleistocene cold and warm intervals into grosser units (such as the Basal, Lower, Middle, and Upper Pleistocene) has considerable utility in Pleistocene studies. One such grouping, becoming ever more widely accepted, is the last item of interest in Table 1 (last column). It will be referred to repeatedly in the following pages.

The Purpose of This Book

Man-made artifacts, constituting the earliest concrete evidence of human cultural activity, appear in the early Pleistocene, more exactly in the terms of Table 1, in the Basal Pleistocene. These earliest artifacts are restricted almost entirely to Africa. Human beings (using this term in the broad sense to include all members of the zoological family Hominidae) do not seem to have colonized Europe and Asia, at least not in any major way, until the Lower Pleistocene. By the end of the Lower Pleistocene and during the succeeding Middle Pleistocene, evidence for human occupation of much of Europe and Asia is quite substantial. A fact relevant to this book, however, is that such evidence is not present anywhere in the vast area (one-sixth of the earth's land surface) occupied today by the Soviet Union. Here scientists have not uncovered any traces of human occupation which can be reliably dated to a time preceding the earlier part of the Upper Pleistocene, or more particularly the Eem. In the later Eem or perhaps the earlier Würm, bearers of one or more variants of the so-called Mousterian culture, widespread at this time over Europe and Southwestern Asia, settled at least the European part of the Soviet Union.

From that point on we have evidence that human occupation there was more or less continuous and relatively intensive. At some time within the later Upper Pleistocene, more specifically within the later Würm, the Mousterian culture in European Russia and elsewhere was supplanted by a culture or complex of cultures referred to as Upper Paleolithic.[1]

A major purpose of this book is to acquaint the reader with the principal features of Upper Paleolithic culture through a detailed analysis of a spectacular group of Upper Paleolithic sites which have been uncovered on the banks of the Don River in the eastern part of European Russia. More generally, the data from these sites will be used to illustrate the procedures whereby Pleistocene prehistorians gain information on early man and his culture. Later chapters will discuss ways of describing and analyzing the cultural remains at the sites, the history of discovery of the sites, their relations to one another in time, the reconstruction of environments at the times they were occupied, the physical appearance of their former occupants, actual descriptions of their contents, and finally, what can be said about the ways in which their ancient inhabitants survived and perhaps even thrived during the last part of the Würm ice age.

[1] Sometimes, particularly in the past, the variants of the Mousterian culture have been grouped together as the Middle Paleolithic, their predecessors as the Lower.

chapter 2. The Cultural Remains of Pleistocene Man

Features and Artifacts

Early man is best known by the remains of his material culture. Prehistorians frequently divide these remains into two principal categories—features and artifacts. *Features* are humanly made or modified phenomena which are generally impossible or at least very difficult to remove intact from a site and which are thus frequently destroyed once excavations have been completed. Obvious examples are remains of buildings, fireplaces, storage pits, post holes, and the like. Features can only be exposed through careful horizontal excavation of a site, usually in conjunction with a well-laid-out grid system. The grid aids in the construction of horizontal maps or plans on which features can be recorded and thus, in a sense, can continue to exist. The discovery of features in a site almost invariably allows a prehistorian to make more inferences about the nature of the ancient occupation than if the features were absent. Much of the interest and excitement generated by the particular Late Pleistocene sites on which this book focuses derives directly from the numerous features found in them.

Artifacts are humanly made or modified phenomena which, in distinction from features, are rather easily removed from the ground. They can thus be studied and preserved in laboratories or museums long after excavations have been completed. The distinction between artifacts and features is purely an analytic one, and anyone can imagine objects whose characterization as one or the other would be difficult. Further, it is important to realize that the web of spatial relations among artifacts in the ground (and among artifacts and features) is itself a feature of a site and, if properly recorded, can give information on the nature of the ancient occupation of the site.

Stone Artifacts

In the range of time with which this book is concerned (the Pleistocene and more particularly its terminal phase), man seems to have used no metals for artifact manufacture, but to have restricted himself entirely to stone, wood, bone, ivory, antler, shell, and sometimes baked clay. Artifacts of stone are by far the most frequently found, if for no other reason than that under ordinary circumstances stone is far less destructible than the other raw materials. In the Pleistocene of Europe the kind of stone most often used in making artifacts was flint. The abundant use of this material presumably reflects Pleistocene man's awareness of its particularly favorable flaking properties (versus those of most other kinds of stone) in combination with its relatively frequent natural occurrence over most of the continent. To be sure, other kinds of stone, for example quartzite and limestone, were also used by man in Pleistocene Europe, but the sum total of artifacts made of these other materials is only a fraction of the total number made of flint. Sometimes when flint, or at least high-quality flint, was not available in an area (for example the region of principal concern to this book), the inhabitants transported (or imported) it from considerable distances.

An understanding of flint, or more generally of stone artifact technology and typology, is crucial for any discussion of Pleistocene prehistory. This understanding is required principally because the "cultures" isolated by Pleistocene prehistorians are usually defined simply by the kinds (and sometimes also by the frequencies of the kinds) of stone tools they contain. More rarely, artifacts of bone and related materials are considered as well. The next few pages deal with those aspects of stone-tool technology and typology which are particularly important for an understanding of the delineation of cultural units among the sites to be considered in this book.

The most basic step in transforming a raw piece of flint (or other stone) into an artifact is the intentional removal from it of a smaller piece. This can be accomplished either by striking the raw object with another piece of rock, known then as a *hammerstone,* or by striking the raw object against a stationary rock, known thereafter as an *anvil.* It is also possible to substitute a piece of some other hard material, for example, bone or wood, for a hammerstone. Most generally, a small piece of stone removed through the use of a hammerstone or anvil is called a *flake.* If it is genuinely man-made, a flake will possess some important features resulting from the fact that the entire force of the blow which removed it was concentrated at a relatively small point on the parent rock. The most prominent of these features is referred to as the *bulb of percussion.* This is a pronounced bulge occurring on the flake near the point where the blow to remove it was struck, on the surface which was inside the parent piece (see Fig. 1#1). This surface is generally referred to as the lower or *ventral surface;* the opposite surface, originally forming part of the outside of the parent piece, is then called the upper or *dorsal surface.* In addition to the bulb of percussion the ventral surface will also bear a series of ripples or undulations concentric around the bulb. If the flake is the first or one of the first to be struck from a raw parent piece, the dorsal surface will frequently possess a quite different color and texture than the ventral one, because, having been on the outside, it has been altered by the elements. The depth to which alteration has occurred may vary from piece to piece. The altered layer is generally called the *cortex* of the piece.

Very frequently, stone knappers more or less systematically removed a series of flakes from a parent piece; in such a case, the piece is referred to as a *core* or nucleus. The part (or parts) of the core which was (were) struck to remove a flake (or flakes) is (are) known as the *striking platform* (or platforms) of the core. Sometimes a flake is also said to have a striking platform, namely that part of it which was once part of the struck surface (striking platform) of a core. François Bordes, an outstanding expert on flint knapping, has suggested that this part of the flake might be more logically known by some other name. The term *butt* will be used here (see Fig. 1#1). It is conventional to orient flakes in drawings with the butt down; only in special cases is this convention disregarded.

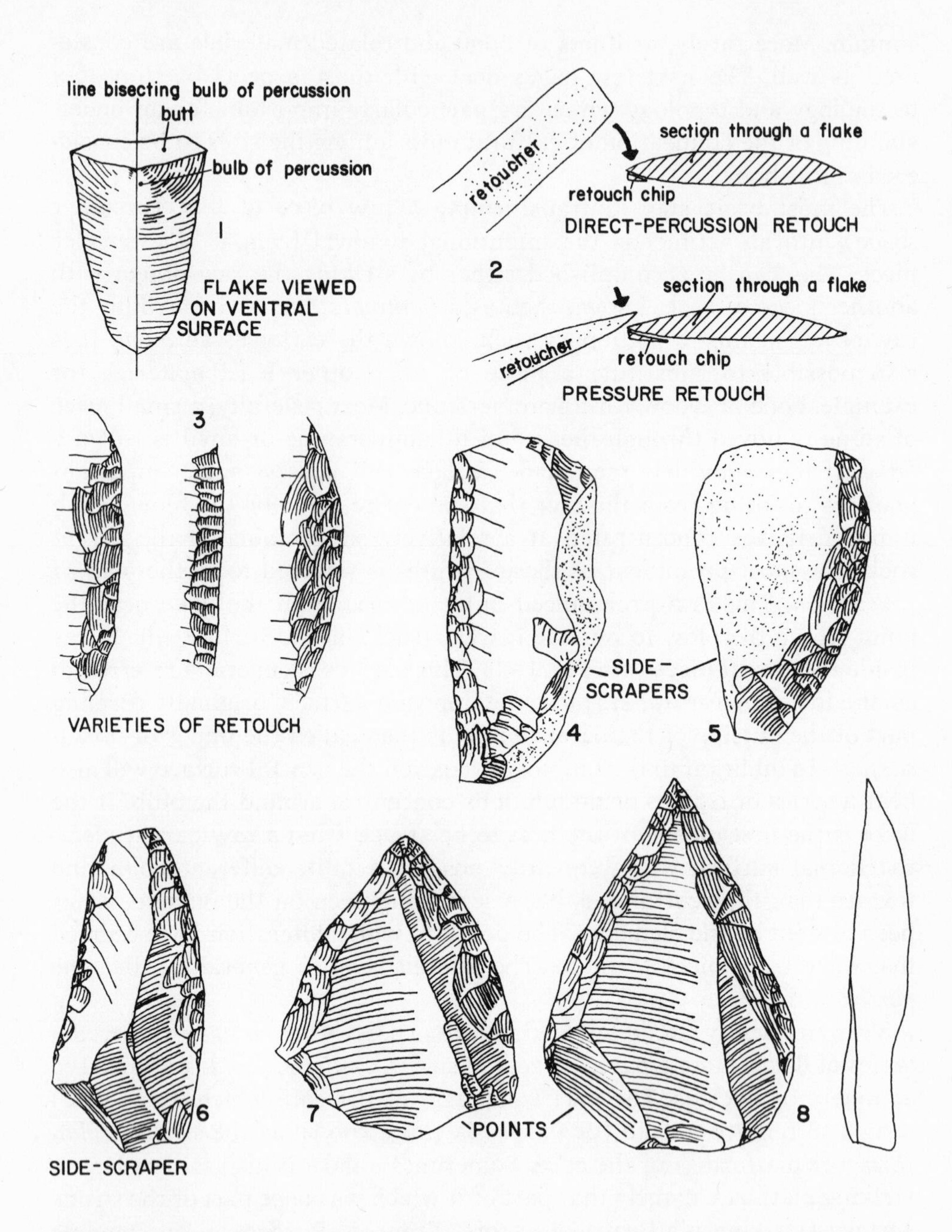

Figure 1. Stone-Artifact Technology and Typology I (redrawn after Bordes 1961: Figures 1 and 2, Plates 10, 16, and 18).

The fresh edge of a flint flake is very sharp, and there is no doubt but that early man was aware of this fact and took advantage of it. But at the same time that it is very sharp a fresh edge is also very brittle. Consequently, if it is used to scrape some kinds of substances, it will chip and soon become ragged and unsuitable for the work. Pleistocene man early discovered he could make an edge more useful for some types of operations, for example for the scraping of some materials, by modifying it through the use of what is termed *retouch.* Pleistocene knappers most commonly produced retouch by striking a flake repeatedly along an edge on one surface, almost always the ventral, in order to remove a more or less continuous series of small flakes or chips from the other surface (see Fig. 1#2,3). Sometimes, particularly in the later Pleistocene, approximately the same effect was achieved by the repeated application of concentrated pressure along an edge on one surface (Fig. 1#2). Regardless of how retouch was obtained, however, it seems certain that it was produced to give an edge a quality or qualities (for example, solidity and/or shape) which its unretouched counterpart did not possess.

By far the most common artifact manufactured by the retouching of one or more edges of a flake is a *side-scraper* (Fig. 1#4–6).[1] Side-scrapers may be divided into several varieties, depending upon such factors as the shape of the retouched edge (convex, concave, or straight), the position of the edge relative to the butt of the flake (to the side or opposite the butt), and the abruptness and general quality of the retouch forming it. Side-scrapers can also be multiple; that is, more than one edge can bear retouch, and a whole variety of subtypes may be defined on the basis of particular combinations of particular kinds of retouched edges.

A second prominent category of retouched flake artifacts consists of *points* (Fig. 1#7,8). Frequently, prehistorians have labeled as points all flakes on which two retouched edges converge; but, following François Bordes, the present book will restrict this label to thin flakes on which the retouched edges converge at a relatively acute angle. All other flakes with two convergent edges are then regarded simply as varieties of side-scrapers.

Side-scrapers and points on flakes do not by any means exhaust the number of possible retouched flake-artifact types, but for the purposes of this book, it is not necessary to consider additional types at any length. Mention should be made, however, of notches (Fig. 2#1) and denticulates (Fig. 2#2). A *notch* is a flake on the periphery of which one or more

[1] The name is somewhat misleading since it is not certain that even a large proportion of the objects so called were used principally for scraping.

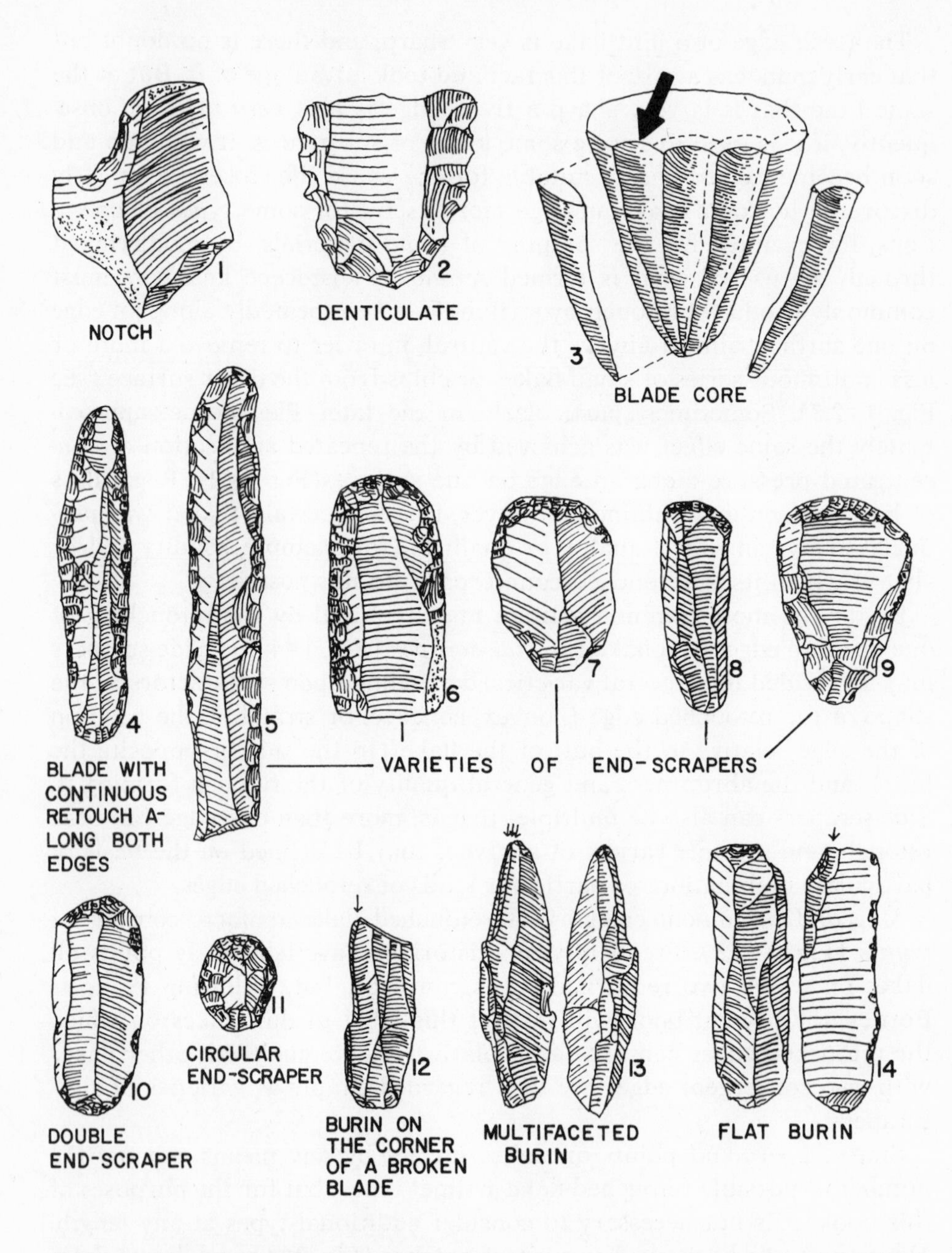

Figure 2. Stone-Artifact Technology and Typology II (1 and 2 redrawn after Bordes 1961:Plates 39 and 40; 3 redrawn from *Early Man,* by the Editors of Time-Life Books, © 1965 (p. 113); 4–14 redrawn after de Sonneville-Bordes and Perrot 1954:329, 330, and 1956b:555).

nonadjacent indentations (notches) have been deliberately fashioned. A *denticulate* on the other hand is a flake on which two or more intentional indentations (notches) are adjacent.

A large category of stone-artifact types are called blade tools. A *blade* may be defined (once again, following Bordes) as a flake which is at least twice as long as wide, length being measured along a line bisecting the bulb of percussion, with width perpendicular to this line.[2] Blades are produced in the same general fashion as flakes, though for their consistent manufacture somewhat special procedures must be adopted. These procedures need not be of concern here (see Figure 2#3 for a blade core in the process of being worked). What is important is a discussion of the types of artifacts which can be manufactured on blades through the use of retouch and other procedures. Many of these types could just as well be produced on flakes, and as will become apparent later, it is largely a matter of historical accident that we most frequently know them on blades.

To begin with, there is a category of blade tools analogous to side-scrapers, but usually distinguished from these as *blades with continuous retouch along one or both side edges* (Fig. 2#4). More important generally in determining differences or similarities among artifact assemblages are blades on which it is the end (the edge opposite the butt) that is continuously retouched. Such artifacts are known by the generic name *end-scrapers* (Fig. 2#5–9) and are subdivisible into several types, depending, for example, on whether one or both lateral edges are also retouched, what shape the retouched end has (rounded, ogival, or other), and what the over-all shape of the finished piece is (for example, fan-shaped). Sometimes the butt end is also continuously retouched, in which case the artifact is called a *double end-scraper* (Fig. 2#10). End-scrapers can also be made on relatively narrow flakes (a wide flake with a retouched edge opposite the butt is a variety of side-scraper). If the flake is more or less circular, it is termed a *circular end-scraper* (Fig. 2#11). Finally, some authors like to group together as *steep end-scrapers* all examples made on particularly thick blades or flakes.

[2] If this definition is followed rigorously, it is clear that blades are no more than a variety of flakes. In actuality, prehistorians have generally tended to treat them as something quite distinct. This relatively inconsequential semantic problem could be eliminated by the acceptance of the term *blank* to include both flakes and blades. The definition of a flake could then be made more restrictive to comply with the way in which the term is actually used by most prehistorians today; that is, it would refer specifically to a blank which is less than twice as long as wide. Throughout this book the terms flake and blade are to be understood as referring to mutually exclusive categories of objects distinguished by differences in proportion.

After end-scrapers, perhaps the most important category of stone tools most often made on blades is that of burins. A *burin* may be defined as a blade (or flake) from which a second blade has been removed in such a way that the ventral surface of the second blade forms a considerable angle (generally near to right) with the ventral surface of the parent blade. The second or subsidiary blade is known as a *burin spall.* The process of manufacturing one kind of burin is illustrated in Figure 3. One begins by dulling, or in technical terminology "truncating," the end of a blade. Then using the more or less flat surface formed as a striking platform, one strikes the spall from the edge of the blade. The particular

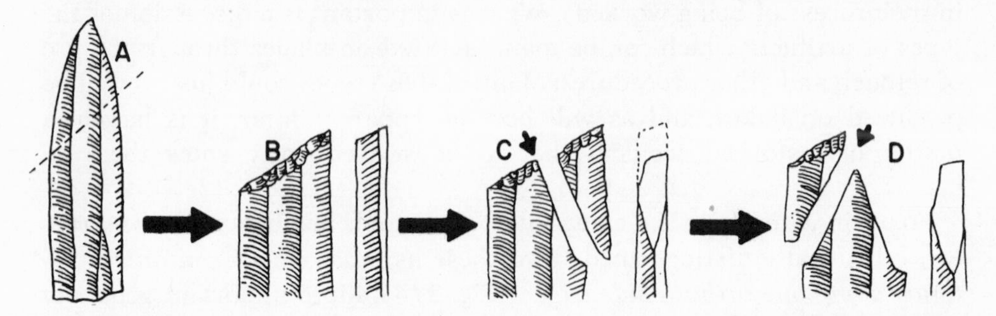

Figure 3. The Manufacture of a Burin (redrawn from *Early Man,* by the Editors of Time-Life Books, © 1965 (p. 113). A. Fresh blade; B. Truncated blade; C. Burin on a retouched truncation; D. Dihedral Burin.

kind of burin that results is called a *burin on a retouched truncation,* and several varieties may be recognized depending upon whether the truncation is straight, convex, or concave. It is also possible to dull the lateral edge of a blade and use this as a striking platform, in which case the spall will come off more or less perpendicular to the line bisecting the bulb of percussion instead of parallel to it. The resulting burin is known as a *burin on a lateral truncation.*

It is possible to take the burin on a retouched truncation and turn it into another kind of burin, as illustrated in Figure 3. To do this one simply uses the flat surface left behind by the removal of the first spall to strike off a second. The resulting artifact is called a *dihedral burin,* and different types may be recognized according to whether the line bisecting the bulb of percussion also bisects the angle formed by the removal of the two spalls or diverges from it to some extent. A third major kind of burin results when a blade is snapped and the fracture surface is used as a striking platform for the removal of a spall. Such burins are called *burins on the corner of a broken blade* (Fig. 2#12).

In the manufacture of each of the above major burin types, it is possible to remove two or more adjacent spalls (each with its ventral surface at a relatively large angle to the ventral surface of the parent piece); such artifacts are called *multifaceted burins* (Fig. 2#13). Many writers classify multifaceted burins as a group independent of whether they are on truncations, dihedral, or on the corner of a broken blade. Sometimes the number of adjacent spalls removed from a piece is so large that it is difficult to determine whether we are dealing with a multifaceted burin or with a core for the removal of small blades or with both. Artifacts which are debatable in this regard are herein called *nucleiform burins.* As yet another category, some authors distinguish as a group all burins from which a spall is removed whose ventral surface is relatively little inclined to that of the parent piece. Such artifacts, which belong only marginally to the general burin class, are called *flat burins* (Fig. 2#14). Finally, it is important to note that two or more burins of the same type or of different types may be combined on the same piece, in which case we may speak respectively of *multiple burins* or of *mixed multiple burins.*

The next major class of blade artifacts comprises pieces referred to as *backed blades.* Most simply these are blades on which one edge has been blunted, or in technical terms "backed," by abrupt retouch. Abrupt retouch is found particularly often on small, narrow blades or bladelets, which are then called *backed bladelets* (Fig. 4#1,2). If the backed edge on a blade or bladelet converges to a point with the opposite-lying edge (which may or may not be retouched, but usually is not), we speak of a *backed point.* Several varieties of backed points can be distinguished, among which the following are worth noting: (1) *Châtelperron points* (Fig. 4#3), which include blades on which a convex, backed edge converges to a relatively sharp point with the opposite-lying, unretouched one; (2) *Gravette points* (Fig. 4#4), which include narrow blades on which a nearly straight, backed edge converges to a sharp point with an edge that is either totally unretouched or retouched only at the point or base; and (3) *Font-Yves points* (Fig. 4#5), which include small, narrow blades with two abruptly or semiabruptly retouched (that is, backed) edges converging to a point.

Another category of artifacts consists of those with truncations, already briefly introduced in the discussion of burins. A *truncated blade or flake* is simply one on which one end has been deliberately blunted, or in technical terms "truncated" by abrupt retouch (Fig. 4#6,7). Different varieties may be distinguished according to the shape of the truncation (straight, convex, or concave) and depending on whether the line bisecting the bulb of percussion also cuts the truncation into two more or less

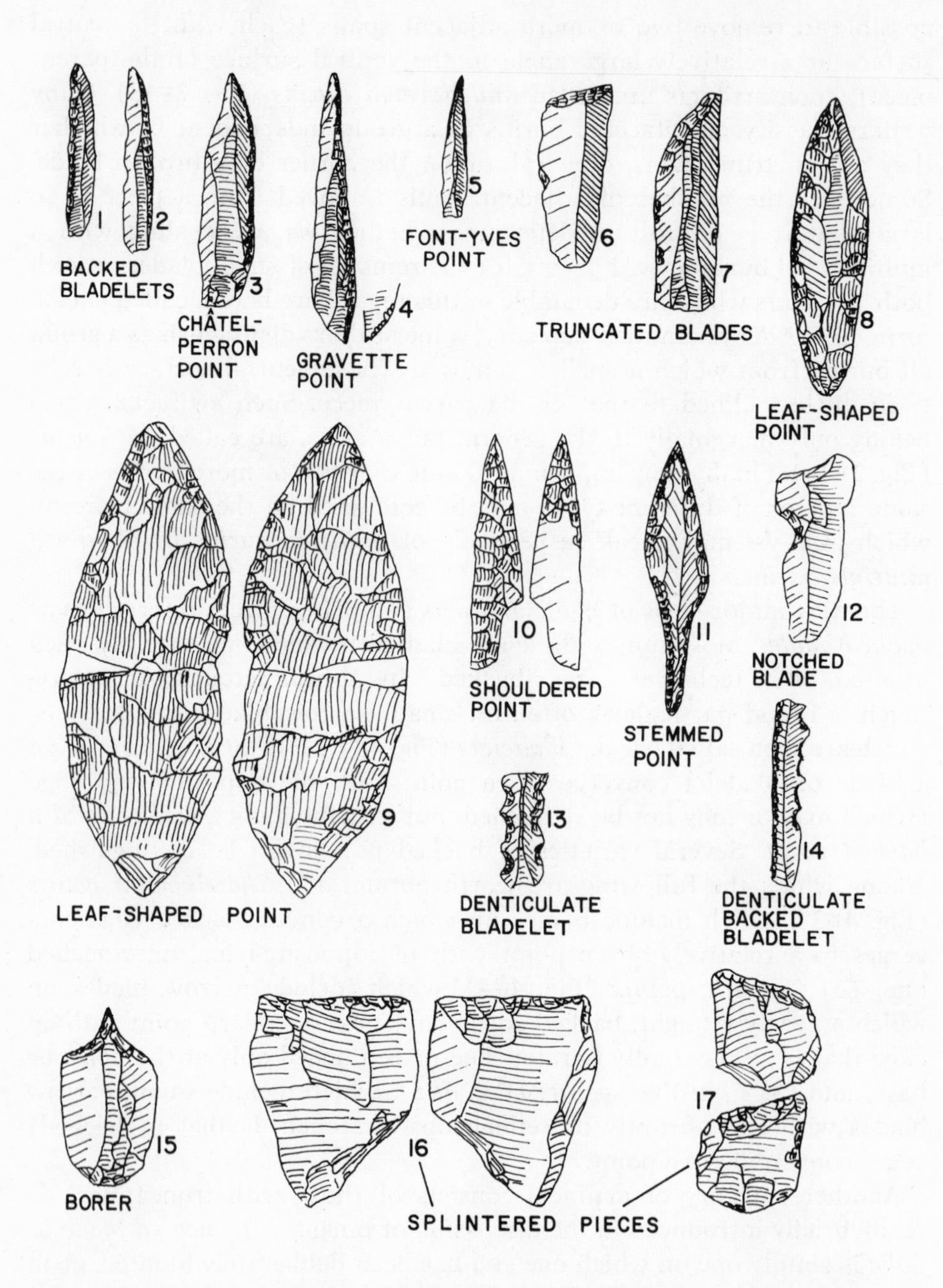

Figure 4. Stone-Artifact Technology and Typology III (Redrawn after de Sonneville-Bordes and Perrot 1954:334; 1955:79; 1956b:549, 551, 553, 555, and 557).

identical halves. Pieces with opposed truncations occur and may be termed *pieces with double truncation.* A particular kind of double-truncated piece on which the abrupt (or often only semiabrupt) retouch is located on the ventral surface is known as a *Kostenki knife.* Like backing, truncation is frequently found on bladelets, where, if it is combined with backing, it may serve to form pieces with geometric shapes, for example, rectangles, trapezoids, and rhombuses.

Still another category of blade artifacts to be considered are *leaf-shaped points* (Fig. 4#8,9). Most generally these are blades which have been given the shape of a leaf, most often of laurel or willow, by non-abruptly retouching the edges so that they converge at both ends, forming a relatively sharp point at least at one end. Important varieties may be isolated depending on whether the retouch is on one surface only (unifacial) or on both (bifacial), and on the extent to which it covers one or both faces.

Typologically similar to the leaf-shaped points as defined above are shouldered points and stemmed points. On *shouldered points* (Fig. 4#10) the base (that is, the end opposite the converging, nonabruptly retouched edges) has a notch or unilateral constriction in one corner forming a so-called shoulder. Several varieties of shouldered points may be defined using differentiating criteria such as those suggested for the leaf-shaped points. Sometimes naturally pointed blades or bladelets with a shoulder set off by abrupt retouch on the end opposite the point are called shouldered points. However, in many if not most instances, it is probable that these shouldered pieces are merely unfinished backed blades or points. A *stemmed (or tanged) point* (Fig. 4#11) is one on which the constriction of the nonpointed end of the blade is bilateral.

As in the case of a flake, the edge of a blade (or bladelet) may bear a notch or series of adjacent notches, in which case the blade is called respectively a *notched blade* (Fig. 4#12) or a *denticulate blade* (Fig. 4#13). Sometimes, the edge opposite the notched or denticulated one is backed, giving a backed notched blade or backed denticulate blade (Fig. 4#14). Sometimes two adjacent notches are formed in such a way that it is the point between them which seems the most important element on the tool, in which case we speak of a *borer* (Fig. 4#15). More generally, however, a borer is any flake or blade on the edge or end of which a small, sharp point has been deliberately set off by retouch.

At many of the sites of particular concern in this book, a prominent category of stone artifacts includes those called battered or *splintered pieces* (Fig. 4#16,17). These pieces are generally rectangular or square flakes, blades, or sections of blades which bear splintering on one or both sets of opposite-lying edges as a result of having been battered along these edges. The splintering is frequently bifacial (that is, located on both the dorsal and ventral surfaces).

Cases are known where one blank (flake or blade) bears examples of two of the major artifact types defined above. Such combinations of types are known as *composite tools* and include more particularly burin/end-scrapers, burin/borers, end-scraper/truncations, and the like.

Of considerable importance is the fact that early man sometimes was at least as interested, if not more interested, in the parent piece from which he struck flakes or blades as in the flakes and blades themselves. Pieces which in this sense are clearly more than cores are sometimes known as *core-tools.* Only three broadly defined varieties need concern us here. The first includes pieces called *choppers* (Fig. 5#1); these consist of pebbles, nodules, or even very thick flakes on which one edge and one edge only has been modified (flaked) on only one surface (that is, unifacially). The second variety comprises *chopping-tools* (Fig. 5#2), artifacts made on pebbles, nodules, or again even on very thick flakes on which a single edge has been modified on both surfaces of the piece (that is, bifacially). Finally, there are objects made on pebbles, nodules, or large flakes on which modification (flaking) is more or less complete over both surfaces. Such pieces are known as *bifaces,* or in some cases as hand-axes (Fig. 5#3).

The above discussion does not in any sense exhaust the number of imaginable types of chipped-stone artifacts; it has, however, dealt with those types which recur in the sites upon which later chapters focus. Retouched pieces which do not fit any of the types defined previously are considered as "miscellaneous" in later chapters.[3]

It is important to realize that although the artifact types so far discussed are frequently known by names which seem to imply their functions, for example, scrapers, burins, and points, the actual functions of the pieces placed in these categories are presently unknown. Attempts to identify the functions of stone tools may be roughly divided into two major approaches: (1) that which seeks to gain a notion of the function of a tool through the study of its context and associations, that is, through the study of where within a site it is most often found and of what other objects most frequently accompany it, and (2) that which makes use of

[3] More detailed discussions of stone-tool typology and technology, upon which the present discussion has been largely based, may be found in the works of François Bordes and Denise de Sonneville-Bordes cited in the bibliography of this book. Also cited there is a recent attempt by James Sackett to pass beyond the intuitive identification of types through the application of statistical procedures.

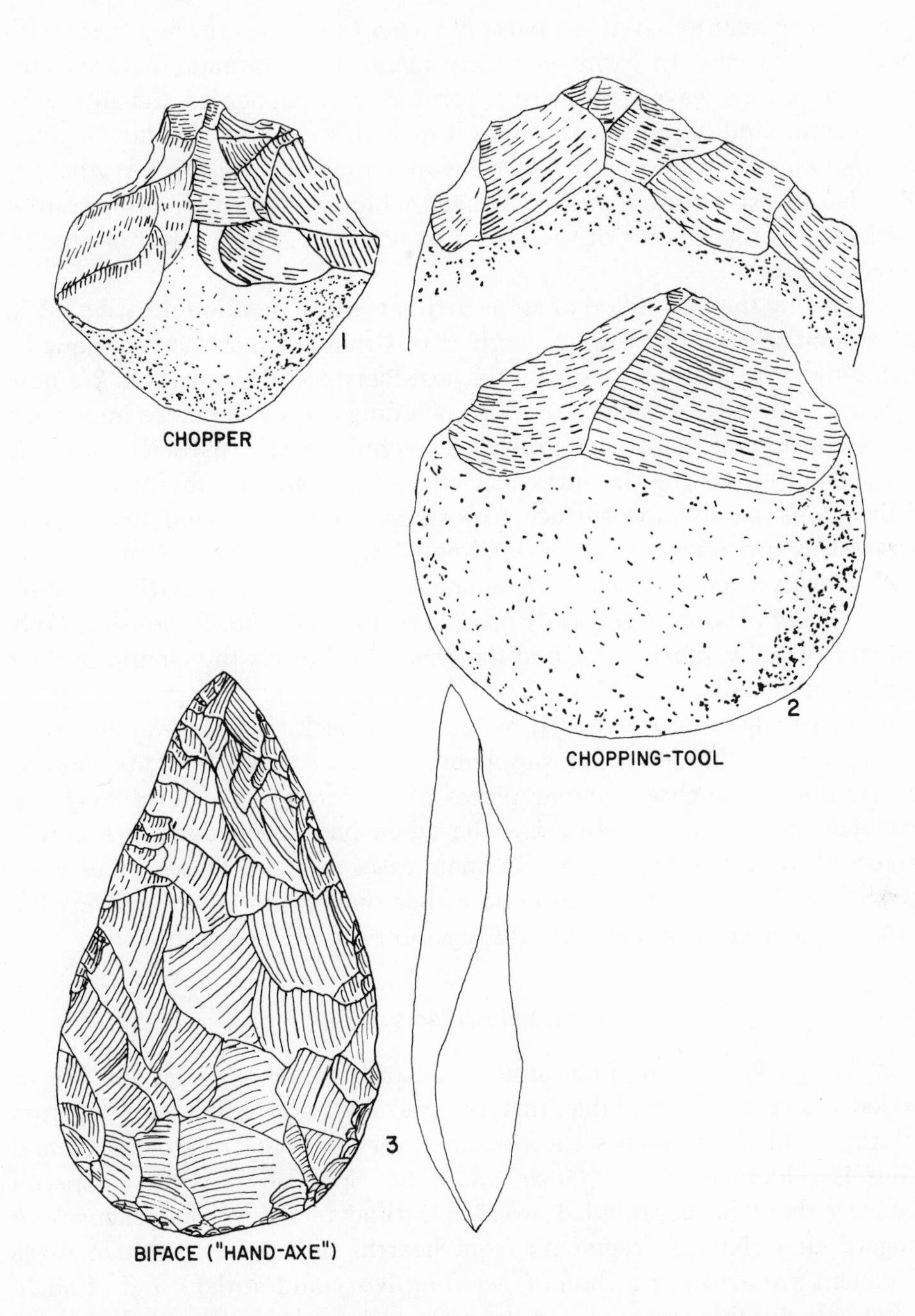

Figure 5. Stone-Artifact Technology and Typology IV (redrawn after Bordes 1961: Plates 46 and 61).

patterns of wear apparent on parts of ancient tools, comparing these with patterns observed to form on nearly identical tools manufactured and used in various ways in modern laboratories. A particular difficulty with the second kind of procedure is that it may only demonstrate how a given artifact *may* have been used, never how it actually *was* used. Nevertheless, Russian investigators in particular have achieved some interesting results with this method. Some of these results, where pertinent, are reported in later chapters.

In closing the discussion of stone artifacts some mention must be made of *ground stone tools*. Until recently it was thought that the technique of grinding stone to make tools was a post-Pleistocene innovation. We now know a number of Pleistocene sites, including one of the more important ones considered below, at which the technique was used. Basically it consists of modifying the surface or edge of a stone by rubbing it repeatedly against an abrasive surface, for example, a piece of sandstone. Sometimes this procedure is also termed polishing; but as S. A. Semenov, the well-known student of primitive technology, has pointed out, the grinding or abrading process is generally used to form a tool, not to polish it (this effect is usually subsidiary), and the term polishing is thus inappropriate and should be dropped. Most often the piece of stone to be ground has its surface or edge first roughened by flaking or pecking. Grinding may thus be seen as a technique which supplements, rather than supplants, flaking. Stone objects, such as tabular pieces of sandstone, on whose rough or roughened surfaces grinding is believed to have been done, are herein referred to as *grinding stones*. In some cases at least, these stones were probably used for smoothing bone rather than stone, or for pulverizing coloring matter or processing wild vegetable materials or even meat.

Nonstone Artifacts

Although Pleistocene man almost certainly made considerable use of wood where it was available, this material does not withstand the rigors of time and the elements except under very special circumstances and thus is seldom found in Pleistocene sites. None of the sites of special concern here have provided wooden artifacts (unless one chooses to regard tiny charred fragments from hearths as artifacts). Much more frequent are artifacts of bone (including ivory and antler) and of shell, relatively durable materials. In the most technical sense, virtually all the bones found in a Pleistocene occupation site might be regarded as artifactual, since by and large these exhibit at least some traces of human activity—for example, cut marks from butchering, skinning, and so forth;

or splintering as a result of the deliberate splitting or smashing for marrow or brains; or patterning in arrangement resulting from having served as constructional material. In actuality, prehistorians generally regard bones which seem to have been used for constructional purposes as parts of "features," and bones which seem to have been broken up for their food value as "kitchen debris." To avoid confusion, the term artifact will be limited here to bone objects clearly modified to make either a tool, a weapon, or what we suppose to have been an ornament or art object. Bone artifacts have never been subjected to the same detailed typological analysis as stone artifacts. Indeed, such analysis may never be undertaken inasmuch as bone artifacts seem to be more culture-specific; that is, whereas the stone-tool types discussed earlier are found in a variety of so-called cultures, bone-artifact types are quite frequently restricted to a single culture. Recurrent types which are worthy of mention are those referred to as awls, needles, points, polishers, pendants (including pierced teeth), and figurines.

Splinters of bone on which one end has been artificially sharpened and tapers to a point, the other end remaining blunt and relatively thick (frequently even preserving an articular head), are called *awls* (Fig. 6#1,2). Splinters on which one end has been artificially sharpened, the opposite one being only moderately thick and having a hole cut or drilled through it, are called *needles* (Fig. 6#3). Similar though usually bulkier objects without holes are called *points* (Fig. 6#4–6). Points may vary considerably in length, and sometimes a rodlike bone artifact which exhibits a fracture at one or both ends is called a fragmentary point, even though no point is apparent on it.

A *polisher* is a long, flat bone artifact, most frequently made of one half of an animal rib which has been split along its length (Fig. 6#7). One end of the object is convex and displays polish presumed to be derived from the burnishing of a material such as leather. *Pendants* include a variety of objects, all of which share the property of having a hole cut or drilled through them, supposedly so that the pieces might be hung from a cord. Perhaps the most frequent type of pendant is a carnivore tooth with a hole drilled or cut through the root. Sometimes perforated objects, such as teeth, which could conceivably have been hung in a series on a cord (rather than singly) are referred to as *beads.* Another recurrent class of bone artifacts consists of carved (and sometimes supplementarily polished) objects which are more or less clearly representations of human beings or animals. These are referred to as *figurines* or *statuettes.* Examples made of soft rock and even of clay are also known.

In later chapters it will become apparent that the types just described

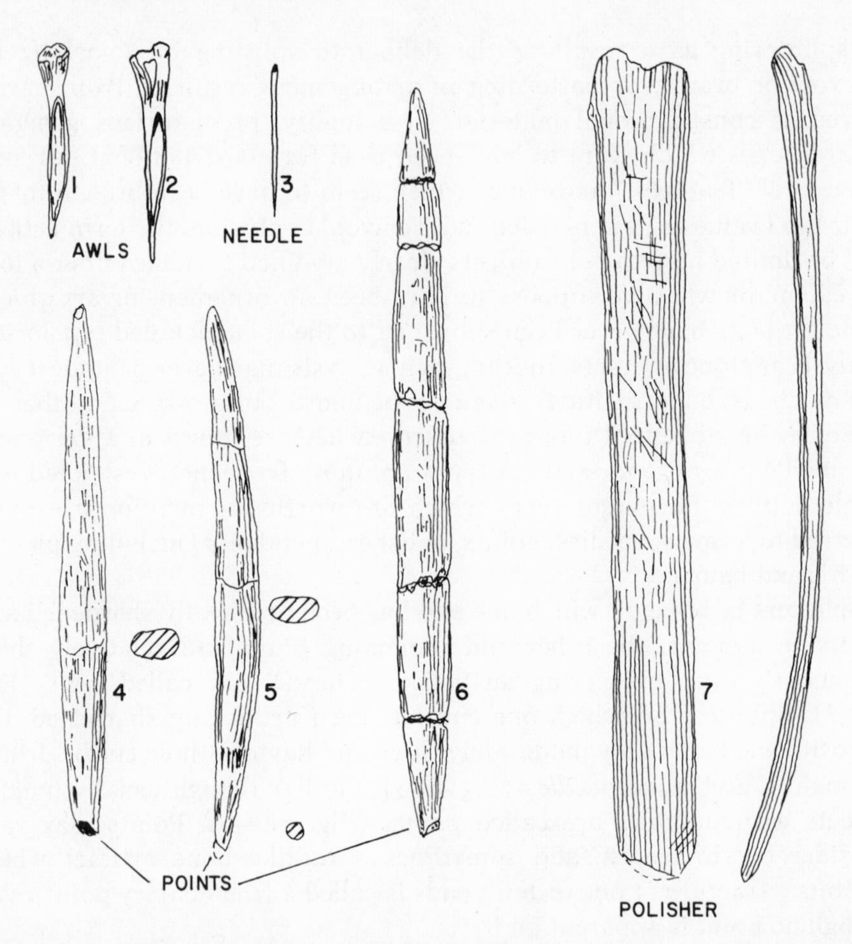

Figure 6. Bone-Artifact Typology (redrawn after Boriskovskij and Praslov 1964: Plates XI and XXIX and Efimenko 1958:313).

include only a fraction of the bone artifacts known from Late Pleistocene sites. Bone objects, in spite of their clearly artifactual nature, are often morphologically so peculiar that it is difficult even to imagine what could have been done with them, much less know what actually was done. In this regard, it is important to realize, as in the case of the stone artifacts, that while we often name bone artifacts in a way which seems to imply a knowledge of how they were used, in reality their functions remain a matter for conjecture.

Artifacts and Pleistocene Prehistory

As stated earlier, a major purpose of this book is to acquaint the reader with the principal determinable features of Upper Paleolithic culture.

Having discussed artifact typology, we are now in a position to examine Upper Paleolithic artifacts and to determine how they contrast with those of the Pleistocene cultures which preceded the Upper Paleolithic.

The oldest artifacts on record belong to the so-called Oldowan culture of Africa. They consist largely of modified hunks of rock and pebbles—crude choppers and chopping-tools—and of flake tools. Oldowan artifact assemblages seem to characterize the Basal Pleistocene. In some parts of the world, particularly in the Far East, assemblages consisting of basically the same kinds of tools (choppers, chopping-tools, and flakes), said to be better made, seem to have continued throughout much of the later Pleistocene as well. In Africa and Europe, however, the Lower Pleistocene witnessed the rise to prominence of bifaces at the expense of choppers and chopping-tools. By the end of the Lower Pleistocene, biface/flake-artifact "cultures," generally grouped together under the name Acheulean, were widespread on both continents. Cultures fitting broadly within the Acheulean tradition continued to exist throughout the Middle and into the Upper Pleistocene. In the course of the Upper Pleistocene, however, the Acheulean in both Africa and Europe was replaced by other cultures. Of particular interest here is the replacement which occurred in Europe and in parts of Asia and Africa fringing the Mediterranean. In this area the earlier part of the Upper Pleistocene saw the Acheulean give way to the so-called Mousterian culture or complex of cultures. The appearance of the Mousterian was not sudden, and no distinct line can be drawn between it and the preceding Acheulean. Like the Acheulean, the Mousterian was characterized by a large variety of flake tools—side-scrapers, points, denticulates, and the like. Where it differed most markedly from the Acheulean was in the biface category; bifaces are either absent in the Mousterian culture or are represented by special types.

The Mousterian culture complex lasted in Europe and in parts of Southwest Asia and North Africa through much of the Würm Glacial period, until at some time within the later part of this glacial, perhaps 30,000 or 40,000 years ago (the exact date possibly depending upon the place), it was replaced by the complex of cultures of central concern here, those termed Upper Paleolithic. The outstanding feature of Upper Paleolithic cultures which may be said to characterize them and distinguish them from their Mousterian predecessors is a marked tendency towards the systematic production of blades, coupled with the consistent manufacture of special kinds of tools, particularly end-scrapers and burins, which had only been sporadically (and perhaps accidentally) manufactured earlier. The side-scrapers and other flake implements, which are the hallmark of the Mousterian culture and are so prominent in the cultures which preceded it, are generally rare in Upper Paleolithic cultures; the same is true of bifaces. On the other hand, Upper Paleolithic peoples seem to have far exceeded the Mousterians and earlier peoples in their use of bone as a raw material. Bone artifacts are known from the earlier cultures, but not in anything like the profusion in which they occur in the Upper Paleolithic. Finally, Upper Paleolithic peoples made a large number and variety of artifacts clearly interpretable as art objects or ornaments. These artifacts appear to be entirely absent in earlier cultures.

The appearance of the Upper Paleolithic in most if not all places where it is known seems likely to have heralded a cultural revolution. The questions of where, how, and why it originated are far from settled and constitute a major focus of ongoing research. These questions are particularly important, since at least in Europe the appearance of the Upper Paleolithic seems to be intimately associated with the appearance of anatomically modern man, *Homo sapiens sapiens*. One of the questions taken up in the concluding chapter of this book is: what do the particular sites described here reveal about the origins of the Upper Paleolithic?

chapter 3. The History of Investigation of the Kostenki-Borshevo Sites

Introduction

With this chapter begins the detailed discussion of the spectacular group of Upper Paleolithic sites located on the banks of the Don River in the eastern part of European Russia (Maps 1 and 2). This discussion is meant to acquaint the reader both with the major features of Upper Paleolithic culture and with the general manner in which the prehistorian obtains information on man and culture in the Pleistocene. The particular sites to be discussed are clustered in and around the neighboring villages of Kostenki, Aleksandrovka, and Borshevo, roughly forty kilometers south of the city of Voronezh. They are frequently combined as the Kostenki-Borshevo group.

Site, Cultural Horizon, and Occupation Horizon

Before learning the history of discovery of the Kostenki-Borshevo sites, it is important to know what is meant by the term site and by the related terms cultural horizon (or level) and occupation horizon (or level). A *site* is quite simply a location where material remains of archeological interest have been discovered. These remains can occur directly on the surface, in which case we speak of a *surface site.* Or they can occur buried in deposits, in which instance two possibilities arise. The first is that the remains lie in the very positions they did when they were left by the ancient occupants of the site. In this case, the remains are said to be *in situ* (= in place) and the site is called a *primary site.* The other possibility is that the remains were moved from their original positions before or during burial. In this case, the materials are said to be derived and the site is called a *secondary site.* A primary site will obviously be of greater value to a prehistorian. On the one hand, it will generally allow more precise placement of its contents in time, and on the other, it is much more likely to contain clearly expressed features. And features are crucial in any attempt to reconstruct the way of life of the ancient occupants of a site.

In a buried site of the Pleistocene age, such as those at Kostenki and Borshevo, the cultural remains (stone tools, bones, and the like), whether in situ or not, are generally concentrated in a stratum of earth from a few centimeters to as much as a meter thick. Such a stratum is referred to as a *cultural horizon* (or level). If the materials in a cultural horizon are in situ, then the more precise term *occupation horizon* (or level) may be used. Frequently, several cultural horizons are found to overlie one another at a particular place. The term site may then be used rather loosely to refer to the general locality and/or to each of the horizons within it. Site is used in this book in both senses, but the reader should have no trouble in discerning from the context which sense is intended in any particular instance.

The History of Discovery of the Kostenki-Borshevo Sites

The manner in which archeologists discover buried sites is frequently a mystery to the layman. It may come as a surprise to learn that many if

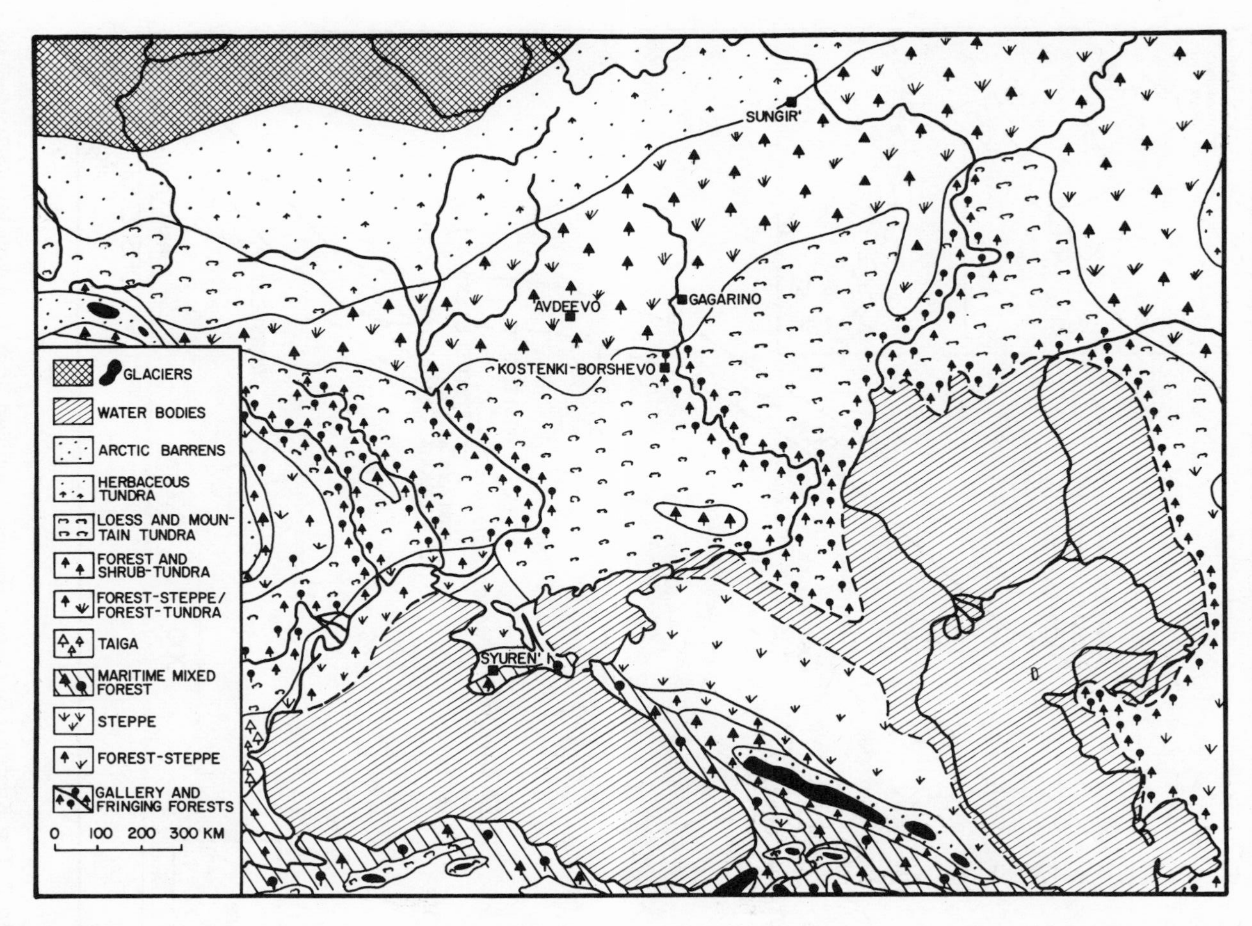

Map 1. Vegetation Zones of European Russia at the Maximum of the Last Glacial (modified after Frenzel 1959–60).

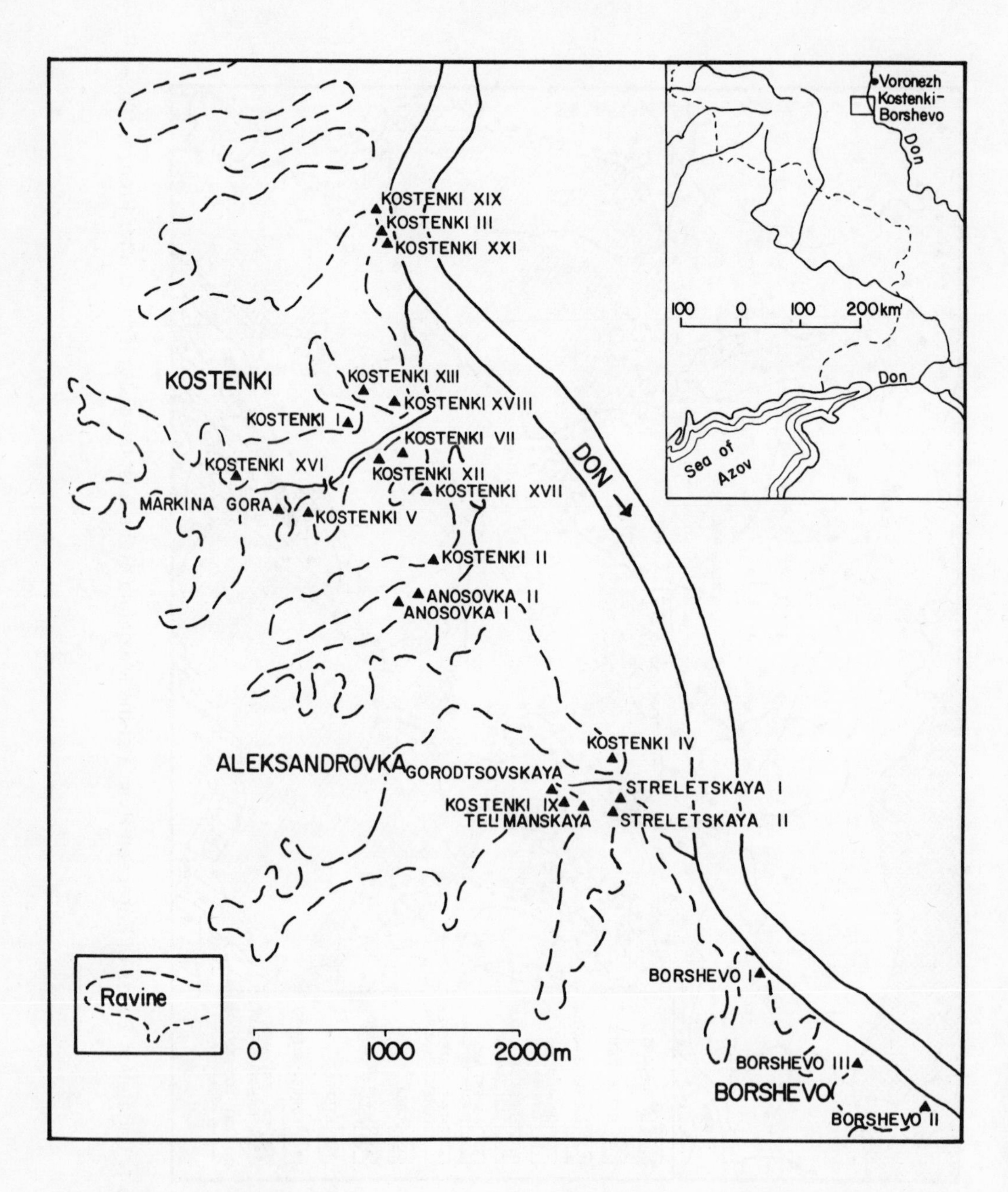

Map 2. The Kostenki-Borshevo Region (modified after Boriskovskij 1963; Map 1).

not most Pleistocene sites have been discovered by accident when a road sliced through a buried cultural horizon or erosion exposed one in the sides of a gully. At Kostenki, most sites were discovered as a result of the economic activities of the local peasants, who have been plowing the area for centuries as well as sinking cellars, house foundations, and the like into the subsoil. To a considerable extent, erosion by the Don and small tributary streams has also aided in the discovery of sites. Only a few have been discovered as a direct result of reconnaissance and test excavation by professional archeologists. And it must be remembered that these test excavations might never have been undertaken if the discoveries of the peasants had not first called attention to the region.

The occurrence of large bones in the general vicinity of the village of Kostenki has been known for a very long time. This knowledge is reflected in the village name (Kostensk in the seventeenth and eighteenth centuries), derived from the Russian word for bone, *kost'*. In medieval times a legend sprang up among the populace of the Kostenki region that the large bones often encountered in the vicinity were those of "antediluvian giants." The legend spread more widely and eventually came to the attention of Peter the Great and of the eighteenth-century scholars, Corneille de Bruin and S. G. Gmelin. In 1768–1769, Gmelin conducted excavations at Kostenki and uncovered a number of large bones which he correctly recognized as those of elephants. Although it is likely that these bones occurred in association with stone artifacts, Gmelin made no mention of them. In the latter part of the eighteenth and earlier part of the nineteenth centuries, a number of historians attempted (always incorrectly) to explain the clearly enigmatic occurrence of elephant bones on the Don. Particularly imaginative was the notion that the bones represented the remains of war elephants left behind by one or another Asiatic army. It was not until the second half of the nineteenth century, after the initial accumulation of data on early man in western Europe and the discovery of stone tools in association with remains of mammoths at Gontsy on the Udaj (in 1873) and Karacharovo on the Oka (in 1877–1878), that the occurrence of elephant bones at Kostenki was at last correctly appreciated. In June, 1879, I. S. Polyakov visited Kostenki to check personally Gmelin's findings and succeeded in discovering the now famous Upper Paleolithic site of Kostenki I. In the report on his excavations at Kostenki I, Polyakov wrote, "At Kostenki we have undeniable proof that man of the far-removed Paleolithic period was a contemporary of the mammoth."

In the years following Polyakov's pioneering work, a number of other archeologists visited Kostenki and conducted excavations at Kostenki I. But only in 1905, through the efforts of A. A. Spitsyn, was a second site discovered in the same region. This second site was located 4 km. south of the first in the village of Borshevo. Today it bears the name of Borshevo I.

It was not until the early years of the Soviet period that the first systematic work was undertaken at Kostenki. Over the years 1922–1928, expeditions primarily under the direction of S. N. Zamyatnin and P. P. Efimenko conducted scientific excavations at Kostenki I and Borshevo I and discovered eight new sites in the vicinity (see Table A-1 in the Appendix). The year 1927 may be seen as particularly important, for in that year Zamyatnin, excavating at Gagarino, a site in the Don Valley to the north of the Kostenki-Borshevo group, uncovered what appeared to be incontrovertible evidence of the remains of a structure in a Paleolithic occupation level, the first such discovery in Europe. With this discovery fresh in mind, Soviet investigators, in particular Efimenko and Zamyatnin and Efimenko's student, A. N. Rogachev, initiated in the 1930's the kind of large-scale, horizontal excavations at Kostenki which would permit the isolation of ancient structural remnants in the ground. These excavations began with the horizontal division of a site into a grid of adjacent squares, one meter on a side. All objects and features uncovered were then carefully plotted on maps on which the meter-square grid system was reproduced in miniature. To the extent that it was possible, major features were maintained intact until the excavations had been completed. As a result of these painstaking procedures, spectacular "ruins" were uncovered at many sites, as data below will attest. The 1930's also saw the discovery of yet more sites in the general Kostenki-Borshevo region (see Table A-1 in the Appendix); and near the very end of the decade the first professional attempt at an analysis of the geological conditions of occurrence of the sites was undertaken by the geologist M. N. Grishchenko.

World War II brought a halt to all investigations at Kostenki, and the years immediately after the war were devoted largely to analysis of materials gathered in the 1930's. It was not until 1948 that investigation in the field was renewed, again with the participation of Grishchenko. He was soon joined in his work by other earth scientists, most notably, G. I. Lazukov and somewhat later, A. A. Velichko. Discovery of still more sites and of new occupation horizons at old ones provided Grishchenko, Lazukov, and Velichko with more than enough material to study. During the 1950's principal responsibility for investigation of archeological materials in the Kostenki-Borshevo region passed to A. N. Rogachev and P. I. Boriskovskij. As a result of their work the number of known sites reached its present level (approximately 24), and for the first time human remains were found (at Kostenki II, XIV, XV, and XVIII). At the same time many details of the geological circumstances of the various sites were worked out so that it became possible to establish reliably the ages of occupation horizons of various sites relative to one another.

Work at Kostenki and Borshevo has continued into the 1960's, and even if no new major field expeditions were to be undertaken in the future, the full description and analysis of the materials already on hand would require many years to come. It is with the description and analysis of the available materials that this book is largely concerned. The next chapter deals specifically with the geological conditions in which these materials occur, an essential prelude to their description.

chapter 4. The Geology of the Kostenki-Borshevo Sites

Introduction

This chapter discusses the geological circumstances in which the Kostenki-Borshevo sites occur. Of special concern here is what these circumstances may tell us about the relation of the sites to one another in time and about the environment at the time the sites were occupied. In order to deal effectively with these topics, it is first necessary to define some sedimentological and geomorphological terms.

Earth scientists commonly divide the continuum of particle sizes which may compose a sediment into a number of discrete size categories called grades. One such scheme of division, differing only in minor respects from others in general use, is presented in Table 2. An analysis of the particle-size composition of a particular sediment, using the categories in the table, can often provide valuable information about the circumstances which led to the formation of the sediment. Some combinations of particle-size categories are so common that it is convenient to give them special names. For example, a sediment in which clay and especially sand and silt are all well represented, is often called a *loam.*

Certain types of deposits are particularly important for understanding the conditions of occurrence of the Kostenki-Borshevo sites. First, there are stream-laid or *alluvial deposits.* These deposits vary from quite coarse (pebble beds = gravels) to quite fine (silts). They are generally characterized by internal stratification—the arrangement of materials into distinct beds or strata within the over-all deposit. Frequently the beds are disposed horizontally, that is, with their interfaces parallel to the surface of the river which deposited them. However, other kinds of bedding are possible, depending on such factors as whether the beds were laid down near to or far from the river banks, whether the river was subject to frequent changes in the velocity of flow, and so forth.

TABLE 2. Modified Atterberg Scale (from Butzer 1964:158)

Nomenclature	*Particle sizes*
Cobbles	>60 mm.
Coarse pebbles	20–60 mm.
Medium pebbles	6–20 mm.
Fine pebbles	2–6 mm.
Coarse sand	0.2–2.0 mm.
Medium sand	0.06–0.2 mm.
Fine sand	0.02–0.06 mm.
Silt	0.002–0.02 mm.
Clay	<0.002 mm.

A second major class of deposits includes those termed colluvial. *Colluvial sediments* are ones which have accumulated on or at the base of a hillside, largely as a result of rainwash and the force of gravity. The particle-size composition of the deposits can vary, depending, for example, on the inclination of a slope or the extent to which water action (slope wash) was involved in the accumulation. The fact that the action of water is only one factor in the origin of colluvial deposits means that they tend to be less well sorted then alluvial ones, that is, they are more likely to consist of large percentages of particles of several distinct grades. Further, coarser elements (pebbles) tend to be more angular and less rounded in colluvial sediments than in alluvial ones. Like alluvial deposits, colluvial ones may exhibit bedding, though with the interfaces of the beds commonly at an angle to the horizon, since they parallel the surface of a slope. A special kind of colluvial deposit results from the process of *solifluction* (literally "soil flow"). This flow involves the down-slope oozing of loose sediment saturated with water. When present in fossil form, solifluction deposits may provide valuable information about past climate, since they are especially likely to form in areas where the subsoil is permanently or temporarily frozen. This condition inhibits the downward percolation of water during the spring thaw and promotes water saturation of surface materials.

Another major category of deposits is *till* or *moraine,* a sediment laid down by a glacier. Till is generally distinctive in displaying neither bedding nor sorting; the variously sized rocky elements are dispersed without system in a clayey matrix. The final category is *loess,* a loamy sediment made up principally of fine sand and silt (size composition: 70–95% of material < 0.06 mm.; 97–99.5% < 0.2 mm.). Loess is generally believed to be wind-deposited, and at least in midlatitude Europe, to have originated during glacial periods when powerful winds blew over the unvegetated barrens immediately in front of the great ice sheets. Besides the absence of vegetation, the ongoing disintegration of rock as a result of frost is thought to have made the areas immediately contiguous to the glaciers especially favorable for wind erosion (deflation). The fine particles picked up by strong winds were frequently transported considerable distances, often being deposited several tens of kilometers away from their point of origin in loessic beds reaching tens of meters in thickness. Loessic deposits in pure form usually do not exhibit any stratification, except where deposition was temporarily interrupted and soil formation begun (see below). Sometimes, after their original deposition by wind, loesses were redeposited ("reworked") on slopes or by streams. The ultimate loessic origin of such sediments may only be apparent in their peculiar silty-sandy composition.

Once formed, deposits may subsequently be altered. Unless very peculiar conditions prevail, whenever a land surface is exposed to the elements, the surface will gradually undergo chemical and physical changes in a process known as *weathering.* The total subsurface depth to which such changes are effective is known as the *zone of weathering.* The uppermost part of the zone is admixed with organic materials and is known as the *soil.* The features of a particular soil—horizons within it, coloration, texture, chemical composition, and the like—depend in large part on the particular environmental features which obtained while the soil was developing. Sometimes, after a soil has been formed, sedimentation is renewed and the soil becomes buried beneath the surface. The analyzable features of a buried soil (exposed in a vertical section or profile through a series of deposits) can provide a paleogeographer and thus a prehistorian with valuable information about past environment. For example, a soil found within a loess deposit may be taken to represent a time when loess accumulation was interrupted or limited, and milder, so-called interstadial conditions prevailed. Soils may form on virtually any kind of sediment—for instance, on alluvium, colluvium, till, and loess.

The concept of *stream terrace* is also important in studying the geology of the Kostenki-Borshevo sites. A terrace is a more or less flat strip of land paralleling the course of a river at some height above the present-day level of the river. A terrace is generally interpreted as the remnant of the ancient floor (flood-plain) of a valley at a time when the river in it flowed at a higher level. Subsequently, the river downcut its bed and the adjacent valley floor to a new level. Downcutting may be initiated by one or several factors operating either to increase the gradient of a stream and/or decrease the amount of detrital material it carries relative to the amount of water in it. Stream terraces may be divided into two principal types—erosional or degradational, and aggradational. Erosional terraces are simply ones marking the approximate level of flow of an ancient river which was actively planing its valley floor, leaving few or no deposits. An aggradational terrace marks the approximate level of an ancient river which was actively depositing along its course. Both erosional and aggradational terraces may become subsequently covered with colluvial and/or windborne deposits. Many Pleistocene sites, including nearly all those considered below, have been found within nonalluvial deposits overlying the surfaces of old river terraces.

The Geology of the Kostenki-Borshevo Region

The villages of Kostenki and Borshevo are located in the Don Valley, roughly forty kilometers south of Voronezh. The western slope of the Don Valley in the vicinity of the villages and for some distance further south forms the eastern boundary of the Central Russian Upland, the eastern slope, the western boundary of the Tambov Lowland. The eastern part of the Central Russian Upland, in contrast to the Tambov Lowland, appears to have been undergoing continued uplift, and partly as a consequence, the Don Valley in the Kostenki-Borshevo region is markedly asymmetrical—the western slope is quite steep, the eastern one quite gentle. Since all the sites of interest here occur on the western side of the valley, our attention will be devoted to the geological/geomorphological structure of that area (Fig. 7).

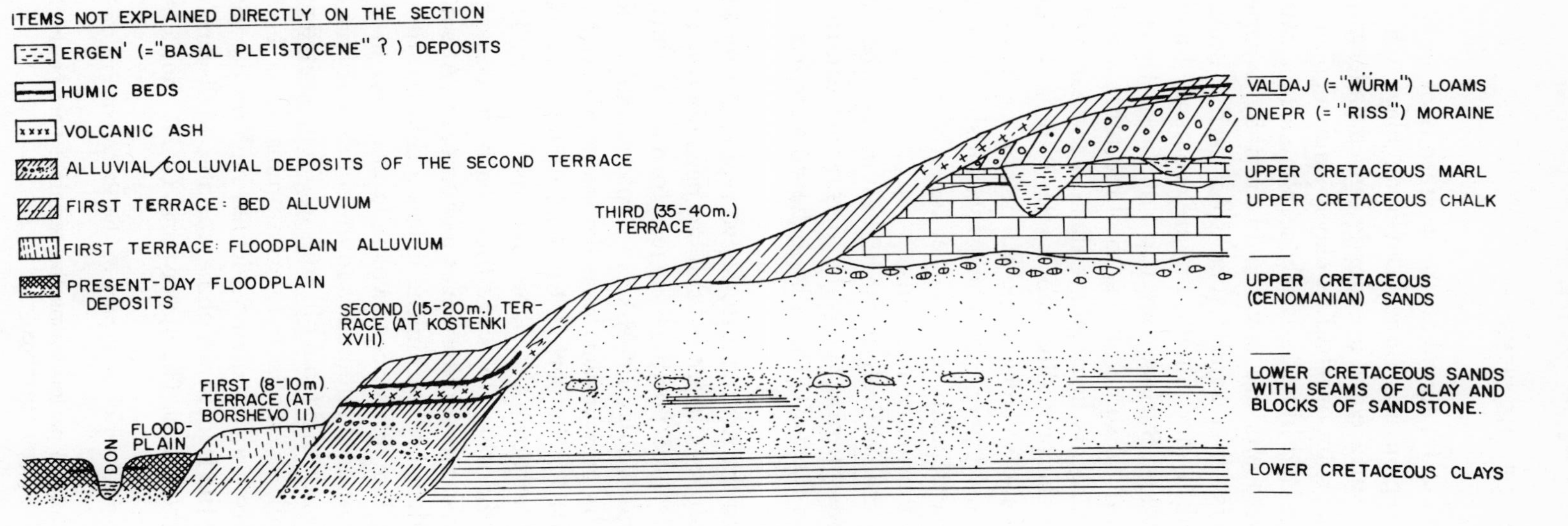

Figure 7. Section through the Western Slope of the Don Valley in the Kostenki-Borshevo Region (redrawn after Lazukov 1957b:86).

The oldest deposits so far found on the western bank of the Don in the Kostenki-Borshevo region are Upper Devonian clays which only very rarely outcrop at the surface and are mostly buried under younger deposits.[1] The Devonian clays are overlaid by clayey-sandy deposits assigned to the Lower Cretaceous and likewise rarely seen in surface exposures.[2] The Lower Cretaceous deposits are covered in turn by a series of Upper Cretaceous sediments—first sands; then soft, earthy limestone (often referred to as "chalk"); and finally, impure, compact limestone (often referred to as "marl"). Surface outcrops of these Upper Cretaceous deposits are abundant. In some places, the limestones are directly overlaid by "Ergen' " sediments belonging either to the early Pleistocene or the terminal part of the preceding epoch (the Pliocene). The remaining deposits making up the western slope all belong with certainty to the Pleistocene (Middle and Upper) and consist variously of till (moraine) or colluvial loams. These deposits occur either directly on the surface or not far below it in natural or man-made cuts.

Glacial till is restricted entirely to the highest part of the western slope, that is, to the uplands forming the water divide between the Don Valley and the next valley to the west. The till is believed to represent a remnant of extensive deposits left behind by the Don lobe of the great Dnepr glacier which covered the Kostenki-Borshevo region during Riss times. In places atop the till, a partially eroded soil has been observed whose major features and stratigraphic position suggest formation during the Eem Interglacial (= Dnepr/Valdaj or Mikulino Interglacial in local terms). The soil is overlain by grey-brown, loesslike loams believed to date from the Würm (= Valdaj) Glacial period. Unlike the till or the soil formed on it, the loams extend far down the slope towards the river. The top of the loams was weathered during Holocene times with the consequent formation of a kind of grasslands soil known as a chernozem. At some localities, investigators have identified within the loams a thin stratum of volcanic ash derived from a late Pleistocene volcanic eruption in the Caucasus Mountains, several hundred kilometers to the south. They have also found beds of buried humus eroded from old soils and redeposited as colluvium. More interesting still, the Polish geologist-prehistorian L. Sawicki has described a profile from a clay quarry located high on the western slope, roughly 90 m. above the Don, in which he was able to discern three in situ buried soils within the loams. The upper parts (= "A" horizons) of all the

[1] The Devonian geological period is a part of the Paleozoic Era and ended about 350 million years ago.

[2] The Cretaceous geological period forms the terminal part of the Mesozoic Era, which ended roughly 70 million years ago.

soils had been more or less completely eroded away, but the lower parts (= "B" horizons) are clearly preserved. Most investigators believe the loams to represent Würm (= Valdaj) Glacial loess reworked by colluvial action immediately after deposition; the soils would then represent milder interstadial periods when loess deposition nearly or entirely ceased. The correlation of interstadials reflected in the sediments at Kostenki with interstadials detected elsewhere will be discussed below.

Examination of the western slope of the Don in the Kostenki-Borshevo region by a number of workers has led to identification of remnants of three stream terraces, all covered and thus masked to some extent by nonalluvial deposits. Each terrace is known by the height its colluvial cover reaches above the low-water (August) level of the river. For the third (and highest) terrace this amounts to an average of 35–40 m., for the second 15–20 m., and for the first 8–10 m. The modern alluvial floodplain has a surface roughly 4 m. above the August level of the Don. The terraces are very narrow; the maximum width attained by the third is 40–50 m., by the second 30–40 m., and by the first seldom more than 60–70 m. The floodplain averages 2.5–3 km. wide.

The entire western slope in the Kostenki-Borshevo region has been strongly dissected by a branching network of ravines and gullies, some of which carry small brooks flowing to the Don. Many of the larger ravines seem to be of considerable age since as many as three terraces are developed on their slopes. These terraces merge at the mouths of the ravines with the terraces of the Don proper. Consequently—and also because of the fact that the colluvial covers of the ravine terraces are strikingly similar in internal structure to their counterparts in the valley—Soviet researchers frequently speak of a site as occurring in the colluvium overlying one or another terrace (First, Second, or Third) without specifying whether the site is located directly in the valley or in a large tributary ravine. This practice will be followed here (though see Map 3); and further justification for it will be presented below.

The uppermost (= Third) terrace is of the erosional type; sections through it in the Kostenki-Borshevo region have never exposed alluvial deposits. Most commonly, sections reveal late Pleistocene grey-brown colluvial, loesslike loams (reworked loess) directly overlying Late Cretaceous sands. Sites related to the Third Terrace are rare. The site of Kostenki XIII is located in the colluvial loesslike loam covering it, while that of Kostenki XVIII, consisting of a grave, intrudes into the Late Cretaceous sands forming its base.

The Second Terrace is the most important from the prehistorian's point of view, since the majority of sites in the region are in colluvial

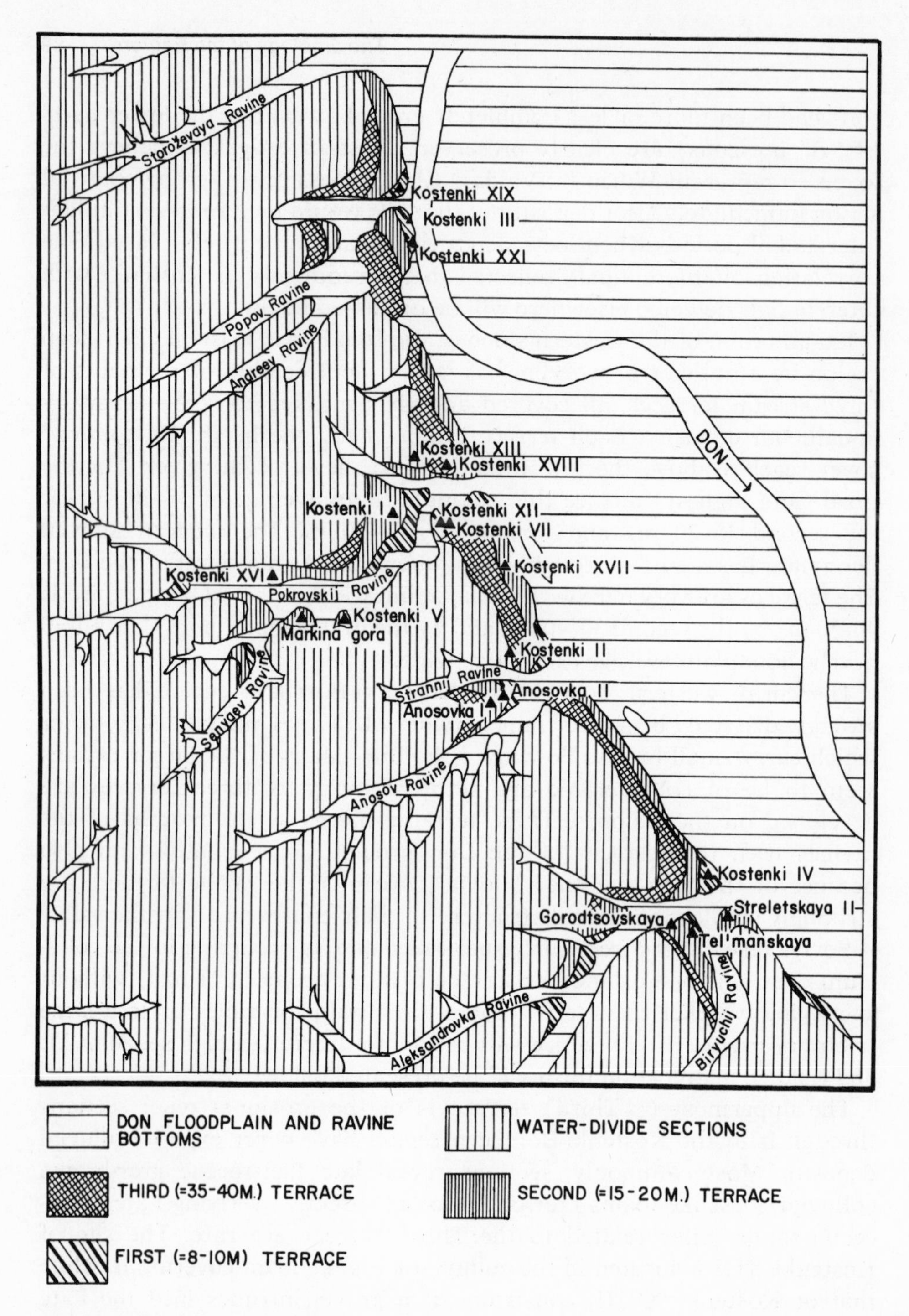

Map 3. Geomorphological Map of the Environs of the Village of Kostenki (redrawn after Lazukov 1957b:Figure 1).

deposits which overlie it. These deposits are poorly preserved in the Don Valley proper, and as a consequence few sites are known on the Second Terrace there. They are well preserved in many of the ravines, however, and this, in combination with the intensive use of the terrace for agriculture, has led to the discovery of numerous sites. Many sections have been made through the colluvial cover of the second terrace and into the alluvium below. Interestingly, in the overwhelming majority of cases these sections have exposed approximately the same sequence of deposits (Fig. 7). Above Late Cretaceous sands at the base of the profile are usually found bedded loams and sandy loams with thin strata and lenses of moderately to well-rolled chalk pebbles. These deposits are believed to be of mixed alluvial-colluvial origin. Higher occur two beds of humic loam separated by a bed of nonhumic loam. The "humic beds" are apparently made up of redeposited (colluvial) soil material; they are clearly not remnants of in situ soils. The humic material is usually distributed throughout each bed in ragged, wavy lenses alternating with lenses of nonhumic loam. The "upper humic bed" generally exhibits greater dip (inclination to the horizontal) than the lower, as well as more pronounced internal bedding (lamination) and less uniform internal composition and structure, which has led investigators to suppose an increase in the intensity of colluviation during the time of its deposition. The extraordinary crumpling of some of the humic lenses within the "upper humic bed" is seen to indicate that it may have accumulated in part through solifluction. At four sites (Kostenki VI, XII, XIV, and XVII) the nonhumic loam separating the "humic beds" contains lenses of volcanic ash derived from the same late Pleistocene volcanic eruption in the Caucasus Mountains that was mentioned earlier. The deposits overlying the "upper humic bed" usually consist of uniform, nonbedded, grey-brown, loesslike loams, representing a continuation downslope of similar loams found overlying the till on the uplands and in the quarry discussed previously.

In some profiles, alluvium at the base of the sequence is entirely absent and the "lower humic bed" rests on pure colluvial deposits or more or less directly on Upper Cretaceous sands. The absence of alluvium may be explained by the location of some sites near the rear junctures of the terrace, that is, far from the river in places where alluviation may have been weak or may not have occurred at all. Likewise, differential location of the sites with regard to important topographic features, such as steep slopes, may be seen as responsible for differences in the thickness and detailed composition of corresponding colluvial beds at different sites. Differences in detail from site to site should not, however, be allowed to obscure the widespread occurrence of the general sequence outlined above. The utility of the sequence lies in allowing the clear placement in time, relative to one another, of sites occurring within the colluvial deposits overlying the Second Terrace (see Fig. 8). The presence of striking similarities among widely separated profiles is illustrated in Table A-2 (in the Appendix), where a profile from Kostenki XVII, located directly in Don Valley is compared with one from Kostenki XIV (Markina gora), located more than 2 km. from the valley on the southern slope of Pokrovskij Ravine.

Unfortunately, no one has yet succeeded in linking the colluvial humic beds overlying the Second Terrace with the in situ soil formations from which they were derived. However, the presence of in situ buried soils higher on the slope in the quarry profile described earlier suggests that this task will prove possible. Satisfactory clarification of these field relationships is prerequisite to reliable geological dating of the Second Terrace sites.

On occasion, a section through the colluvial deposits overlying the Second Terrace has failed to expose a profile with two humic beds separated by a bed of nonhumic loam. So far this has happened at only one site, Kostenki V, where colluviation seems to have followed a peculiar trend, probably related to the peculiar topographic circumstances in which the site is located. Essentially two distinct profiles have been described from the site, one from its more downslope portion, the other from its upslope part (see Fig. 9). Upslope, beneath the Holocene chernozem is a brown, loesslike loam containing the occasional flint artifacts of the uppermost (= first) cultural level. The brown loam is underlaid by a light-brown loam, at the very bottom of which (3.2 m. from the surface) occurs the middle (= second) cultural level. It is 10 cm. thick and contains flint artifacts and fragments and splinters of both charred and uncharred bone. Directly below it is found a bed of rounded chalk rubble and below that laminated loam containing more such rubble. The bottom of the laminated loam has not been reached.

Downslope (more than 20 m. from the profile just described), the Holocene chernozem is underlaid by redeposited Late Cretaceous sand. The sand in turn rests on successive beds of brown, loesslike loam, rounded chalk fragments, laminated loam with rounded chalk fragments, more redeposited late Cretaceous sand, and finally at a depth of ca. 2.60–3.40 m., the lowermost (= third) cultural level. This level consists principally of a thick accumulation of horse and mammoth bones in a matrix of rounded chalk fragments. The bone accumulation lies directly on yet more redeposited late Cretaceous sand. The anomaly of Kostenki V among the Second Terrace sites is apparent.

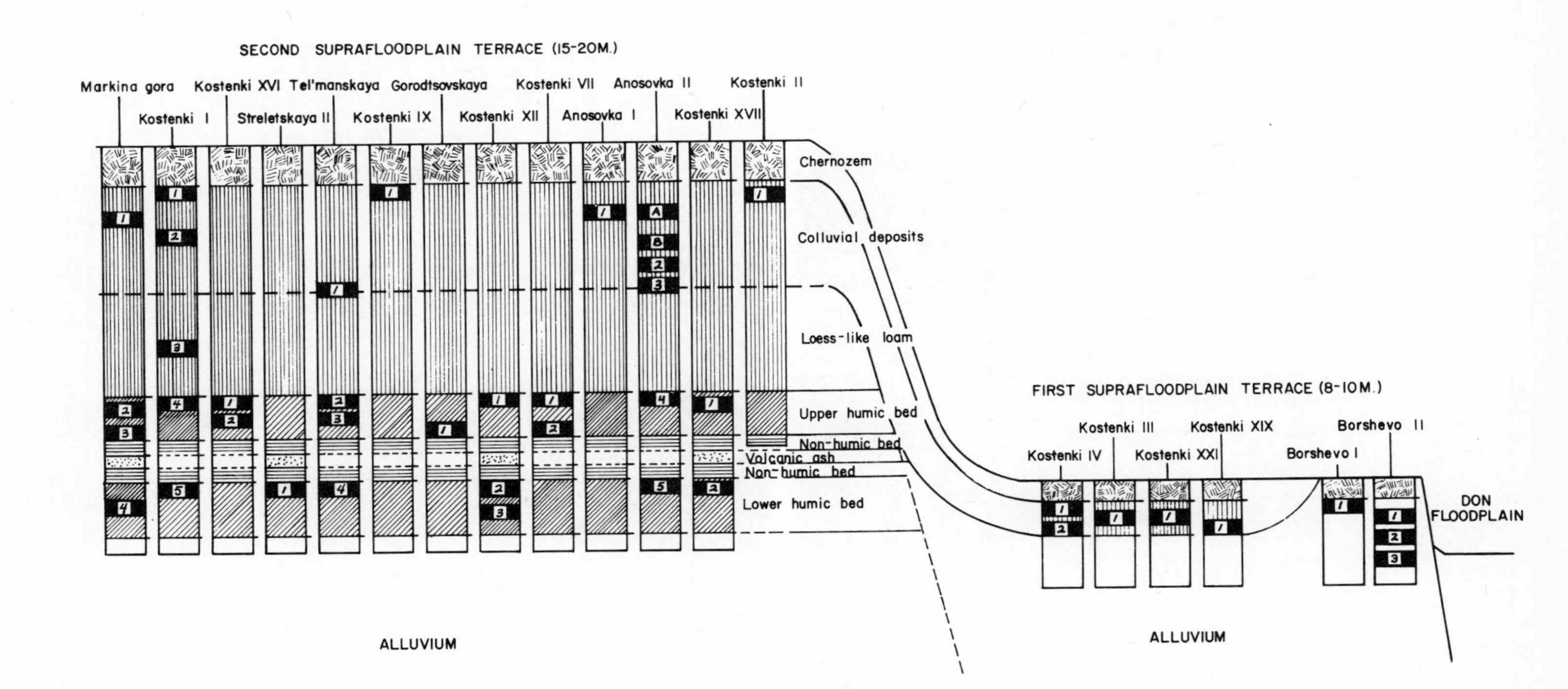

Figure 8. Comparative Stratigraphy of the Kostenki-Borshevo Sites (Modified after Rogachev 1961a:401).

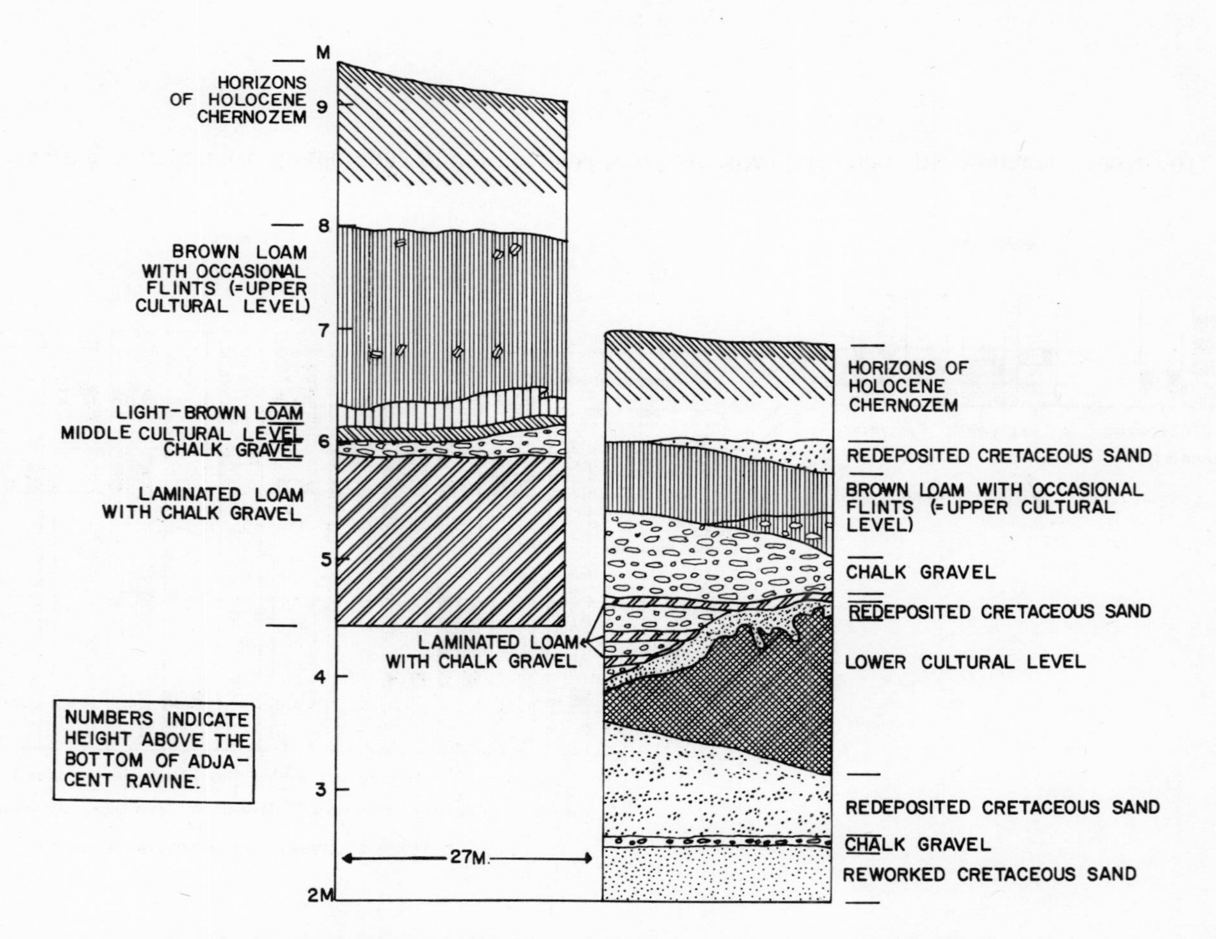

Figure 9. Profiles of Kostenki V (redrawn after Rogachev 1957:Figure 47).

We may now turn our attention to the First Terrace, whose alluvial/colluvial sequence has supplied a relatively small but nonetheless interesting group of sites. Unlike the colluvial series overlying the Second Terrace, that overlying the First has provided no "marker beds" by reference to which it would be possible to order the known sites in time. First Terrace sites have provided a variety of profiles, only some of which can be said to resemble the others closely. The most common profile is one in which sandy-loamy alluvial deposits are overlain by grey-brown, loesslike colluvial loams, somewhat greyer and coarser than those covering the Second Terrace and the higher slopes. A chernozem soil of Holocene origin is generally found developed on the loams. At several localities, the grey-brown loams covering the First Terrace contained a horizon of lime nodules believed to have been formed in a soil whose upper parts have been eroded away. The erosional hiatus thus represented may ultimately turn out to be a First Terrace analogue of the humic "marker beds" of the Second Terrace. The absence of a bed of lime nodules, as well as of an erosional hiatus, in the grey-brown loams overlying the Second Terrace has led some investigators to suppose that these loams are all older than those on the First Terrace. On the other hand, some workers have supposed rough temporal comparability between the upper part of the loams covering the Second Terrace and those overlying the First (see Fig. 8).

One very important First Terrace site, Borshevo II, has provided a completely unique profile, in which a buried meadow or floodplain soil is represented (see Fig. 7). In Table A-3 (in the Appendix), this peculiar profile with soil is compared with the more typical section through First Terrace deposits found at Kostenki III.

Sections through the floodplain of the Don have revealed a series of sandy-silty alluvial deposits. In the upper part of these sections are sometimes found buried soils (up to three in some places) consisting mainly of dark bands of semidecomposed vegetative material. The entire sequence of floodplain deposits is believed to date from the Holocene, and the buried soils, which may or may not have climatic significance, need not concern us.

Radiocarbon Dating of Kostenki-Borshevo Sites

Before considering in detail the geological ages of the various Kostenki-Borshevo sites, it is first necessary to discuss briefly the small number of radiocarbon dates so far available from them. The radiocarbon-dating technique is basically a method for determining how long ago a particular carbon-containing object ceased to acquire fresh carbon. Organic remains constitute by far the most frequently dated materials; what is measured then is the time of death of the organism(s) providing the remains. The radiocarbon technique is far from infallible, and great caution must be exercised in evaluating its results. Perhaps the most difficult problem to deal with is the possible contamination of a buried object by fresh carbon—for example, of old charcoal by younger humic material brought down by percolating water. Such contamination will lead to the charcoal coming out "too young" when the radiocarbon technique is

TABLE 3. Radiocarbon Dates from Kostenki-Borshevo Sites*

Stratigraphic level (from younger to older)	*Radiocarbon dates (in years Before Present)*	*Material dated, site*
First Terrace	11,800 ± 500 (GIN-107) 12,300 ± 100 (GIN-88)	Charred bone, Kostenki XIX Humic loam, Borshevo II
Second Terrace, grey-brown loam above upper humic bed	14,020 ± 60 (GIN-86) 15,200 ± 600 (Ta-34) 9,610 ± 190 (GIN-85) 11,000 ± 200 (GIN-93)	Charred bone, Kostenki I, Level 1 ???, Anosovka II, Level 2 Fossil bone, Anosovka II, Level 1 Fossil mammoth bone, Kostenki II
Second Terrace, upper humic bed	20,000 ± 350 (GIN-77) 23,060 ± 300 (GIN-89) 14,300 ± 460 (GIN-79)	Humic loam, Kostenki XVII Humic loam, Kostenki XII Fossil horse bone, Markina gora (=Kostenki XIV), Level 3
Second Terrace, lower humic bed	20,100 ± 200 (GIN-78)	Humic loam, Kostenki XVII

* Geological Institute (GIN) dates from Cherdyntsev et al. (1965:1413–1414); Tartu (Ta) date from Rogachev (1966:41).

applied. Even in the presumed absence of contamination, certain aspects of the dating method make it necessary to state all dates with a plus or minus figure. This figure is to be understood as providing the range in which the dated object is likely to fall *two times out of three;* there is always one chance in three that the actual age of the object falls outside this range. (The likelihood of actually bracketing the correct age of an object may be considerably increased—to 96 times out of 100—by doubling the plus or minus figure.) It is probably obvious that radiocarbon dates for an archeological or geological horizon are most reliable when a number of samples from it have been dated and when the dates exhibit consistency among themselves. It is always dangerous to rely on a single date.

With this in mind, we can now turn to the dates from the Kostenki-

Borshevo sites, presented in Table 3. From the table it is apparent that there is a clear tendency for stratigraphically older levels to possess older dates—as they should. At first it may appear surprising that the dates from the two humic beds should be so close (discounting for the moment the date from Markina gora), but this proximity would be entirely reasonable if the humus from both beds was derived from a single fossil soil. In any case, it is important to remember that the humus in the humic beds must antedate the actual periods of accumulation of these colluvial deposits.

The Geological Age of the Kostenki-Borshevo Sites

Already presented evidence makes it clear that the Kostenki-Borshevo sites belong within the Würm Glacial period. It is presently known that this time interval was far from uniformly cold; rather, it was interrupted on several occasions by interstadials, distinct oscillations towards warmer conditions. The fullest information on the number and chronology of Würm interstadials comes from studies made in the Netherlands and Denmark. The earliest interstadials detected there are those known respectively as the Amersfoort and Broerup, both of which seem to have occurred prior to 55,000–60,000 years ago.[3] The cold climatic conditions which succeeded the Broerup seem to have continued more or less unabated until they were punctuated between approximately 39,000 and 37,000 years ago and again between 32,000 and 29,000 years ago by two marked warm oscillations called the Hengelo and Denekamp Interstadials respectively. The Denekamp was followed by what is believed to have been a time of intense cold, terminating at about 12,400 B.P. with the Boelling Interstadial. The Boelling lasted until about 12,000 B.P., when there was a brief fluctuation towards colder conditions followed by the Alleroed Interstadial in the interval 11,800–11,000 B.P. Finally, after one more cold lapse, the Würm Glacial was terminated approximately at 10,000 B.P.

In the loess areas of central and eastern Europe, Würm Glacial stratigraphy and chronology are unfortunately not quite so clear as in Holland and Denmark. The Amersfoort and Broerup Interstadials seem to be incorporated in a soil complex involving the Eem Interglacial as well. This complex is frequently referred to as Stillfried A. The Hengelo and

[3] More exact dates cannot be obtained because these interstadials fall at or just beyond the present maximum range of the radiocarbon dating technique.

Denekamp Interstadials are presumably both to be correlated with an interval in the loess regions known as Paudorf or Stillfried B, during which time loess deposition ceased and soil development was once again initiated.

Given the present evidence, it is possible to suppose that the colluvial humic beds overlying the Second Terrace in the Kostenki-Borshevo region were derived from a soil formed during the Paudorf Interstadial. The

TABLE 4. Provisional Sequence of Pleistocene Events in the Kostenki-Borshevo Area

1. Deposition of the Ergen' clays. Late Pliocene or Basal Pleistocene.
2. Extended period of erosion, probably interrupted by temporary periods of alluviation. *Lower to Middle Pleistocene.*
3. Deposition of till by the Don lobe of the Dnepr Glacier. *Late Middle Pleistocene* (*Early Riss*).
4. Downcutting by the Don and its tributaries. *Late Riss Glacial or Eem Interglacial.* Soil formation atop Dnepr till. *Eem Interglacial.*
5. Planation of the Third Terrace (with surface of colluvial cover at 35–40 m. above the modern low water level of the Don). Loess accumulation and colluvial reworking, with the formation of a loamy mantle on the uplands (interfluve). Brief periods of interruption of loess accumulation marked by buried soils in the colluviated loess. *Early Würm.*
6. Downcutting of the Don to beneath the level of the modern floodplain. Continued loess accumulation and reworking on the uplands (interfluve) and on the Third Terrace. *Early Würm.*
7. Deposition of the alluvium of the Second Terrace (with surface of colluvial cover at 15–20 m. above the modern low-water level of the Don). Formation of a soil on the loamy mantle of the uplands and the Third Terrace. *Paudorf Interstadial* (?).
8. Partial destruction of the Paudorf Interstadial (?) soil and consequent deposition of the "lower humic bed" over Second Terrace alluvium. Occupation of Markina gora-4, Kostenki I-5, Streletskaya II-1, Tel'manskaya-4, Kostenki XII-2 and 3, Anosovka II-5, Kostenki XVII-2. *Later Würm* (ca. 20,000–22,000 B.P.?).
9. Major volcanic eruption in the Caucasus recorded locally by lenses of ash in colluvium. *Later Würm.*
10. Further destruction of the Paudorf Interstadial (?) soil and deposition of the "upper humic bed" on the Second Terrace. Occupation of Markina gora-2 and 3, Kostenki I-4, Kostenki XVI-1 and 2, Tel'manskaya-2 and 3, Gorodtsovskaya, Kostenki XII-1, Kostenki VII-1 and 2, Anosovka II-4, and Kostenki XVII-1. *Later Würm* (ca. 20,000 B.P.?).
11. Downcutting by Don to beneath modern floodplain level. Further loess accumulation and colluvial reworking on the uplands and on the Second and Third Terraces. Occupation of Kostenki I-3, Tel'manskaya-1, and Anosovka II-3. *Later Würm* (ca. 18,000 B.P.?).
12. Deposition of alluvium of the First Terrace (with surface of colluvial cover 8–10 m. above the modern low-water level of the Don).
13. Loess accumulation and colluvial reworking on uplands and on the Third, Second, and First Terraces. Occupation of Markina gora-1, Kostenki I-1 and 2, Kostenki XIII, Kostenki IX, Anosovka I, Anosovka II-1A, 1B, and 2, Kostenki II, Kostenki IV-1 and 2, Kostenki III, Kostenki XXI, Kostenki XIX, Borshevo I, and Borshevo II-1, 2, and 3. *Terminal Würm* (ca. 15,000–10,000 B.P.?).
14. Downcutting of the Don to beneath the level of the modern floodplain. *Terminal Würm or Early Holocene.*
15. Renewed aggradation of the Don; formation of the modern floodplain. *Holocene.*

radiocarbon dates from the humic beds may be "too young" because of sample contamination; in any case they are too few at present to contribute conclusively to an answer to this question. If it is true that at least the lower humic bed is made up of material redeposited from a soil formed in the Paudorf Interval, then all the known Upper Paleolithic sites in the Kostenki-Borshevo region must be more recent than that interval. As we shall see further on, this conclusion means that these sites would be considerably later than the earliest known Upper Paleolithic sites elsewhere. It is conceivable that the buried soil at Borshevo II and the one which seems to have been eroded away at many other First Terrace sites dates from the Boelling, or perhaps from the Alleroed Interstadial. So far no convincing scheme has been put forth to link the formation of the alluvial deposits of the First and Second Terraces with Würm glacial climatic events. No linkage may ever be established inasmuch as it is quite possible that the origins of the terraces are to be traced to local crustal movements rather than to climatic change.

Much of the information presented in this chapter is summarized in Table 4. The discussion has indicated that there are still some major gaps in our knowledge of the Pleistocene stratigraphy of the Kostenki-Borshevo region. It is important to emphasize that the sequence of Pleistocene events postulated in the table for the area must remain provisional until these gaps are filled in.

chapter 5. The Environment of Pleistocene Man in the Kostenki-Borshevo Region

The Modern Setting of Kostenki and Borshevo

The villages of Kostenki and Borshevo are located on the southern fringes of what Russian geographers call the forest-steppe zone. Just a few kilometers to the south the true steppe begins. The climate of the forest-steppe zone is continental with marked seasonal extremes; mean July temperature in the vicinity of Kostenki and Borshevo is 21–22° C (ca. 71° F), mean January temperature roughly −11° C (ca. 12° F). Annual precipitation in the forest-steppe is moderate, ranging according to place from 300 to 500 mm. (12 to 20 inches). In the Kostenki-Borshevo area maximum precipitation comes in June.

As one might expect from the name, the vegetation of the forest-steppe is composed of alternating woodland and steppe. However, it is widely believed that the forest would take over completely were it not for human interference. In the part of the zone of interest here, the forests are deciduous and consist principally of oak (*Quercus*), secondarily of linden (*Tilia*), aspen (*Populus*), elm (*Ulmus*), maple (*Acer*), and hornbeam (*Carpinus*). Pine (*Pinus*) is found in those areas where sandy soils are developed. In the steppe portions of the zone dicotyledons (herbaceous flowering plants) tend to predominate in contrast to the pure steppe where grasses rule. The fauna of the forest-steppe is a mixture of forest and steppe species. In fairly recent times the local forests contained relatively abundant bear (*Ursus arctos*), elk (*Alces alces* = American moose), red deer (*Cervus elaphus*), and roebuck (*Capreolus capreolus*). Elk and roebuck may still be found in some places. The aurochs (*Bos primigenius*), now extinct, formerly inhabited both the forests and steppes of the zone, while the wild horse or tarpan (*Equus gmelini*), also extinct, was not long ago fairly numerous in the steppes. Steppe rodents such as susliks (*Citellus* spp.) and jerboas (*Allactaga jaculus*, etc.) are still common, but the steppe marmot (*Marmota bobac*), once widespread in the zone, has now virtually disappeared from it, at least in Europe. The destruction of habitats through cultivation may have been as much (or even more so) the cause of recent impoverishment of wildlife in the forest-steppe as hunting has been.

Floral Remains and Past Kostenki-Borshevo Environment

The analysis of data derived from the study of sediments and of plant and animal remains allows us to make some clear statements about the conditions under which late Pleistocene man lived in the Kostenki-Borshevo region.

Recent research has revealed that pollen is by far the most useful class of organic remains in reconstructing Pleistocene environments. Pollen is frequently identifiable as to genus, sometimes even as to species. Under certain relatively common (but not universal) conditions, it is all but indestructible. Given the technical means for isolating it in sediments, it can provide very valuable information about the natural conditions which prevailed at the time the sediments were formed.

In the process of analysis, the pollen found in a sediment sample is classified according to the kinds of plants from which it was derived, and the amount of pollen of each kind of plant is stated as a percentage of the total.[1] The list of percentages of different kinds of plants represented by pollen in a sediment sample is called the *pollen spectrum* of the sample. It is often presented graphically. Usually the presentation involves a broad breakdown into the percentages of arboreal (= tree) pollen, nonarboreal (= herbaceous) pollen, and spores, and then a finer breakdown into the percentages of grains of different kinds of plants within each of these three categories. From a pollen spectrum inferences can be made about the composition of an ancient vegetational community. Very often, several spectra are placed on a single graph with percentages laid out on the horizontal axis, stratigraphy on the vertical. The result is a *pollen diagram,* from which one can infer change through time in the vegetation of an area. Several pollen diagrams are presented here (Figures 10, 11, 12, and 13).

The use of pollen data to gain information about past vegetation is not unrestricted. One difficulty which is especially noteworthy here arises from the possibility that a certain proportion of the pollen in a given bed may be derived (redeposited) from older sediments. The vegetational community inferred from the pollen spectrum of the bed would then be a composite of vegetational communities from two different times; obviously its utility for reconstructing environment would be limited at best. It should further be obvious that if it is desired to use pollen data to infer change through time in vegetation, it is necessary that pollen-containing samples be removed at regular and fairly frequent intervals from a profile. (The nature of the beds making up the profile should in large part determine the frequency and regularity of intervals between samples.) Substantial gaps without samples may plainly conceal important vegetational changes. Without knowledge of such changes any attempt to reconstruct the history of vegetation in a region is of questionable value. Finally, inferences about the vegetation which existed at a particular time or about vegetational change through time are most reliable when they are based on the analysis of samples from several comparable profiles and not just on those from one.

Turning now to pollen data from the Kostenki-Borshevo region, we have first to contend with the problem of the nature of the sediments from which most samples for analysis were taken. By and large these sediments are colluvial; and particularly in the case of those sediments which make up the "humic beds" on the Second Terrace, the possibility

[1] Identification of pollen is a tedious business, and generally only the first 100 or 200 grains encountered in a sample are identified. This simplifies the calculation of percentages, but gives rise to certain kinds of statistical problems.

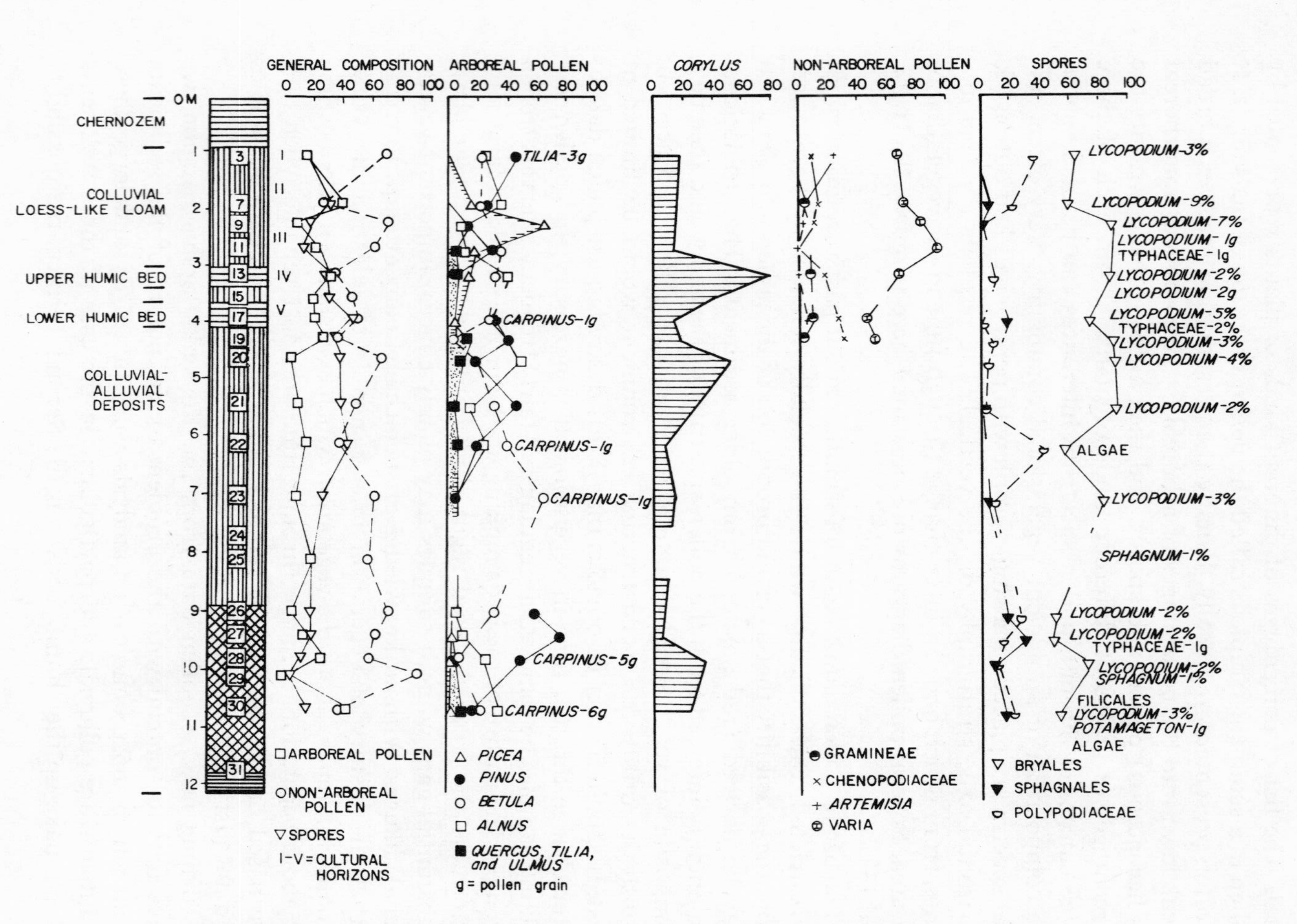

Figure 10. Pollen Diagram from Kostenki I (redrawn after Lazukov 1957b:88).

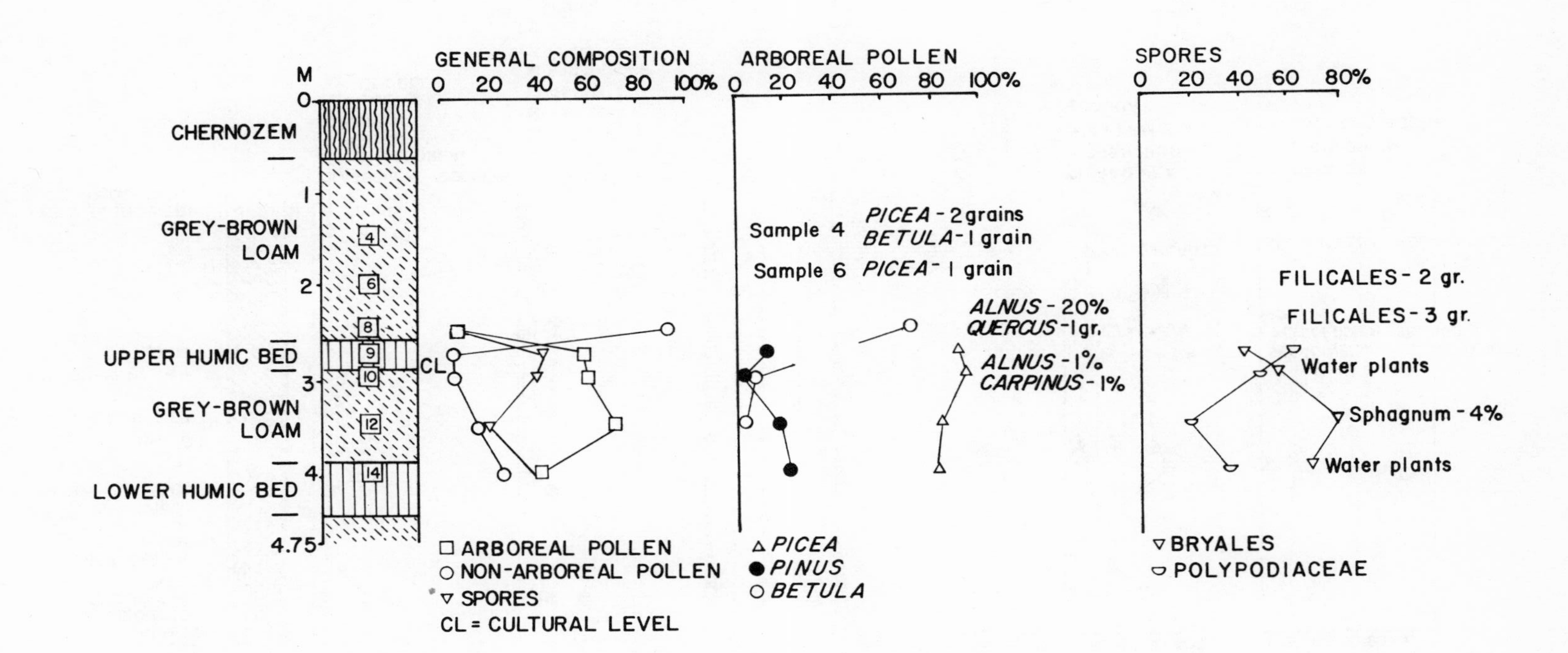

Figure 11. Pollen Diagram from Gorodtsovskaya (redrawn after Lazukov 1957b:90).

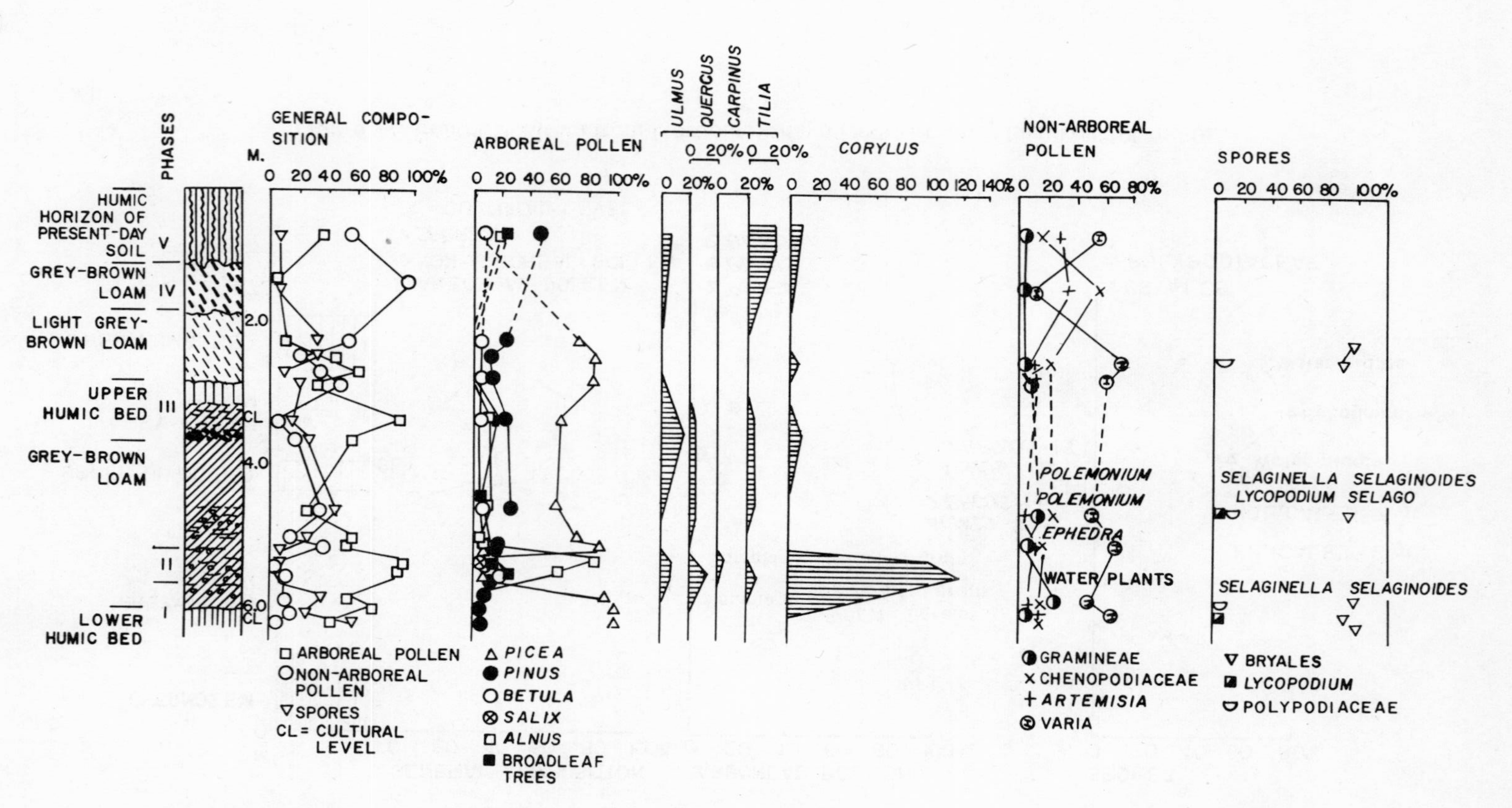

Figure 12. Pollen Diagram from Kostenki XVII (redrawn after Fedorova 1963:221).

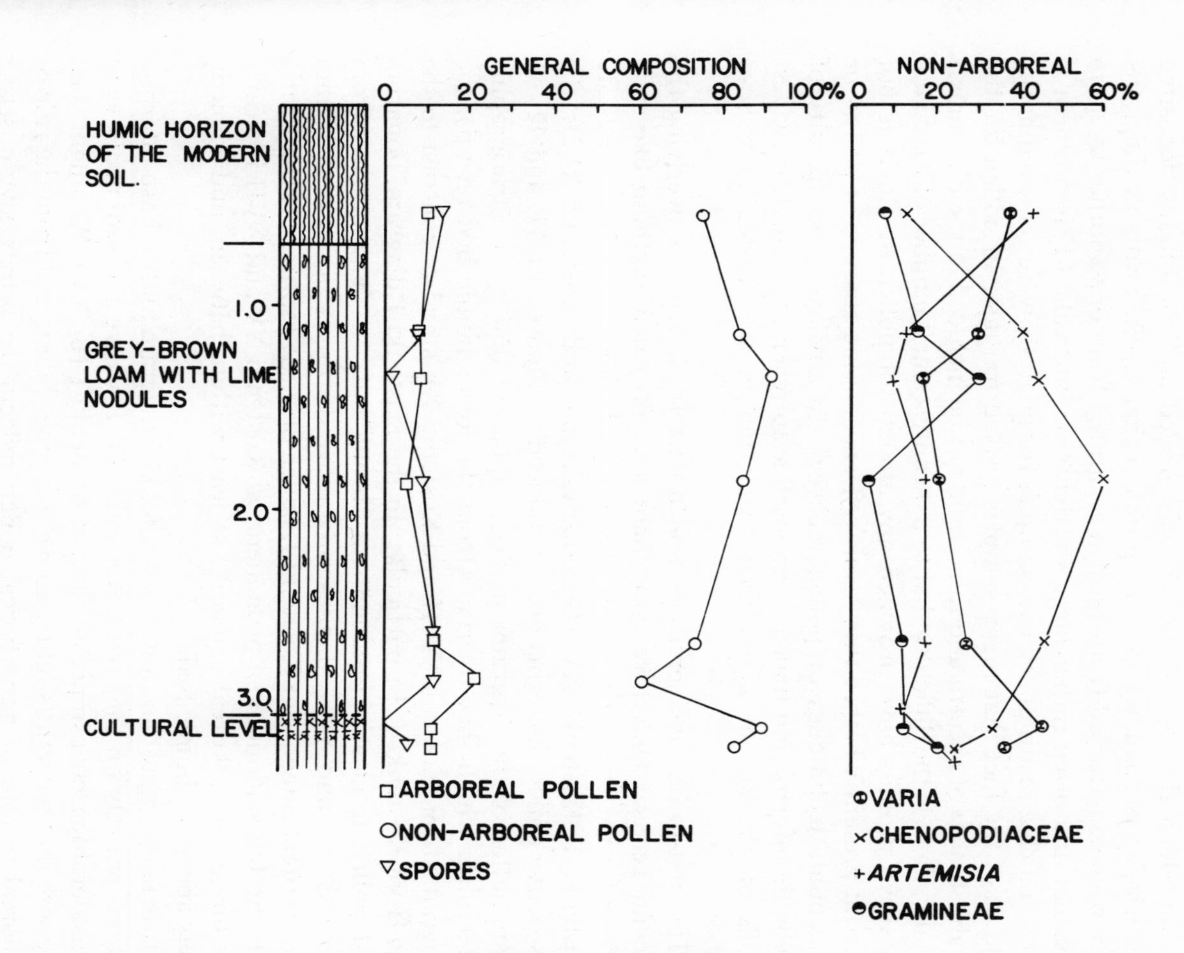

Figure 13. Pollen Diagram from Kostenki XIX (redrawn after Velichko and Fedorova 1961:Figure 10).

seems quite good that a single sediment sample might actually contain pollen from two quite distinct time periods (namely, the time of the formation of the soil from which the humus was derived and the time during which the top of the soil was eroded and the humus deposited downslope). Second, we face the problem that all the available diagrams have been constructed from spectra separated from one another by quite irregular and often rather large stratigraphic intervals. (This problem is not so much a result of the way samples for analysis were removed in the field as of the fact that many samples proved too poor in pollen for the establishment of spectra and thus could not be included in the diagrams.) Finally, there is the difficulty that to date only a small number of Kostenki-Borshevo profiles have provided any amount of pollen at all. It is not clear at present whether this result reflects genuine absence of pollen, or inadequate techniques of pollen recovery. In any case, the sparsity of available information makes it impossible to reach any but the broadest kinds of conclusions about past vegetation in the Kostenki-Borshevo region.

The first to be considered are pollen data from deposits overlying the Second Terrace. Only three sites here have provided anything like sufficient information for the construction of pollen diagrams. These sites are Kostenki I, Kostenki XV (Gorodtsovskaya), and Kostenki XVII; the respective pollen diagrams are reproduced as Figures 10, 11, and 12. An examination of the diagrams makes it apparent that in the stratigraphic interval in which they overlap (from the lower humic bed on up), the diagrams from Kostenki XVII and Kostenki XV stand in contrast to the one from Kostenki I. In particular, in the Kostenki I diagram, nonarboreal pollen is clearly predominant throughout; in the diagrams from Kostenki XV and XVII, it rules only above the upper humic bed. Within the arboreal category at Kostenki I, pollen of *Picea* (spruce) is frequently present, but seldom most prominent; at Kostenki XV and XVII it clearly dominates the arboreal category, at least within, between, and immediately above the humic beds.

It is tempting to discount the Kostenki I diagram and to base interpretations entirely on that from Kostenki XVII, where the sediments were considerably richer in pollen than at Kostenki I (or XV). We might then suppose that the shift slightly above the upper humic bed from the rule of arboreal to that of nonarboreal pollen reflects the progressive onset of colder conditions (climatic deterioration). This climatic change would follow the time (Paudorf?) of formation of the soil which provided the humus. (It is possible that much of the arboreal pollen in the humic beds was derived from this soil and thus that the actual shift toward less forested conditions took place earlier than the deposition of the upper humic bed.) But no matter how appealing such an interpretation may be, it must remain purely hypothetical until confirmatory data are forthcoming from other profiles. Certainly, more detailed interpretations (such as a five-phase scheme proposed by the Kostenki XVII pollen analyst, R. F. Fedorova) are completely untenable at present. This is particularly true in view of the irregular and frequently large stratigraphic gaps between spectra from Kostenki XVII.

Whatever inferences may ultimately be drawn about vegetational change during the accumulation of the colluvial deposits overlying the Second Terrace, the available pollen data do allow us to draw one very interesting conclusion about the contemporary environment. In whatever forests existed, to whatever extent, both spruce (*Picea*) and the plants which frequently accompany it, such as the club moss *Selaginella selaginoides,* were present. Since spruce and its companions today do not occur south of 60° N in European Russia (Kostenki is at ca. 51° N), the implications are that local climate was colder in the late Pleistocene than it is now. The prominence of *Picea* and the presence of other trees at the time when the Second Terrace colluvium was deposited is substantiated by the discovery of charcoal in the cultural horizons of Paleolithic sites (see Table 5).

Pollen data from First Terrace deposits are even sparser than those from the Second. Among First Terrace sites, only Kostenki XIX has supplied enough pollen from different levels for the construction of a diagram (Figure 13). From this diagram it is clear that pollen of herbaceous plants dominated all the analyzable samples. Although the meagerness of the data makes conclusions tentative, it is tempting to suppose that the predominance of nonarboreal pollen indicates the continuation of the same cold, relatively unforested conditions that seem to be indicated by the spectra from the upper part of the Second Terrace at Kostenki XVII. The presence of at least some trees during the time when the First Terrace deposits were formed is demonstrated by the occurrence of charcoal of spruce (*Picea*), larch (*Larix*), and willow (*Salix*) or aspen (*Populus*) in the lowermost cultural horizon of Borshevo II. Further, analysis of sediment samples from the buried soil above this horizon provides considerable evidence (both macro- and microbotanical—see Tables 6 and 7) that forested conditions with prominence of alder obtained during the time of soil development. This evidence appears to substantiate the notion put forth earlier that the Borshevo II buried soil was formed under interstadial conditions (Boelling?, Alleroed?).

It is clear that the sparsity of the available paleobotanical data makes

TABLE 5. Plants Represented by Charcoal in Cultural Horizons in the Kostenki-Borshevo Area (Based on Data in Lazukov 1957c:91 and Gromov 1948:307)[a]

Stratigraphic level (from younger to older)	*Picea (spruce)*[b]	*Larix (larch)*	*Betula (birch)*	*Salix (willow)*	*Quercus (oak)*	*Tilia (linden)*	*Crataegus (hawthorn)*	*Viburnum? (cranberry?)*	*Padus or Prunus (bird cherry or prune)*	*Indeterminate conifers*	*Indeterminate broadleaf trees*	*Various vascular plants*
First Terrace (Borshevo II, lowermost horizon)	X	X		X[c]								
Second Terrace, grey-brown loam above the upper humic bed (Kostenki I-Horizon 3)	XX				12					18		2
Second Terrace, upper humic bed (Kostenki XV)	XX		3	2	6	1	1?	1	1	XX	4	3
Second Terrace, lower humic bed (Kostenki I-Horizon 5, and Streletskaya II)	XX						X				X	XX

[a] X = present; XX = much; number = number of coals.

[b] Blokhina (1964) has reported charcoal of spruce (*Picea*) in samples she examined from the Second Terrace Sites of Kostenki I, Kostenki XII, and Kostenki XIV, but she has not specified what cultural levels are involved. Thus her data could not be incorporated in the table.

[c] This could be either willow (*Salix*) or aspen (*Populus*).

it impossible to reconstruct in detail the late Pleistocene vegetation of the Kostenki-Borshevo region. At present, it may be said that these data do indicate clearly colder conditions than current ones, in which spruce grew and perhaps at times even thrived. The information on hand suggests, but

TABLE 6. Pollen from Samples of the Buried Soil at Borshevo II (Identifications of K. Bitner as Reported by L. Sawicki 1965:186)*

Pollen types	*Sample A*	*Sample B*
Pollen—over-all percentage composition		
Arboreal pollen	84	85
Nonarboreal pollen	10	13
Spores	6	2
ARBOREAL POLLEN (pollen of each form as a percentage of all grains)		
Pinus (pine)	7.0	6.0
Betula (birch)	0.5	3.5
Corylus (hazel)	1.5	1.5
Ulmus (elm)	10.0	2.5
Tilia (linden)	5.5	12.5
Quercus (oak)	6.5	24.5
[Quercetum Mixtum (mixed oak forest)]	[22.0]	[39.5]
Alnus (alder)	69.0	51.0
Picea (spruce)	1.0	——
Fagus (beech)	0.5	——
NONARBOREAL POLLEN (pollen of each taxon as a percentage of all grains)		
Cyperaceae (sedge family)	1.5	0.5
Gramineae (grass family)	1.0	1.0
Artemisia (wormwood)	3.0	3.5
Compositae (sunflower family)	——	1.5
Centaurea (centaury)	0.5	——
Ranunculaceae (buttercup family)	1.0	——
Centrospermae (goosefoot family)	0.5	2.0
Umbelliferae (parsley family)	1.5	0.5
Typha (cattail)	——	0.5
Varia	3.5	5.5
SPORES (spores of each form as a percentage of all grains)		
Sphagnum (sphagnum moss)	0.5	——
Filicales (true ferns)	6.0	0.5

* Sawicki does not say how many grains were counted, but simply that more were available than it was possible to count. The percentages of the various kinds of arboreal pollen, nonarboreal pollen, and spores for Sample A should total 84, 10, and 6 respectively; for Sample B they should total 85, 13, and 2. However, it is apparent in both cases that they do not. It can only be assumed that the figures were miscalculated by Bitner or misprinted in Sawicki (1965:186).

TABLE 7. Seeds Identified in Samples of the Buried Soil at Borshevo II (Identifications of K. Bitner as Reported by L. Sawicki 1965:185–186)

Seed types	*Number of seeds*
Anantha cf. *anatica* (dropwort)	34
Lepidium sp. (canary grass)	24
Najas marina (najas)	1
Betula alba (white birch)	9
Betula sp. (birch)	5
Alnus glutinosa (European alder)	8
Alyssum cf. (alyssum)	7
Carex sp. (sedge)	2
Lycopus auropacus (bugleweed)	5
Mentha ? (mint)	2
Characeae (stonewort family)	1 oogonium

does not confirm, that forests were more widespread during milder, interstadial intervals, while areas of herbaceous vegetation predominated in colder, stadial periods.

Faunal Remains and Past Kostenki-Borshevo Environment

Paleozoological remains from the deposits in the Kostenki-Borshevo region consist of molluscan shells and of mammal bones. Shells of both terrestrial and aquatic species have been recovered, the latter presumably reflecting the proximity of the river and the possibility of periodic innundation or ponding. The composition of the molluscan fauna in each of the four major stratigraphic units from which the shells have been identified is presented in Table 8. Ecological assessment of a molluscan faunal assemblage is a job for a trained specialist. Unfortunately, to date the Kostenki-Borshevo assemblages have not been evaluated by such a person. In fact, a conclusive evaluation would require more complete information than is now available on the Kostenki-Borshevo molluscan faunas. Particularly important would be reliable data on the frequencies of the various species in the different stratigraphic levels. In the absence of expert evaluation and more complete information, only a few broad generalizations can be made here.

First, it is apparent that roughly the same species are represented in both colluvial humic beds above the Second Terrace; at least in the absence of quantative information, the molluscan faunas provide no rea-

TABLE 8. Molluscan Species Represented by Shells in Deposits in the Kostenki-Borshevo Region*

Stratigraphic level (from younger to older)	*Terrestrial (T) or aquatic (A)*	*Environments in which terrestrial molluscs are presently found in the USSR (from Likhachev and Rammel'meier)*			
		Tundra	*Taiga*	*Mixed and broadleaf forest*	*Steppe*
FIRST TERRACE AT BORSHEVO II (from Gromov 1948:207, and Sawicki 1965: 184–187)					
Bed 2—loesslike loam above buried soil					
Succinea oblonga	T		X	X	X
Vallonia costata	T	X	X	X	X
Bed 3—buried soil					
Succinea oblonga	T		X	X	X
Helix rubiginosa	T	X	X	X	
Pisidium amnicum	A				
Anadonta sp.	A				
Bed 4—loesslike loam below buried soil					
Succinea oblonga	T		X	X	X
Cochlicopa lubrica	T	X	X	X	X
Pupilla muscorum	T	X	X	X	X
Pupilla sterri	T	A mountain species no longer found in European Russia (Likhachev and Rammel'meier 1952:1948)			
Perpolita radiatula	T	X	X	X	X
Helix rubiginosa	T	X	X	X	
Pisidium amnicum	A				
Lymnaea palustris	A				
Bed 5—sandy loam at base of profile					
Pupilla muscorum	T	X	X	X	X
Pupilla sterri	T	A mountain species no longer found in European Russia (Likhachev and Rammel'meier 1952:1948)			
SECOND TERRACE, UPPER HUMIC BED (from Lazukov 1957c:99)					
Succinea putris	T	X	X	X	X
Succinea oblonga	T		X	X	X
Vertigo alpestris	T	X	X		

* X = present.

TABLE 8. (*Continued*)

Stratigraphic level (from younger to older)	Terrestrial (T) or aquatic (A)	*Environments in which terrestrial molluscs are presently found in the USSR (from Likhachev and Rammel'meier)*			
		Tundra	*Taiga*	*Mixed and broadleaf forest*	*Steppe*
Vertigo parcedentata ?	T	A taiga/tundra species no longer found in European Russia (Likhachev and Rammel'meier 1952:77)			
Pupilla muscorum	T	X	X	X	X
Pupilla sterri	T	A mountain species no longer found in European Russia (Likhachev and Rammel'meier 1952:1948)			
Vallonia pulchella	T	X	X	X	X
Vallonia tenuilabris	T		X	X	X
Goniodiscus ruderatus	T	X	X	X	X
Planorbis planorbis	A				
Bathyomphalus sp.	A				
SECOND TERRACE, NON-HUMIC LOAM BETWEEN THE HUMIC BEDS (from Lazukov 1957c:99)					
Succinea putris	T	X	X	X	X
Succinea oblonga	T		X	X	X
Trichia hispida	T			X	
SECOND TERRACE, LOWER HUMIC BED (from Lazukov 1957:99)					
Succinea putris	T	X	X	X	X
Succinea elegans	T			X	X
Succinea oblonga	T		X	X	X
Cochlicopa lubrica	T	X	X	X	X
Pupilla muscorum	T	X	X	X	X
Pupilla sterri	T	A mountain species no longer found in European Russia (Likhachev and Rammel'meier 1952:1948)			
Vallonia pulchella	T	X	X	X	X
Vallonia costata	T	X	X	X	X
Vallonia tenuilabris	T		X	X	
Fruticicola fruticum	T		X	X	
Helicella striata	T				X
Trichia hispida	T			X	
Limnaea trunculata	A				

son to suppose that the two beds were formed under very different environmental circumstances. Further, they do not allow specification of the exact conditions under which either bed was formed. In particular, it is impossible to make a conclusive statement about the kind of vegetation cover which might have been present. Almost all the species found in the humic beds are known to exist (or to have existed) in several distinct vegetation zones. To compound this obstacle to precise interpretation, there is reason to suppose that the present-day habitat preferences of some molluscan species need not have characterized their Pleistocene representatives. For example, the Czech expert on Pleistocene molluscan faunas, Vojen Ložek, has pointed out that *Succinea oblonga,* which today seems to favor more or less moist situations, is frequently encountered in European loess believed to have accumulated under relatively dry, periglacial conditions. Only one important generalization seems possible on the basis of the molluscan faunas in the humic beds, namely, that they imply colder climatic conditions than prevail in the region at present. Such conditions are especially indicated by the occurrence in both beds of the boreal mollusc, *Vallonia tenuilabris,* found today only in much colder areas. In the upper humic bed, *Vertigo alpestris* also indicates harsher climate.

The molluscan assemblages from the First Terrace deposits at Borshevo II shed very little light on the conditions under which the deposits accumulated. Hopefully, data on molluscs from other First Terrace sites will eventually be forthcoming.

The mammalian remains found in the occupation horizons of the Kostenki-Borshevo sites have both temporal and paleoenvironmental implications. The temporal ones are fairly clear: since the particular species represented (see Tables 9 and 10) are those commonly found in late Würm sites in various parts of middle-latitude Europe, their occurrence in the Kostenki-Borshevo sites may be regarded as confirmation that these sites also date from the late Würm. It is not so simple to deal with the paleoenvironmental implications, however.

The reconstruction of a particular environment at a given time using the mammalian fauna which occurred there depends in large part upon knowledge of the distribution of living forms. This knowledge can be misleading because an ancient form may be extinct and the living counterpart whose known distribution is used may be only a near relative, perhaps existing under quite different environmental circumstances. Possibly an even greater hindrance to environmental reconstruction by means of mammalian species is the fact that the distribution of a species, living or extinct, is influenced by a number of factors. So, for example, in attempting to reconstruct environment in the Kostenki-Borshevo region by means of the mammalian fauna found in the sites there, G. I. Lazukov has supposed that species are distributed only with respect to climate and vegetation. While we know these two factors are vital, we also know that the distribution of a given species is usually very much dependent upon the distributions of other species. This dependence is complex and generally difficult to evaluate, particularly when some of the species we are dealing with are extinct. These qualifications to environmental reconstruction through the use of mammals cannot be emphasized too strongly. They do not, however, rule out the possibility of making some interesting statements about late Würm environment in the Kostenki-Borshevo region on the basis of the then-living mammalian species.

In the first place, it seems clear from the fauna that the climate was by and large colder than at present. This conclusion is indicated by the presence in all the major stratigraphic units (see Table 9) of arctic fox (*Alopex lagopus*) and reindeer (*Rangifer tarandus*). The occurrence of musk ox (*Ovibos moschatus*) in the upper part of the Second Terrace colluvium (in Horizon 1 of Kostenki I) underscores cold conditions for the time when that colluvium accumulated. Perhaps also indicative of cold conditions is the absence or near absence anywhere in the deposits of bones of wild boar (*Sus scrofa*), whose Pleistocene and Holocene distributions seem to indicate a preference for relatively warm climate. It has frequently been supposed that both the woolly mammoth (*Mammonteus primigenius*) and the woolly rhino (*Coelodonta antiquitatis*) imply cold climate for sites in which their bones are found. While this supposition is likely to be true for some areas, it may not hold for European Russia, where at least the woolly mammoth is known for interglacial (Eem) deposits. Both creatures would perhaps best be characterized as extremely cold-tolerant rather than strictly cold-loving. The same description may perhaps apply to other major herbivores, particularly the wild horses and bovines found in many Pleistocene sites, including those at Kostenki and Borshevo.

If the large herbivores do not provide evidence for making absolute statements about past climatic conditions in the Kostenki-Borshevo region, they would seem to permit some inferences about past vegetation cover. In particular, their presence in some numbers in all major stratigraphic units would seem to imply the occurrence of considerable expanses covered by herbaceous as opposed to forest vegetation. Perhaps the late Würm forests, even at their maximum, were largely restricted to the more sheltered sections of the Don Valley, while open steppes or even herbaceous tundras prevailed on the adjacent uplands (interfluve). The

TABLE 9. Major Game Animals Represented in the Kostenki-Borshevo Sites

Species	Second Terrace, Lower Humic Bed	Second Terrace, Upper Humic Bed	Second Terrace, Grey-Brown Loam Above Upper Humic Bed	First Terrace	Present Status (E = Extinct, LE = Locally Extinct)	Ecological/Latitudinal Characterization (after Lazukov 1957c) (NB: No., Mid., and So. Lats. = within U.S.S.R.)
Mammonteus primigenius, woolly mammoth	X	X	X	X	E	Various zones/various lats.
Coelodonta antiquitatis, woolly rhinoceros	X	X	X	X	E	Various zones/various lats.
Equus caballus, wild horse	X	X	X	X	LE	Forest and steppe/so. lats.
Bos sp. (*Bison priscus*?), wild bovid	X	X	X	X	LE	Forest and steppe/so. lats.
Ovibos moschatus, musk-ox			X		LE	Tundra/no. lats.
Cervus elaphus, red deer	X	X	X	X		Forest and steppe/so. lats.
Megaloceros euryceros, giant deer		X			E	Forest/mid. lats.
Alces alces, elk (moose)				X	LE	Forest/mid. and no. lats
Rangifer tarandus, reindeer	X	X	X	X	LE	Tundra and forest/no. lats.
Saiga tatarica, saiga antelope	X	X		X	LE	Steppe/so. lats.
Sus scrofa, wild boar				?	LE	Forest and steppe/so lats.
Panthera spelaea, cave lion			X	X	E	Various zones/various lats.
Lynx lynx, lynx				X	LE	Forest/mid. and no. lats.
Gulo gulo, wolverine	X		X	X	LE	Forest/no. lats.
Ursus arctos, brown bear			X	X	LE	Forest/mid. lats.
Vulpes vulpes, ordinary fox		X	X	X		Various zones/various lats.
Vulpes cf. *corsac*, steppe fox		X	X		LE	Steppe/so lats.
Alopex lagopus, arctic fox	X	X	X	X	LE	Tundra/no. lats.
Canis lupus, wolf	X	X	X	X		Various zones/various lats.
Martes foina, beech marten				X	LE	Various zones/various lats.
Lutra lutra, otter			X			Various zones/various lats.
Lepus sp., hare	X	X	X	X		Various zones/various lats.

TABLE 10. Species of Rodents Represented by Bones in Different Major Stratigraphic Units in the Kostenki-Borshevo Region*

Species	*Second Terrace, lower humic bed*	*Second Terrace, upper humic bed*	*Second Terrace, grey-brown loam above the upper humic bed*	*First Terrace*	*Present status*	*Ecological/latitudinal characterization (after Lazukov 1957c) (NB: So., Mid. and No. lats. = within USSR)*
Marmota bobac (steppe marmot)			X	X	LE	Steppe/So. lats.
Spalax microphthalmus (European mole rat)		X	X	X		Forest and steppe/So. lats.
Allactaga jaculus (great jerboa)			X	X		Forest and steppe/So. lats.
Lagurus lagurus (sagebrush vole)				X		Steppe/So. and Mid. lats.
Citellus citellus (European suslik)			X		LE	Forest and steppe/So. lats.
Citellus rufescens (russet suslik)		X	X	X	LE	Steppe/So. lats.
Citellus pygmaeus (little suslik)		X			LE	Steppe/So. lats.
Castor fiber (beaver)		X			LE	Forest/Mid. lats.
Cricetus cricetus (ordinary hamster)		X	X	X		Forest and steppe/So. lats.
Apodemus sylvaticus (forest mouse)			X			Forest/So. and Mid. lats.
Arvicola amphibius (water vole)	X	X	X			Various zones/various lats.
Microtus oeconomus (northern vole)				X	LE	Forest/Mid. and No. lats.
Microtus arvalis (continental field vole)				X		Forest and steppe/So. and Mid. lats.
Microtus sp. (vole)		X				
Ellobius talpinus (mole vole)			X	X	LE	Steppe/So. lats.

* LE = locally extinct.

ancient inhabitants may have exploited both vegetation settings, finding some animals, such as mammoth and horse, primarily in the open country, and others, such as the red deer (*Cervus elaphus*), primarily in the forests. Arctic fox and wolf (*Canis lupus*), the two most frequent carnivores found in the Kostenki-Borshevo sites, could have ranged through either setting, though more likely preferring the open one.

Thus, on the basis of the kinds of mammals present, we can say that during the late Würm time interval represented by the Kostenki-Borshevo occupation sites climate was generally colder than today and that extensive unforested areas always existed in the vicinity. At the same time, it is important to point out that it is difficult, if not impossible, to use the mammalian fauna to reconstruct fluctuations in climate and vegetation during the late Würm. In part, this difficulty exists because paleontologists have not investigated and reported on the different stratigraphic units to an equal extent. The lower humic bed, for example, has provided fewer sites and far fewer faunal remains than have the other stratigraphic units. This, in combination with the near absence of published systematic analyses of the available lower-humic-bed bones, may well account for the apparent paucity of rodent remains in that unit.[2] But even if we had equally abundant and thoroughly described paleozoological materials from all stratigraphic units, problems would persist. The paleoenvironmental significance of any differences among units would still be suspect since it is clear that the different species and especially their frequencies at a given site (or a group of sites) are a result of cultural (hunting) choices as well as of more general environmental (climatic and vegetational) conditions.[3] Because the presence of animal bones (at least those of game animals) in a site is a result of cultural activity (in a sense, the over-all species composition is a feature of the site), the particular species represented in the various cultural levels will be listed in the discussions of the site contents (Chapters 7, 8, 9, and 10).

[2] It should also be pointed out that in many cases rodent remains were derived from animals which died in their burrows and which are thus likely to postdate the level in which they were found. This fact too makes difficult the assessment of differences among levels as presented in Table 10.

[3] In this context, it is tempting to suppose that the appearance of elk (*Alces alces*) in First Terrace deposits, more specifically in the uppermost horizon of Borshevo II, is a reflection of environmental change rather than of altered hunting tastes, because the same horizon which contains the elk remains is virtually unique in having supplied no remains of mammoth. Further, it is believed by many to be the youngest occupation horizon in the Kostenki-Borshevo region, possibly dating from the time of the Pleistocene/Holocene transition when relatively drastic environmental change took place.

Summary and Conclusions

In general summary and conclusion, it may be said that the various classes of organic remains—floral, molluscan, and mammalian—found in late Würm colluvium overlying the First and Second Terraces indicate colder climatic conditions than exist now in the area. Relying on inferences derivable from a composite analysis of the floral and mammalian remains, it may further be stated that the late Würm vegetation consisted partly of open, herbaceous expanses and partly of forests. In this regard, it is relevant to note in other, more fully investigated areas with present-day circumstances comparable to those of Kostenki and Borshevo the late Würm seems to have been characterized by forest-steppe or forest-tundra. Forests were most important in the major river valleys, particularly when the cold reached its maximum (see Map 1, p. 27). There is some evidence at Kostenki-Borshevo to suggest that forests were most widespread shortly before and/or during the time the two Second Terrace humic beds were deposited and again later when a now-buried soil developed on the First Terrace. However, the faunal remains indicate that herbaceous expanses were never absent, and they may have been especially significant in the interval between the deposition of the upper humic bed and the formation of the now buried First Terrace soil (this soil has been found in place only at Borshevo II). This interval probably included the cold maximum of the Würm glacial, for which data from other areas suggest that average July temperatures in the vicinity of Kostenki may have been around 12–13° C (= ca. 54° F) and the number of frost-free days per year may have numbered no more than 30 or 40. The manner in which man made a living in this cold, partly forested, partly open environment will be taken up in later chapters and in particular in the concluding one.

chapter 6. Human Remains from the Kostenki-Borshevo Sites

The modern species of man, *Homo sapiens,* seems to have appeared at approximately the beginning of the Middle Pleistocene. The fossil evidence for *Homo sapiens* does not become really substantial, however, until the earlier part of the Upper Pleistocene (especially the early Würm), when it is apparent that several subspecies were present. By far the best known of these subspecies is *Homo sapiens neanderthalensis,* popularly referred to as Neanderthal Man. Neanderthal Man seems to have been the bearer of the Mousterian culture or culture complex; like the Mousterian, Neanderthals appear to have been distributed principally in Europe and Southwest Asia. Sometime in the later Upper Pleistocene, more specifically within the later Würm, Neanderthal Man was supplanted over this entire area by populations of anatomically modern man, *Homo sapiens sapiens.* The nature of this replacement is a matter of dispute. Some experts believe that the evolution of modern man was a repeated and widespread phenomenon, that various widely dispersed populations of Neanderthals evolved more or less simultaneously into the current subspecies. Alternatively, the event may have occurred in a very restricted area, the new subspecies spreading out from there, literally destroying or perhaps genetically absorbing the still extant Neanderthal populations elsewhere. In any case, as was noted earlier, the disappearance of the Neanderthals seems to have coincided closely with the disappearance of the Mousterian, or conversely, the appearance of modern man seems to have coincided closely with the appearance of the Upper Paleolithic. Since it appears likely that more than coincidence is involved here, and since Mousterian and Upper Paleolithic cultural remains are many times more abundant than Neanderthal and early modern physical remains, it may be that the question of the origins of modern man and the disappearance of Neanderthals will ultimately be solved by careful studies of the nature of the Mousterian/Upper Paleolithic replacement/transition in various areas.

The Kostenki-Borshevo region provides no exception to the generalization that traces of Pleistocene man's cultural activity are far more abundant than his bone remains. To date only five of the sites in the region have provided human skeletal remains. Detailed information on these remains, much of which will be of interest only to the specialist, is presented in Tables A-4 and A-5 (in the Appendix). From Table A-4 it is apparent that the oldest of the potentially analyzable remains (those from Kostenki XV and horizon 3 of Kostenki XIV) are younger than the earliest Upper Paleolithic occupation sites in the region. Hence, it might be expected that all the remains would belong quite clearly to the living variety of man, *Homo sapiens sapiens,* and indeed this is the case. Using measurements of the kind presented in Table A-5 as well as visual impressions, Soviet specialists have further attempted a racial analysis of the available remains. They have reached agreement that the individuals represented at Kostenki II, XV, and XVIII were paleo-Europeans. On the other hand, some authors have suggested that the individual from Kostenki XIV was a Negro. Without considering this question in detail, it is pertinent to point out that even the assignment of present-day skeletal remains to one or another race is far from a simple matter. On these grounds alone, any attempt to determine the race of a Pleistocene skeleton must be regarded with suspicion.

Drawings of the skulls from the Kostenki sites are presented in Figures 14, 15, 16 and 17. The circumstances in which the human remains were found at each site are discussed in later chapters. Here, it is sufficient to note that all four nearly complete skeletons come from clearly deliberate burials.

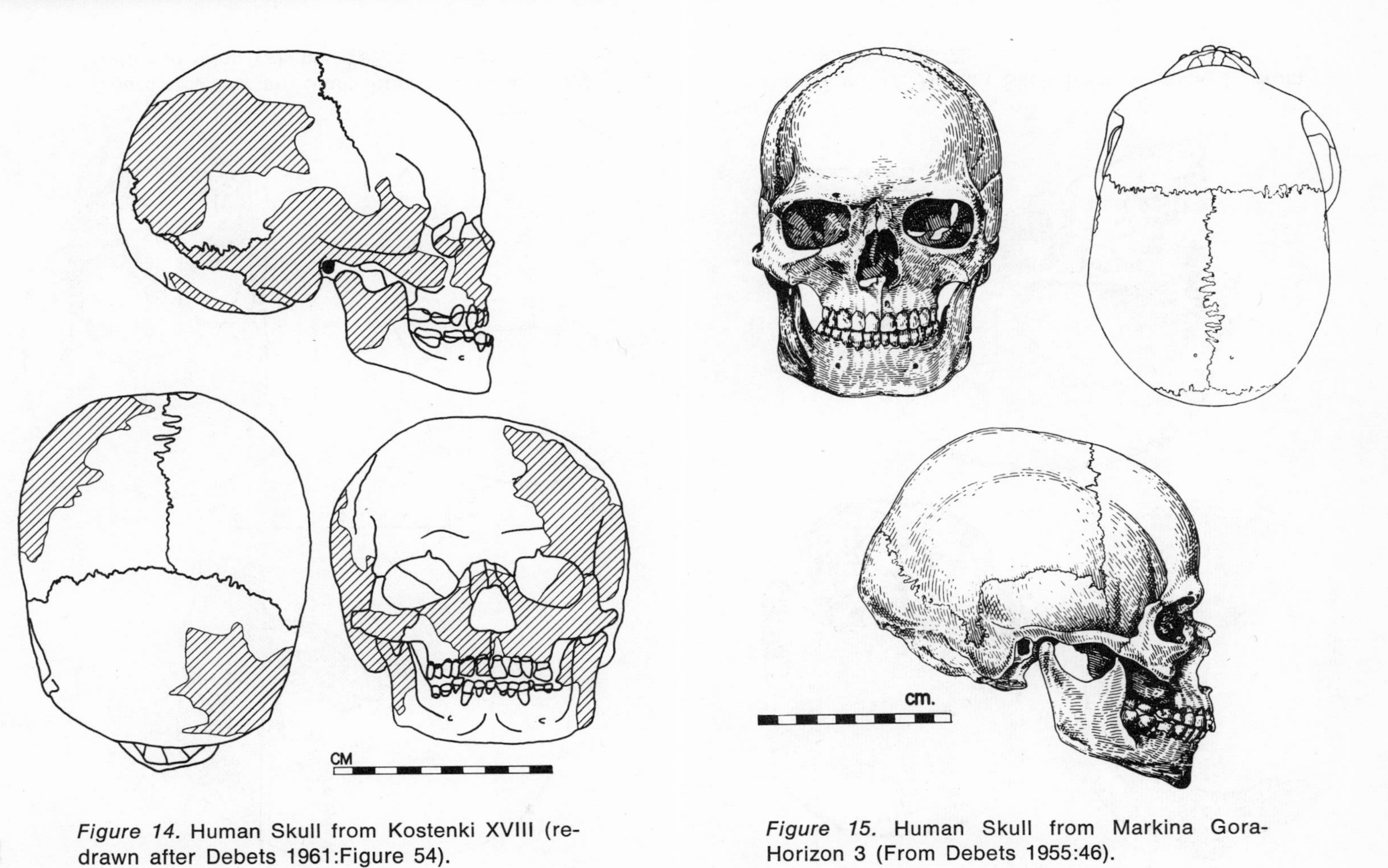

Figure 14. Human Skull from Kostenki XVIII (redrawn after Debets 1961:Figure 54).

Figure 15. Human Skull from Markina Gora-Horizon 3 (From Debets 1955:46).

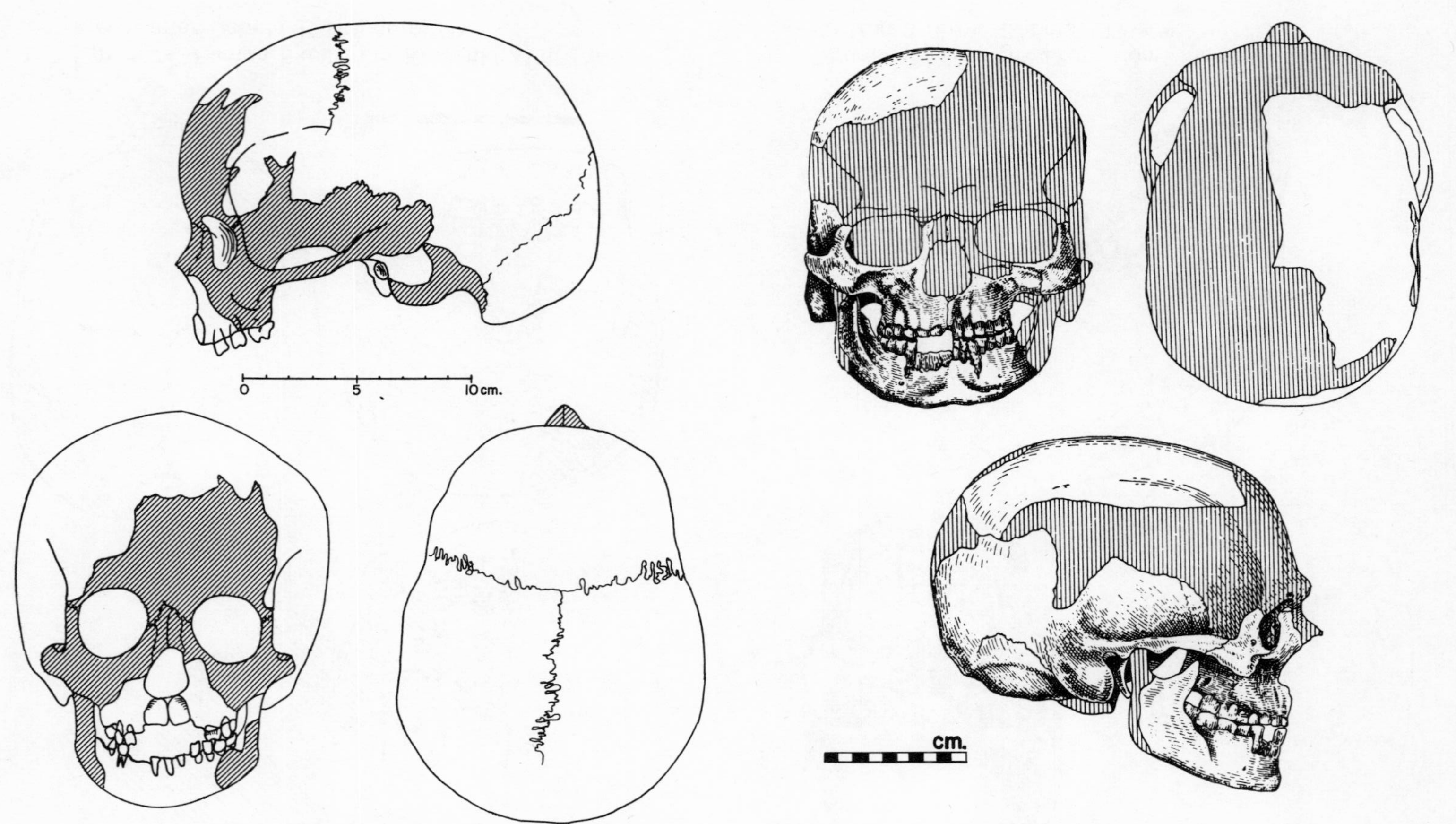

Figure 16. Human Skull from Gorodtsovskaya (redrawn after Yakimov 1957:Figure 5).

Figure 17. Human Skull from Kostenki II (from Debets 1955:47).

chapter 7. Sites in the Lower Humic Bed on the Second Terrace

This chapter deals with the geologically oldest sites so far known in the Kostenki-Borshevo region, those occurring in the lower humic bed on the Second Terrace. Succeeding chapters will deal with the sites found in the upper humic bed, in the loesslike loam above the upper humic bed, and finally in the colluvium overlying the First Terrace.

Eight sites are known from the lower humic bed (see Fig. 8, p. 43): Markina gora(= Kostenki XIV)-horizon 4, Kostenki I-horizon 5, Streletskaya II (= Kostenki VI), Tel'manskaya(= Kostenki VIII)-horizon 4, Kostenki XII-horizons 2 and 3, Anosovka II(= Kostenki XI)-horizon 5, and Kostenki XVII-horizon 2. In addition to these sites, Kostenki V-horizon 3, which is currently not datable on stratigraphic grounds, will also be considered in this chapter, because the artifacts from it are said to resemble those from Markina gora-horizon 4. The faunal assemblages from the various lower-humic-bed sites are presented in Table 11. Since the different sites have not been equally investigated and reported on, it is fruitless at present to speculate on the possible significance of any differences apparent in the table.

Kostenki I-Horizon 5, Streletskaya II, Kostenki XII-Horizon 3, and Anosovka II(= Kostenki XI)-Horizon 5

Kostenki I-horizon 5 was found at a depth of 3.50–3.80 m. from the surface and was exposed over an area of 46 sq. m. The frequent discovery of fragments of flint and quartzite artifacts in nearly vertical positions may indicate that the horizon has been partially disturbed by erosion. The cultural remains were concentrated inside a rough oval with maximum diameter no more than 5 m. (Fig. 18). Each square meter inside this oval provided at least several dozen flints. The number was particularly high near a small mass of ash and charcoal interpreted as the remnants of a hearth. Several small spots of pigment (ochre) were also located near the supposed hearth. Squares outside the oval rarely provided more than ten flints each and no ashy or ochreous spots. The excavator of the horizon (A. N. Rogachev) has supposed that the oval area with the hearth marks the base of an ancient structure. The typological composition of the small but interesting assemblage of artifacts collected in Kostenki I-5 is presented in Table 12 (see also Fig. 19).

Three other sites in the lower humic bed, Streletskaya II, Kostenki XII-3, and Anosovka II-5, are said to have provided materials similar to those of Kostenki I-5. Streletskaya II was relatively rich in both bone and artifacts (Table 12 and Fig. 20), but the materials are all believed to have been somewhat displaced from their original positions, and no features (remnants of structures, fossil fireplaces, and the like) were discovered. Kostenki XII-3 was poor in both fauna and artifacts (Table 12) and, like Streletskaya II, contained no features. The materials from Anosovka II-5 are still in the process of analysis, and only limited information is available on them. They include at least one bifacial, triangular, concave-based point. A. N. Rogachev, who excavated all four sites in question, has labeled the common culture from which he believes they were derived, the Kostenki-Streletskaya culture. A prominent feature of this culture is the high frequency of flakes (retouched and otherwise) versus blades, but Rogachev regards as its hallmark bifacially worked, triangular, concave-

TABLE 11. Species Represented by Faunal Remains in Sites of the Lower Humic Bed*

Species	*Kostenki I-5 (Lazukov 1957: 93–94)*	*Streletskaya II (Lazukov 1957c: 93–94)*	*Kostenki XII-3 (Rogachev 1957)*	*Kostenki XVII-2 (Boriskovskij 1963:87)*	*Tel'manskaya-4 (Lazukov 1957c: 93–94)*	*Kostenki XIV-4 (Rogachev 1957)*	*Kostenki V-3 (Rogachev 1957)*	*Kostenki XII-2 (Rogachev 1957)*
Mammonteus primigenius (woolly mammoth)	X	X		X	11/?	X	X	?
Coelodonta antiquitatis (woolly rhinoceros)		X		X	1/1		X	
Equus caballus (wild horse)	1/1	X	X		5/?	X	X	
Bison or *Bos* (wild cattle)	4/?	X		X			X	
Cervus elaphus (red deer)		X						
Rangifer tarandus (reindeer)		X		X				
Saiga tatarica (saiga antelope)	X			X				
Gulo gulo (wolverine)				X				
Alopex lagopus (arctic fox)		X		X				
Canis lupus (wolf)		X	X	X				
Lepus sp. (hare)		X		X				
Arvicola amphibius (water vole)		X						
Artiodactyla, indeterminate			X					?
Carnivora, indeterminate			X			X		?

* X = present; 0/0 = number of bones/number of individuals.

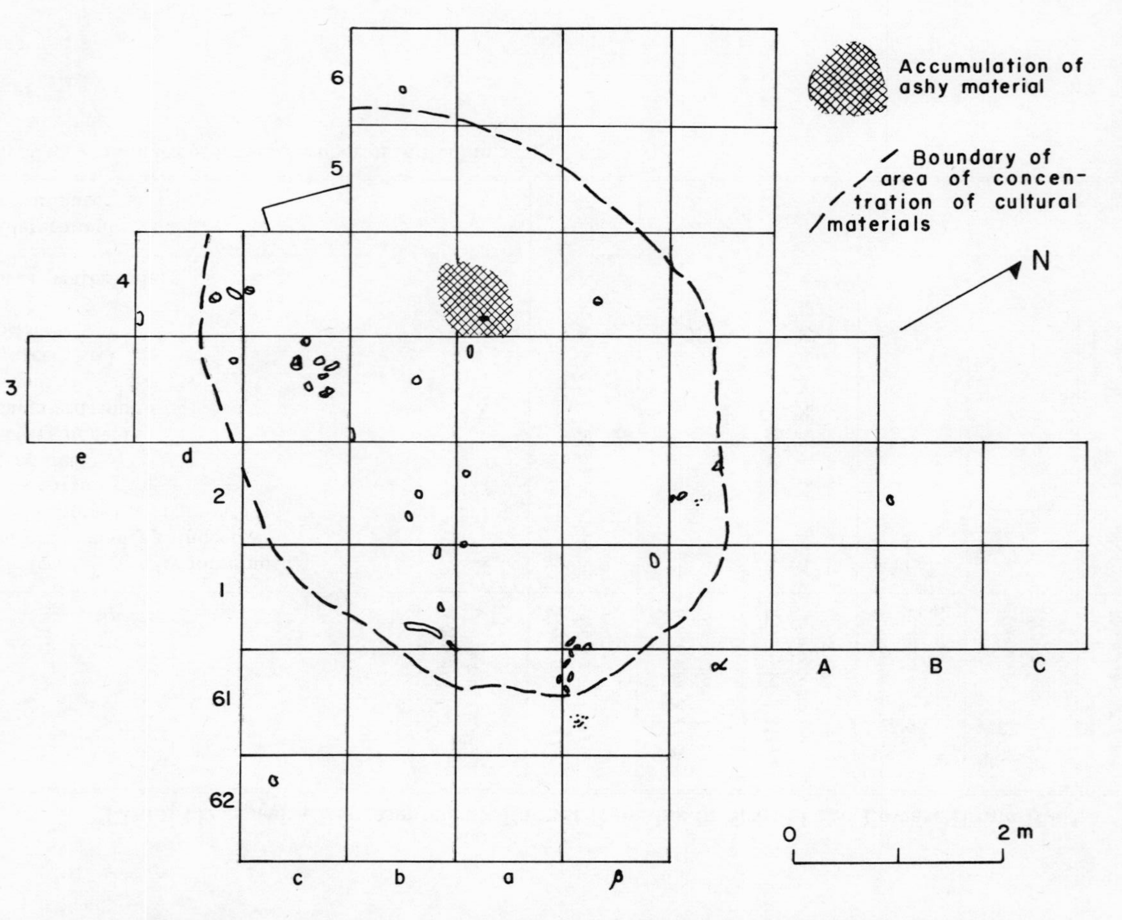

Figure 18. Plan of Kostenki I-Horizon 5 (redrawn after Rogachev 1957:Figure 36).

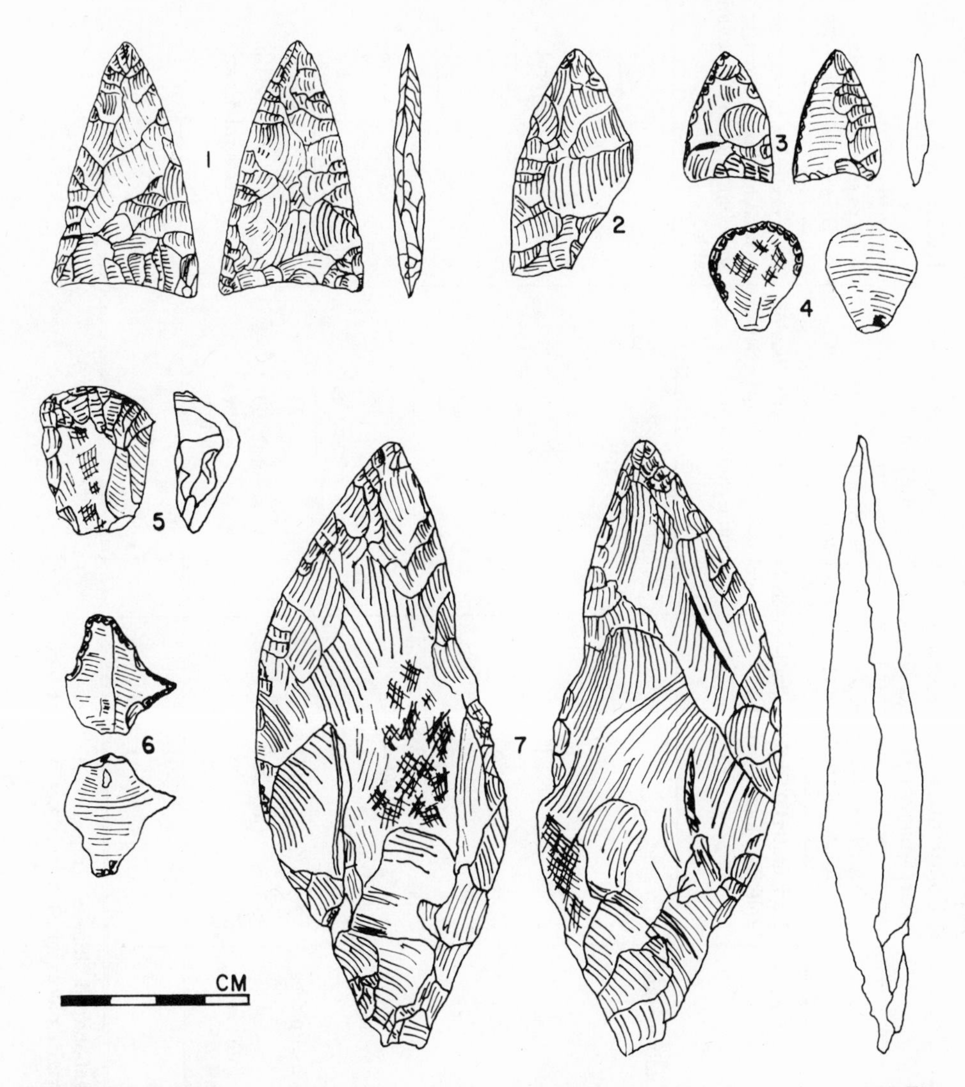

Figure 19. Artifacts from Kostenki I-Horizon 5 (redrawn after Rogachev 1957:Figures 12 and 13).

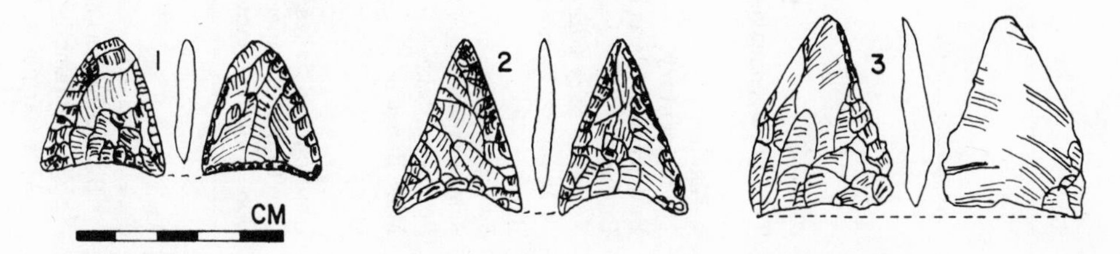

Figure 20. Artifacts from Streletskaya II (redrawn after Rogachev 1957:Figure 54).

TABLE 12. Typological Composition of the Artifact Assemblages from Kostenki I-Horizon 5, Streletskaya II, and Kostenki XII-Horizon 3

Artifacts	*Kostenki I-horizon 5* (*Rogachev 1957:36–41*)	*Streletskaya II* (*Rogachev 1957:97–106*)	*Kostenki XII-horizon 3* (*Rogachev 1957:70–71*)
	Raw material: locally available flint and quartzite.	Raw material: mostly locally available flint and quartzite; also some sandstone.	Raw material: mostly locally available flint and quartzite; some flint not locally available.
STONE			
Triangular, concave-based, bifacially worked points	15	4	—
Whole	(6)		
Fragmentary	(9)		
End-scrapers (largely on flakes)	11	2	several
Burins	6	—	—
On ordinary truncations	(1)		
On lateral truncations	(5)		
Borers	4	—	—
Splintered pieces	2	—	—
Side-scrapers	several	} 13	some
Points on flakes	1		?
Miscellanea	2[a]	4[b]	1[c]
TOTAL retouched pieces	> 41	23	several
Unretouched flakes	ca. 1,200	several 100	
Unretouched blades	a few	a few	several dozen
Cores (all for removal of flakes)	ca. 20	a few	?
BONE			
Awls	1	—	—

[a] Bifacially worked, roughly leaf-shaped "knives" (Fig. 19#7).
[b] Three bifacially worked quartzite pieces and 1 bifacial axelike flint tool.
[c] A "spear point."

based points (Fig. 19#1–3; Fig. 20#1–3). These are absent from Kostenki XII-3 perhaps because of the small size of the collection. Since such points are known from a number of other sites in clearly later stratigraphic contexts, Rogachev has supposed the Kostenki-Streletskaya culture to have had considerable duration. Among the other sites where such points have been found are two in the Kostenki-Borshevo region—Kostenki XII-1A in the upper humic bed of the Second Terrace, and Anosovka II-3 in the loesslike loam overlying the upper humic bed. Perhaps more interesting is the occurrence of such points in the site of Sungir', located 200 km. ENE of Moscow and roughly 530 km. north of Kostenki (see Map 1, p. 27). Two radiocarbon determinations relevant to Sungir'—14,600 ± 600 B.P. (GIN-14) on fossil bone from the occupation horizon and 16,200 ± 400 B.P. (GIN-15) on humus from below it—appear to indicate that Sungir' postdates the lower humic bed sites at Kostenki. In linking the Sungir' and Kostenki-Streletskaya sites, Rogachev and others have assumed that wherever bifacial, triangular, concave-based points are found in Pleistocene sites and whatever their associations, they are indicative of a single (Kostenki-Streletskaya or Kostenki-Sungir') cultural tradition. This assumption may not be warranted, however. Certainly there are no empirical or theoretical reasons to suppose that such points could not have been invented more than once, and, indeed, they are known from contexts which are very unlikely to have any connection with either Kostenki or Sungir'—for example, from the post-Pleistocene (Neolithic Tripol'e Culture) site of Polivanov Yar on the Dnestr River, many hundred kilometers west of Kostenki.

Kostenki XVII-Horizon 2

The cultural debris of Kostenki XVII-2 were confined to a band 0.20–0.30 m. thick immediately at the top of the lower humic bed. They were clearly in situ, since the flint artifacts were very fresh and were accompanied by distinctly bounded accumulations of bone charcoal and ash (= hearth remnants) and by groups of animal bones in anatomical order (Fig. 21). The cultural level was colored by a heavy concentration of red pigment (ochre). No remains of any kind of habitation were found during the excavations.

Both in abundance and composition, the artifact assemblage from Kostenki XVII-2 is unique for the lower humic bed (Table 13). In particular, it contrasts with the collections from the nearby sites of the "Kostenki-Streletskaya Culture" in containing many artifacts made of stone not available locally. It is also distinctive for a large number of burins and for

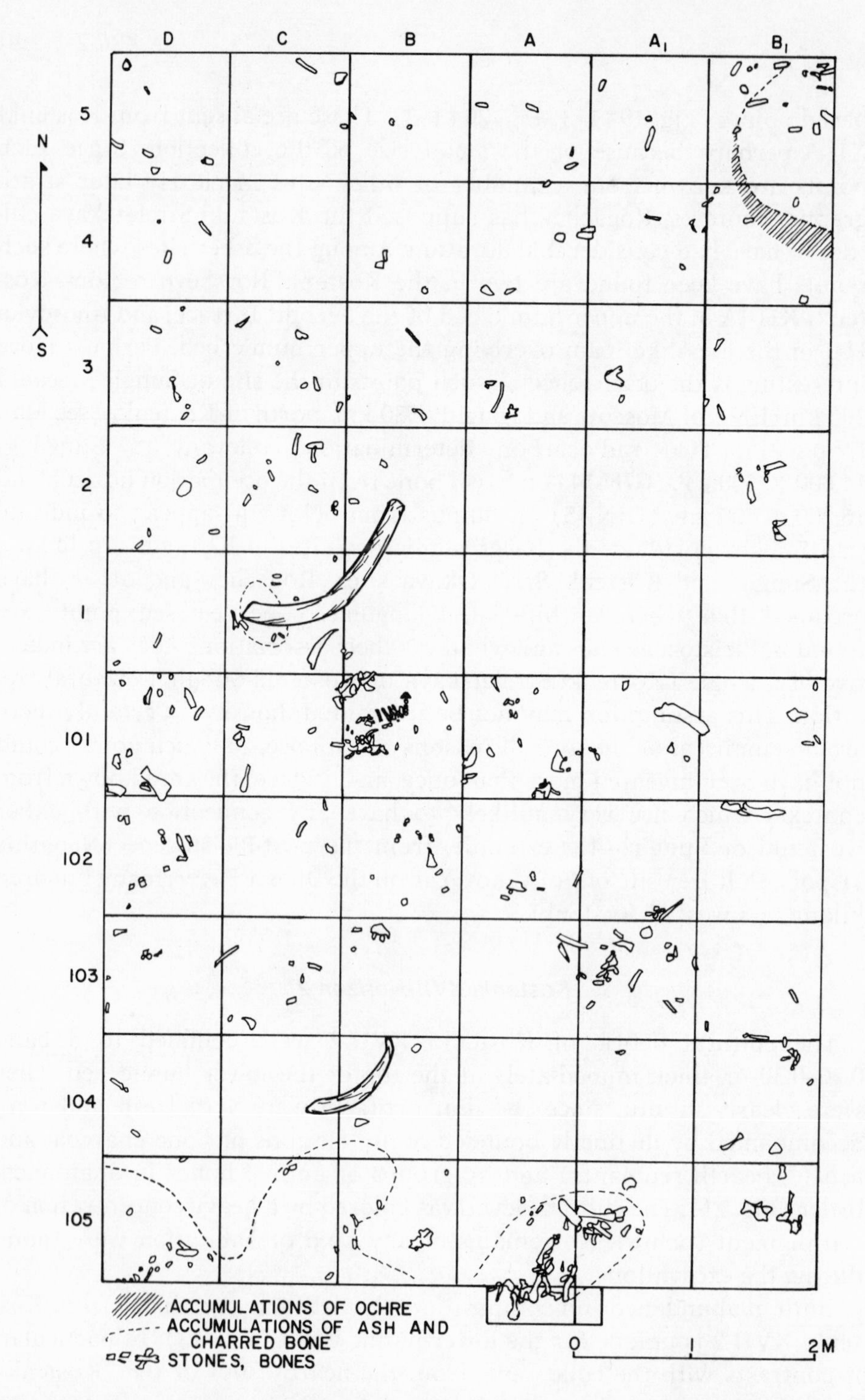

Figure 21. Plan of Kostenki XVII-Horizon 2 (redrawn after Boriskovskij 1963:Figure 11).

TABLE 13. Artifact Inventory from Kostenki XVII-2 (Critically Compiled from Information in Boriskovskij 1963:89 ff.)

Artifacts	*Quantity*
STONE	
(Raw material: almost exclusively flint not available locally.)	
Burins	ca. 140
On the corner of a broken blade	(4)
Dihedral	(10)
On retouched truncations	(ca. 125)
Composite tools (burin/end-scrapers and burin/truncations)	ca. 20
End-scrapers on blades	22
Pieces with double inverse truncation (= atypical "Kostenki knives")	2
Blades and fragments of blades with retouch	ca. 120
Miscellanea	9[a]
TOTAL retouched pieces	ca. 315
Unretouched flakes	ca. 1800
Unretouched blades (and microblades)	ca. 200
Unretouched chips	ca. 7000
Burin spalls	ca. 600
Blade cores	45
Whole	(15)
Fragmentary	(30)
Hammerstones (flint)	2
TOTAL artifactual flint	ca. 9800
Sandstone and slate anvils or hammerstones	several
BONE ARTIFACTS	
Awls	2
Points (fragmentary)	2
Polisher	1
Miscellanea	1[b]
ORNAMENTS ("PENDANTS")	
Drilled arctic fox canines	37
Drilled fragments of belemnite (= a Cretaceous marine fossil)	4
Drilled fossil shells and pieces of coral	several
Drilled pieces of slate and sandstone	7

[a] All pieces with ventral retouch.
[b] Two fragments of an enigmatic ivory artifact.

relatively abundant bone artifacts and "pendants." An analysis of Kostenki XVII-2 artifacts under a binocular microscope yielded some interesting results. The burins exhibited a remarkable variety of wear patterns presumably reflecting a variety of different uses. Many of the burin spalls had traces of wear on their more pointed ends, which suggests that they were used as borers, possibly in making holes in the relatively large number of drilled objects ("pendants") recovered. The majority of end-scrapers displayed some polishing on the scraper end, but only on the dorsal surface; this has been interpreted as indicating that they were used principally for scraping, an operation in which only one surface might be subjected to wear. On some end-scrapers, polishing also was found on the lateral edges, where it occurred on both the dorsal and ventral surfaces. It is supposed that these edges were used principally for cutting, a bifacially wearing operation. Finally, a study of the belemnitic and stone "pendants" showed that the point of the instrument which drilled the holes through them was constantly changing position. This fact has led the analyst S. A. Semenov to suggest that the instrument was operated between the palms rather than by a bow-sash apparatus.

Tel'manskaya-Horizon 4, Markina Gora-Horizon 4, Kostenki V-Horizon 3, and Kostenki XII-Horizon 2

Tel'manskaya-4 contained mostly animal bones; its rare stone artifacts were scattered throughout the lower humic bed at a depth of 4 to 5 m. from the surface. The materials were apparently not in situ since the bones were frequently found in inclined positions and the single ashy mass uncovered was clearly redeposited. The stone artifact collection consisted of 29 pieces made of flint not available locally and included 26 ordinary flakes and blades, 2 end-scrapers, and an end-scraper/burin.

Markina gora-4, like Tel'manskaya-4, is known principally by its faunal contents. Only a few artifacts were found, though in one square a small mass of ash and charcoal was encountered. Slightly more information is available on Kostenki V-3, the artifacts from which are said to resemble those from Markina gora-4. The Kostenki V-3 pieces were all made of flint not available locally and included seven backed blades and points, three burins, and six blades with continuous retouch along one or both edges. The backed blades and points are worth noting since they are absent in both the "Kostenki-Streletskaya" sites and at Kostenki XVII-2, and may indicate the presence of yet a third cultural entity while the lower humic bed was accumulating.

The Kostenki XII-2 site was very poor and provided only a small quantity of animal bones and a few artifacts, said to include some burins.

Conclusions

Perhaps the most general conclusion which may be drawn from this brief survey of sites in the lower humic bed is that they were not all derived from the same culture. At least it seems unlikely that there is any genetic connection between the sites of the Kostenki-Streletskaya group (Kostenki I-5, Streletskaya II, Anosovka II-5, and Kostenki XII-3) and Kostenki XVII-2. Whether other cultural units were also present in the time span involved must await the expansion of excavations and the gathering of additional materials at other known lower humic-bed sites.

Since the lower-humic-bed sites are the oldest so far known in the Kostenki-Borshevo region, they are the best sites to compare to the Mousterian. In making such a comparison, one cannot help but be struck by the paucity of blades (retouched or otherwise) in the Kostenki-Streletskaya sites. We might easily conclude that these sites are transitional between the Mousterian and the later Upper Paleolithic. This question will be considered in more detail in the concluding chapter, but here we may note that such an interpretation would be more easily acceptable if the Kostenki-Streletskaya sites were all demonstrably older than the clearly nontransitional site of Kostenki XVII-2. Presently it is not possible to demonstrate any differences in age. The discovery at Kostenki XVII-2, Tel'manskaya-4, and Kostenki V-3 of artifacts made of raw material not available locally will also be considered in detail in the final chapter. As we shall see shortly, this occurrence is common at the Kostenki-Borshevo sites.

chapter 8. Sites in the Upper Humic Bed on the Second Terrace

The upper humic bed has proven considerably richer in sites than the lower. To date it has provided thirteen, including Markina gora(= Kostenki XIV)-horizons 2 and 3, Kostenki I-horizon 4, Kostenki XVI-horizons 1 and 2, Tel'manskaya(= Kostenki VIII)-horizons 2 and 3, Gorodtsovskaya(= Kostenki XV), Kostenki XII-horizons 1A and 1B, Kostenki VII-horizons 1 and 2, Anosovka II(= Kostenki XI)-horizon 4, and Kostenki XVII-horizon 1. The faunal assemblages from these sites are presented in Table 14. However, because the different sites have been excavated and reported on to very different extents, it is pointless to speculate on the possible significance of any differences apparent in the table.

TABLE 14. Species Represented by Remains in Sites of the Upper Humic Bed*

Species	*Markina gora-3* (*Rogachev 1957*)	*Tel'manskaya 2 and 3* (*Lazukov 1957c:93–94*)	*Gorodtsovskaya* (*Lazukov 1957c:93–94*)	*Kostenki XII-1B* (*Rogachev 1957*)	*Kostenki XVII-1* (*Boriskovskij 1963:87*)	*Kostenki XVI* (*Tarasov 1961*)	*Markina gora-2* (*Rogachev 1957*)	*Kostenki XII-1A* (*Rogachev 1957*)	*Anosovka II-4* (*Rogachev 1961, 1966*)	*Kostenki VII-1* (*Rogachev 1957*)	*Kostenki I-4* (*Lazukov 1957c:93–94*)
Mammonteus primigenius (woolly mammoth)	X	5/?	X	X	X	X	X	X		X	5/?
Coelodonta antiquitatis (woolly rhinoceros)		12/?								X	
Equus caballus (wild horse)	X	10/?	X	X	X	XX	X	X	X	XX	9/?
Bos sp. or *Bison* (wild cattle)		1/1	X				X				
Cervus elaphus (red deer)	X		X		X	X	X				2/?
Megaloceros euryceros (giant deer)			X								
Rangifer tarandus (reindeer)		1/1									
Saiga tatarica (saiga antelope)		10/?									
Vulpes vulpes (ordinary red fox)		16/?									
Alopex lagopus (arctic fox)			X		X	X			X		1/1
Canis lupus (wolf)		30/?	X			X		X			
Lepus sp. (hare)	X	48/?	X			X	X			X	
Spalax microphthalmus (mole vole)		13/?			X						
Citellus rufescens (russet suslik)					X						
Citellus pygmaeus (little suslik)		8/?									
Castor fiber (beaver)		1/1	X								
Cricetus cricetus (ordinary hamster)		3/?			X						
Arvicola amphibius (water vole)		1/?									
Microtus sp. (vole)		11/?									
Carnivora indet.							X	X		X	
Artiodactyla indet.				X				X			
Aves (birds)		15/?	3/?								
Amphibia (amphibians)		2/?									
Reptilia (Ophidiae) (reptiles)		1/1									

* X = present; XX = abundant; 0/0 = number of bones/number of individuals.

Markina Gora-Horizon 3 and Tel'manskaya-Horizon 3

Horizon 3 of Markina gora occurred at the very bottom of the upper humic bed and was 20–25 cm. thick. Although only 20 sq. m. of it were opened, a number of important features were exposed (Fig. 22). Small bits of charred bone and wood were found everywhere in the horizon, but were concentrated in three roundish ashy spots (= fossil hearths?). The most northwestern of these spots was found in a small, bowl-shaped depression, 80 cm. across and 10 cm. deep at center. The edges of this depression were slightly deformed, leading the excavator (A. N. Ro-

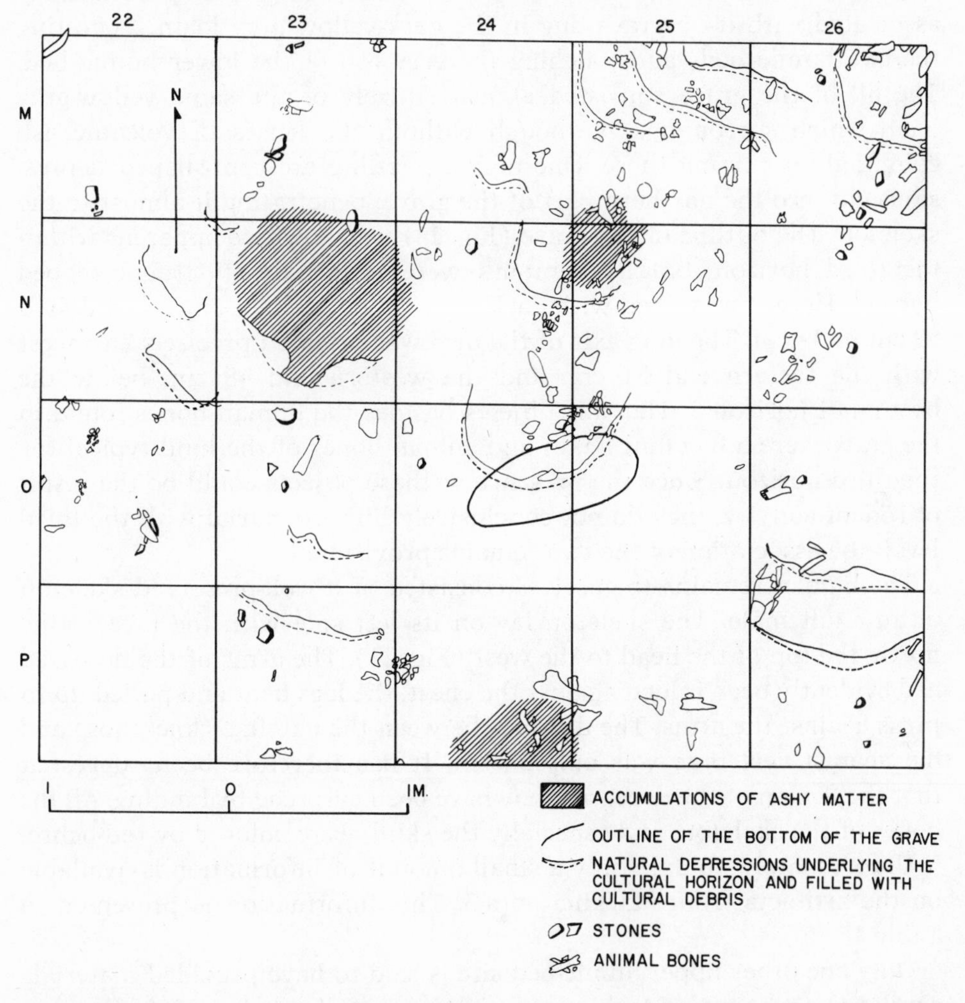

Figure 22. Plan of Markina Gora-Horizon 3 (redrawn after Rogachev 1957:Figure 38).

gachev) to suppose that some of the cultural remains may have been displaced from their original positions. A series of enigmatic, presumably natural depressions provide additional evidence for disturbance of the cultural materials. The depressions tended toward a crescent shape with the bulge of the crescent directed downslope (= south). The upslope (= northern) edge of each depression was usually delineated sharply, while the downslope edge was difficult to discern. The depressions varied in length (between the points of the crescent) from 50 to 90 cm. They were 10–30 cm. deep and filled with black, artifact-bearing loam of the third cultural level. Their mode of origin is not clear.

The most interesting feature of the third horizon is only provisionally associated with it—a grave dug in the dark-yellow grey loam separating the two humic beds and touching the very top of the lower humic bed. The fill of the grave consisted almost entirely of the same yellow-grey loam which surrounded it, though without the lenses of volcanic ash commonly occurring there. One of the puzzling crescent-shaped depressions cut into the northern part of the grave, penetrating it almost to the skeleton. The outline of the grave (Fig. 23) was nowhere apparent within the third horizon, but its contours were visible on its trough-shaped bottom. Here it was lined with dark-red pigment delineating an oval area 99 cm. × 39 cm. The long axis of the oval was oriented precisely east-west with the eastern end 31 cm. and the western end 48 cm. below the bottom of horizon 3. The only objects besides the human bones found in the grave were a few flint flakes and animal bones of the kind typical for the third horizon. Since the presence of these objects could be the result of rodent activity, they do not conclusively link the burial with the third level; the association of the two remains provisional.

The human remains themselves consisted of a well-preserved skeleton of an adult male. The skeleton lay on its left side with the face to the north, the top of the head to the west (Fig. 23). The arms of the deceased had evidently been folded against the chest, the legs bent and pulled up to press against the arms. The distance between the patellae (kneecaps) and the nearest vertebrae was only 28 cm. It has therefore been suggested that the flexion of the deceased may have been enforced by binding. All the bones of the skeleton, and especially the skull, were colored by red ochre.

Unfortunately, to date only a small amount of information is available on the artifacts from Markina gora-3. This information is presented in Table 15.

Only one other upper-humic-bed site is said to have provided materials similar to those from Markina gora-3. This is Tel'manskaya-3. The rather sparse information available on the artifact inventory from this site is

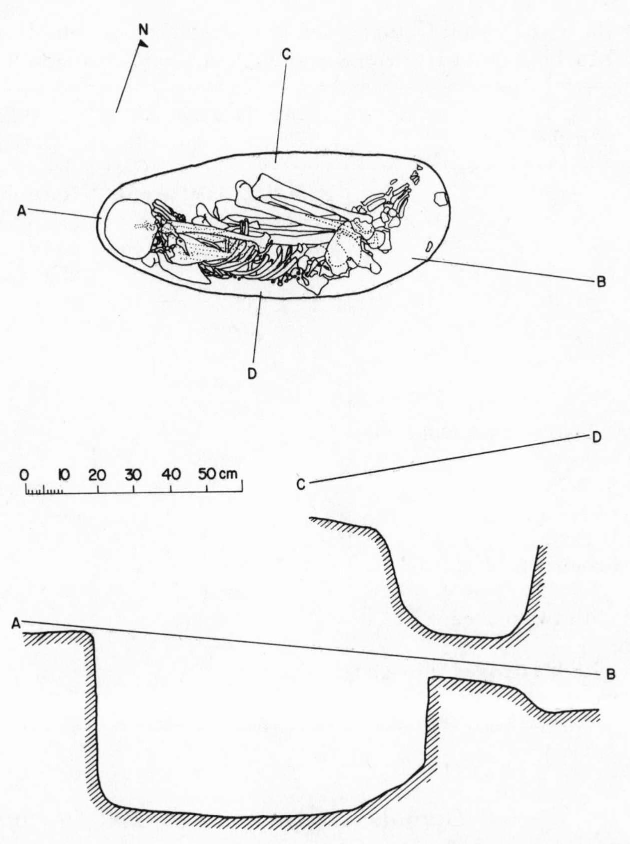

Figure 23. Plan and Profiles of the Grave from Markina Gora (redrawn after Rogachev 1955a:Figure 2). Lines AB and CD above the profiles mark the top of horizon 3.

presented in Table 15. In places, Tel'manskaya-3 occurred on approximately the same level as Tel'manskaya-2 (the immediately higher-lying horizon). It is therefore difficult to make statements about features. In areas where the two horizons were clearly distinct, the raw materials used for artifact manufacture were strikingly different—compare Tables 15 and 17. This distinction allowed division of artifacts in places of mixture. One of the areas where horizon 3 was clearly distinguishable from horizon 2 contained a small accumulation of ash and pieces of charred bone, which apparently represent the remains of an ancient hearth (see Fig. 24). The hearth is believed to have been located within a structure whose base may now be traced only according to the limits of concentration of cultural debris. A large test pit located some distance from the main excavation of Tel'manskaya-3 uncovered a second concentration of debris around an ashy mass. This is also thought to mark the spot of an ancient structure.

TABLE 15. Typological Composition of the Artifact Assemblages from Markina Gora-Horizon 3 and Tel'manskaya-Horizon 3

Artifacts	*Markina gora-3* (*Rogachev 1957:89*)	*Tel'manskaya-3* (*Rogachev 1957:56*)
	Raw materials: almost exclusively flint not available locally; some sandstone.	Raw materials: ca. ⅔ locally available flint and ⅓ locally available quartzite.
STONE		
End-scrapers	some	6
Burins	——	2
Splintered pieces	some	——
Side-scrapers	some	——
Blades with continuous retouch along one or both edges	some	some
Nonretouched pieces	??	several hundred
BONE		
Fragmentary rod-shaped artifacts of ivory	some	some
Antler fragment with two incised parallel grooves	——	1
Carnivore tooth with hole drilled through at base of crown	——	1

Gorodtsovskaya and Kostenki XII-Horizon 1B

Gorodtsovskaya provides a marked contrast to Markina gora-3 and Tel'-manskaya-3. Careful excavation of the site revealed that cultural debris were not scattered randomly over the entire 70 sq. m. exposed. Rather, they were distinctly concentrated in an area which is thought would have been roughly oval, had not the eastern part of it been eroded away (Fig. 25). In the opinion of the excavator (A. N. Rogachev), the rough oval demarcates the base of an ancient structure.

Evidence for fire at Gorodtsovskaya was apparent in the large number of charred bits of bone and wood encountered throughout the cultural horizon and also in two distinct ashy spots. One of these, the less clear, occurred near the southwestern end of the oval concentration of materials. The other, more sharply bounded and containing a large amount of charcoal, occurred beyond the margins of the oval, a little more than a meter from its southwestern end. Small spots of red ochre, as well as lumps of red and yellow ochreous material, were found dispersed throughout the area of maximum concentration of materials.

Investigation of deposits immediately below the cultural horizon dis-

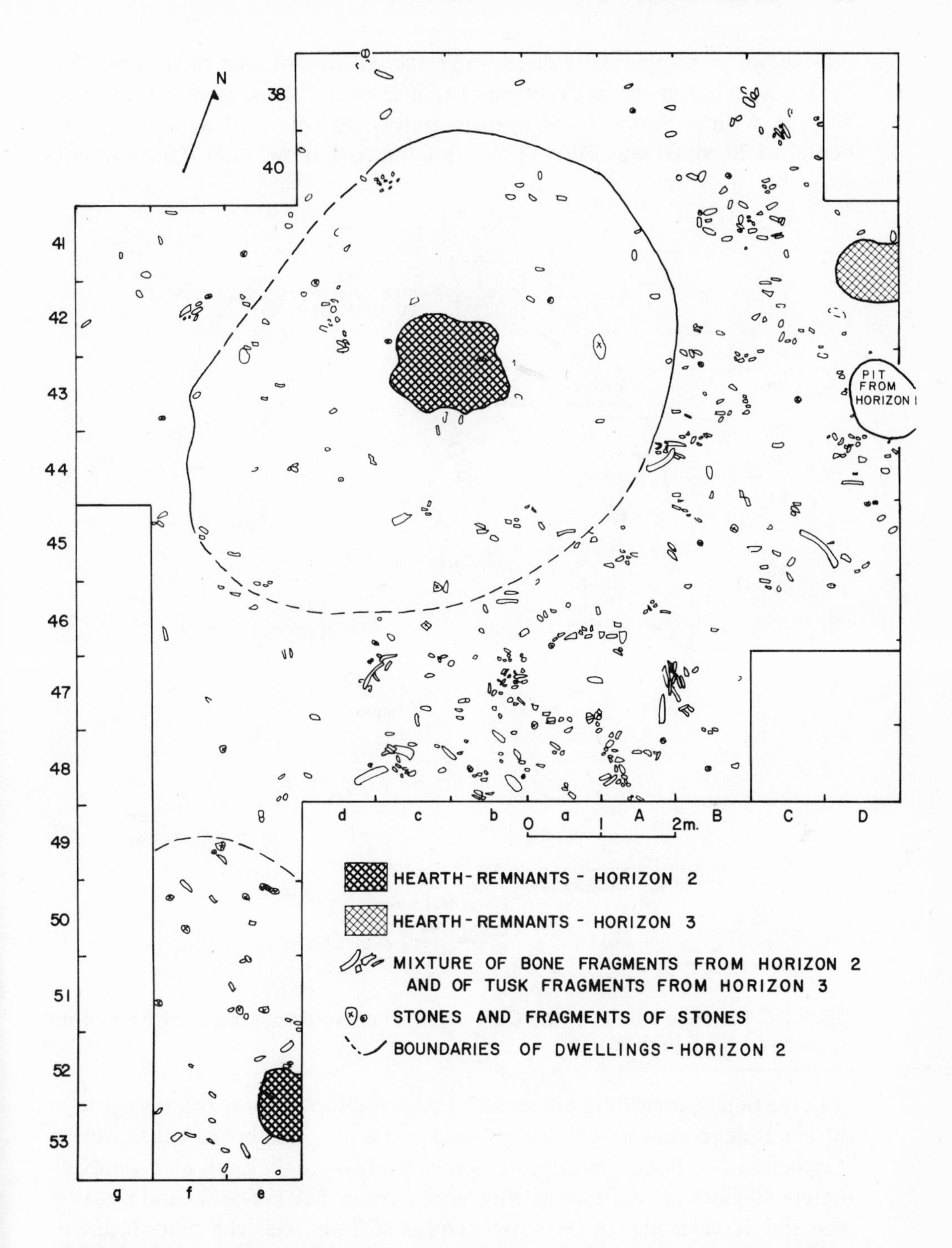

Figure 24. Plan of Tel'manskaya-Horizons 2 and 3 (redrawn after Rogachev 1957: Figure 2).

closed two pits apparently dug by the ancient inhabitants of the site. The first, occurring at the northern end of the oval "house floor," was bowl-shaped, with a diameter of approximately 70 cm., and a depth at the center of 20 cm. It was filled to overflowing with more than 100 fragments

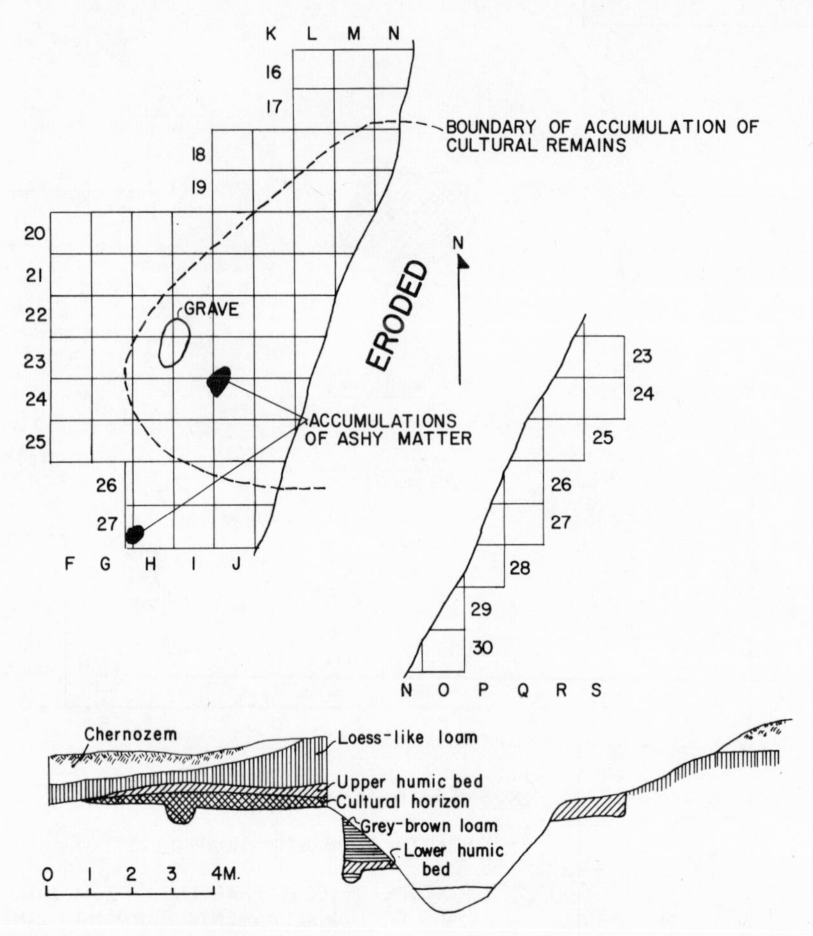

Figure 25. Plan and Profile of the Cultural Level of Gorodtsovskaya (redrawn after Rogachev 1957:Figure 55).

of horse bones, including pieces of long bones, foot bones, and two groups of vertebrae in anatomical order. Scattered among the horse bones were a fragment of a bone "paddle-shaped shovel" (see below) and approximately 40 pieces of artifactual flint (none retouched). The second pit, dug near the western edge of the supposed house floor was even more interesting than the first; its contents indicate that it represents an intentionally dug grave. The grave was oval, measuring 1.24 × 0.80 m., with its major

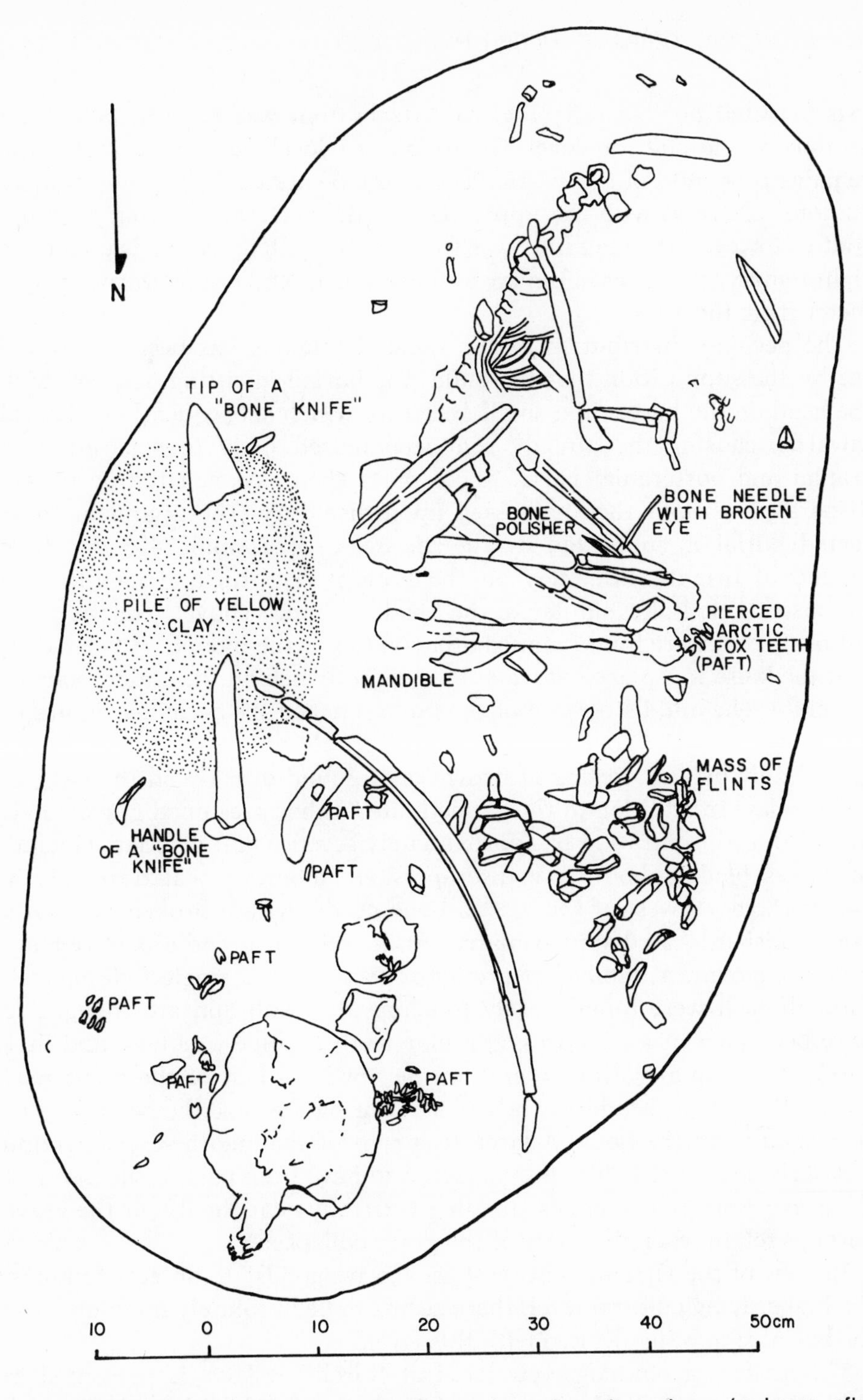

Figure 26. Plan of the Bottom of the Grave from Gorodtsovskaya (redrawn after Rogachev 1957:Figure 56).

axis oriented north-south (Fig. 26). Its bottom was 0.43 m. below the bottom of the cultural level. On its almost level floor were found the remains of a child of 5–6 years. Part of the postcranial skeleton retained anatomical order, with the upper part of the vertebral column pointing south. However, the mandible was found with teeth downwards under the right femur. And the cranium lay at the northern end of the grave nearly a meter from the atlas.

The peculiar distribution of the skeletal remains has been accounted for by the supposition that the child was buried in sitting position with the head on the knees, in a small structure which subsequently collapsed inwards, causing the already semidecomposed body to separate into cranial and postcranial parts. These parts then assumed the peculiarly disparate positions they possessed upon discovery. The argument for a seated burial is supported by the discovery of a small, 4–6 cm. high mound of bright-yellow clay on the bottom. The tip and handle of a supposed bone knife, similar to the "paddle-shaped shovels" of the same cultural level, were found immediately on top of the mound. It is thought that the knife was placed at waist level directly behind the seated body of the child. The middle portion of the knife touched the decaying tissues of the body and as a consequence completely decomposed; it was represented only by a scattering of brown dust, found directly on the heap of yellow clay. In addition to the "bone knife," other presumed grave goods included a concentration of approximately seventy flint artifacts (including flakes, blades, about ten end-scrapers, and a borer) located roughly 30 cm. to the northwest of the seat; a bone needle with a broken eye and a bone polisher located approximately 30 cm. due west; and bits of red and yellow pigment. A number of arctic-fox teeth with a single hole pierced through each were found nearly touching the skull and are thought to have been part of a headdress. Similar teeth (canines, molars, and incisors) occurring at various points in the northern half of the grave may have fallen off the headdress before and during the time the head became separated from the body. A large fragment of mammoth scapula found above the legs of the child is considered to have been part of the cover of the grave. Some horse bones standing vertically near the top of the grave perhaps fell in when the cover of the grave collapsed.

In view of the virtual identity of the "grave goods" to objects found in the higher-lying cultural level, there seems to be absolutely no doubt that the burial is to be associated with this level.

The artifact assemblage recovered at Gorodtsovskaya is presented in Table 16. Among all the artifacts found, the "paddle-shaped shovels" (Fig. 27) present the greatest interest. Similar objects elsewhere are

TABLE 16. Typological Composition of the Artifact Assemblages from Gorodtsovskaya and Kostenki XII-1B

Artifacts	*Gorodtsovskaya (Rogachev 1957: 106–118)*	*Kostenki XII-1B (Rogachev 1957:66)*
	Raw material: locally available and not locally available flint; locally available quartzite.	Raw material: almost exclusively locally available flint.
STONE		
End-scrapers	80	12
Double	(5)	?
End-scraper/burins	5	?
Burins	ca. 18	3
Splintered pieces	108	17
Borers	ca. 10	—
Backed bladelets	—	5
Blades with continuous retouch along one or both edges	75	4
Side-scrapers	9+	6
Points on flakes	?	—
Chopping tools	—	8
Miscellanea	ca. 62[a]	—
TOTAL retouched pieces	ca. 370	ca. 55
Cores	a few	1
Unretouched pieces	ca. 1,600	ca. 440
TOTAL artifactual stone	> 2,000	ca. 500
BONE		
Paddle-shaped shovels	11	1(?)
Whole	(2)	—
Fragmentary	(9)	—
Fragmentary needles	10	—
Fragmentary awls	a few	—
Artificially sharpened fragments of deer antler	2	—
Drilled arctic-fox teeth (canines, incisors, and molars)	ca. 30	—

[a] Mostly flakes with sporadic retouch; also a bifacially worked piece and fourteen fragments of various tools.

exceedingly rare: they are so far known only from Kostenki XII-1 and the site of Předmost in Czechoslovakia. Both nearly whole examples of paddle-shaped shovels at Gorodtsovskaya were cut from the walls of mammoth long bones. Each had an over-all length of at least 26 cm., and a maximum blade width of 6 cm. in one case and 7 cm. in the other. The fragments of paddle-shaped shovels consisted of four pieces of handles and five of blades. In addition, it will be recalled that a similar kind of artifact, partially decomposed, was found in the grave.

Only one other upper-humic-bed site has an artifact inventory said to be closely similar to that of Gorodtsovskaya. This is Kostenki XII-horizon 1. Artifacts in the upper humic bed at Kostenki XII were discovered at three

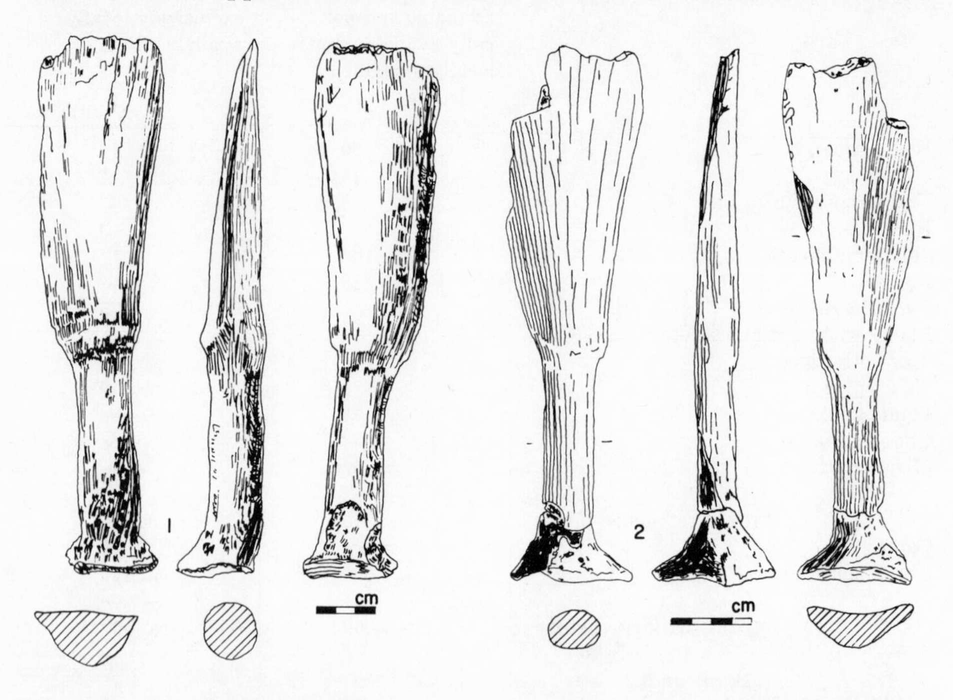

Figure 27. "Paddle-Shaped Shovels" from Gorodtsovskaya (redrawn after Rogachev 1957:Figures 58 and 59).

separate points, each characterized by a distinctive assemblage. It has not been possible to establish the stratigraphic interrelationships of the three points, and they have simply been assigned the letter designations A, B, and C (Fig. 28). Point C is sometimes known as Kostenki VII (it is treated here under this label). Points A and B are referred to as horizons 1A and 1B. It is 1B which has supplied stone artifacts said to be like those of Gorodtsovskaya (see Table 16 for a typological comparison of the assemblages). However, a pit dug in the upper humic bed at point A exposed an accumulation of horse bones with a mammoth-bone paddle-shaped shovel. Since no stone artifacts were found in the pit, it is not out of the question that the shovel may belong to the occupation represented

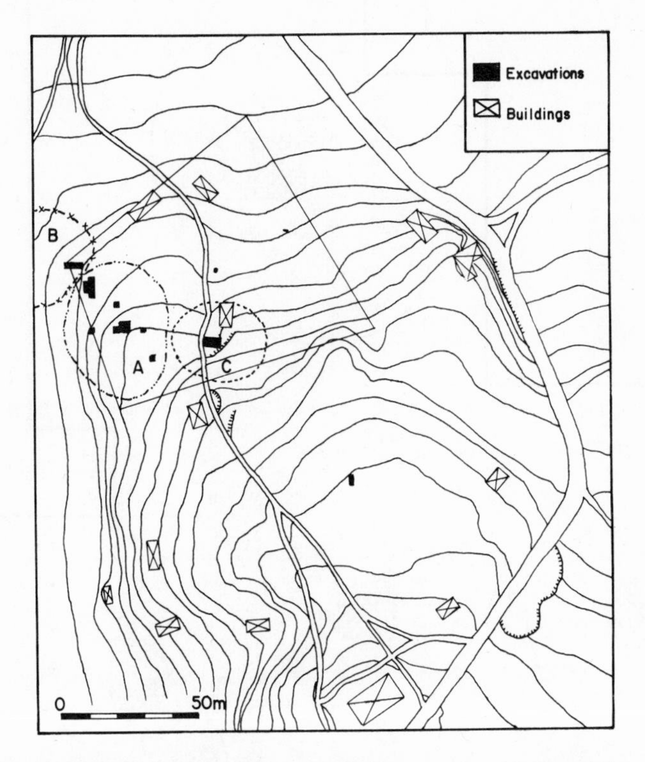

Figure 28. Topographic Map of Kostenki XII (one meter contour interval) (redrawn after Rogachev 1957:Figure 27).

more abundantly at point B. This underscores the possibility that point B is derived from the same culture as Gorodtsovskaya. No features have been reported from point B. This is not surprising since none of the materials found in the upper humic bed at Kostenki XII are believed to have been in situ.

Tel'manskaya-Horizon 2

Two sets of excavations have been conducted in Tel'manskaya-2. The first exposed what the excavator (A. N. Rogachev) believes were the remains of two dwellings (Fig. 24, p. 93). One (the more northern) was excavated completely, the other only partially. In each case, the presence of an ancient structure was thought to be demonstrated by an especially intensive concentration of cultural materials around a distinctly bounded mass of ash and charcoal (= a "hearth"). In the more northern (and completely excavated) example, the concentration of debris was roughly oval, measuring ca. 5.5 × 7.5 m. The second set of excavations (conducted

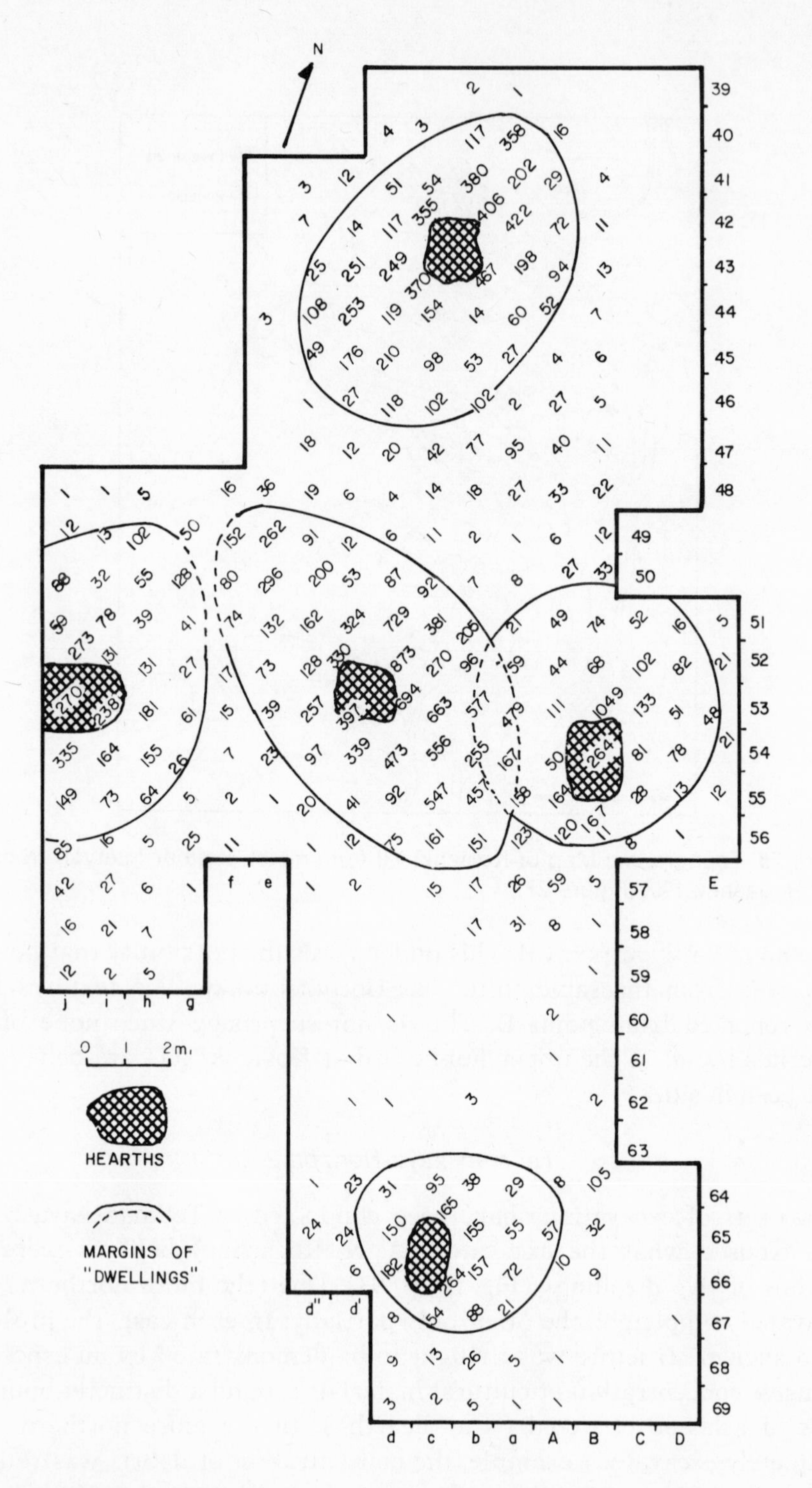

Figure 29. Flints per Square Meter in Tel'manskaya-Horizon 2 (redrawn after Litovchenko 1966).

by L. M. Litovchenko and L. M. Tarasov), added three more supposed house floors (= roundish concentrations of cultural debris, each with a hearth in its center; see Fig. 29). These areas were not always clearly delimited and two (the southern and eastern) even overlapped, which is said to indicate that one dwelling, probably the southern, was slightly more recent. Sizeable concentrations of cultural materials immediately outside the "dwelling bases" are thought to mark the entrances into the ancient structures.

The artifact inventory of Tel'manskaya-2 is presented in Table 17.[1] No other upper-humic-bed site has provided a comparable assemblage.

TABLE 17. Typological Composition of the Artifact Assemblage from Tel'manskaya-Horizon 2, A. N. Rogachev Excavations (Compiled from Information in Rogachev 1957:53–57)

Artifacts	*Quantity*
STONE	
(Raw material: principally flint not available locally)	
Notched and denticulate blades	ca. 17
End-scrapers	ca. 9
End-scraper/burins	ca. 2
Burins (principally dihedral and on retouched truncations)	ca. 100
Backed bladelets and points (including microgravettes and perhaps Font-Ives points)	ca. 475
Geometric pieces (principally trapezoids)	ca. 6
Blades and fragments of blades with continuous retouch along one or both edges	some
Side-scrapers	some
TOTAL retouched pieces	> 600
Cores	a few
Unretouched pieces of stone (mostly small chips from retouching)	several 1,000
TOTAL artifactual stone	> 6,000
BONE	
Polisherlike tools	1
Incised bones	some
Engraved bones	?
Ivory "pendants"	1

[1] The table includes pieces from only the first set of excavations. Those from the second have not yet been described.

Kostenki XVII-Horizon 1

The sparse cultural remains of Kostenki XVII-horizon 1 were scattered over a vertical distance of 0.30–0.40 m. in lenses of dark, humic loam; intercalated lenses of grey, sandyish loam turned out to be artifactually sterile. In addition, no clear hearths or horizontal concentrations of bones or artifacts were found. All this evidence has led the excavator (P. I. Boriskovskij) to suppose that the materials were not in situ. Displacement from primary position cannot have been great, however, since none of the artifacts are markedly rolled. Further, six small, intensive accumulations of red pigment (ochre) were found, and four diffuse, but still visible ashy spots (1.5–2 m. across). The ashy spots were somewhat enigmatic; they were very flat in section (not lens-shaped as is usual for hearth masses) and the earth beneath them was baked dark brown to red. It is thought they may represent the remains of a grass fire. The horizontal distribution of concentrations of red ochre, ashy spots, and important bone and stone objects is depicted in Figure 30.

The artifact inventory of Kostenki XVII-1 is presented in Table 18. Although the number of retouched pieces (54) is perhaps too small for any conclusive statements to be made, the assemblage has been said to bear an over-all resemblance to that of Kostenki XVII-2. It is unique among the assemblages from the upper humic bed.

Kostenki XVI-Horizons 1 and 2

According to the excavator (L. M. Tarasov), the western part of Kostenki XVI contained two cultural horizons, sometimes separated from one another by a 5–10 cm. seam of sterile loam. However, over much of the area exposed, the two horizons touched and were inseparable; their total combined thickness averaged 12–15 cm. and reached a maximum of 30 cm. The upper horizon, where it was clearly distinguishable, was the thinner and poorer of the two, and was characterized by strong coloration from red ochre and by the presence of quartzite and yellow flint. The lower horizon was only weakly colored by ochre and contained black flint. It was, however, thicker and richer, and it seems likely that most, if not all, the features described from the western part of the excavation belong to this horizon. Most prominent among these features were a number of vague carbonaceous, ashy lenses, 2–4 cm. thick, and a shallow pit, about 0.7 m. across. The pit contained a 3–5 cm. thick black carbonaceous mass (Fig. 31). Ten additional small pits were found directly below the lower horizon in the western part of the excavations. Nine of these, with dimensions 0.3–0.6 m. across and 0.4 m. deep, contained materials in the same density as the lower horizon. The tenth, an oval 0.5 × 0.86 m. across and

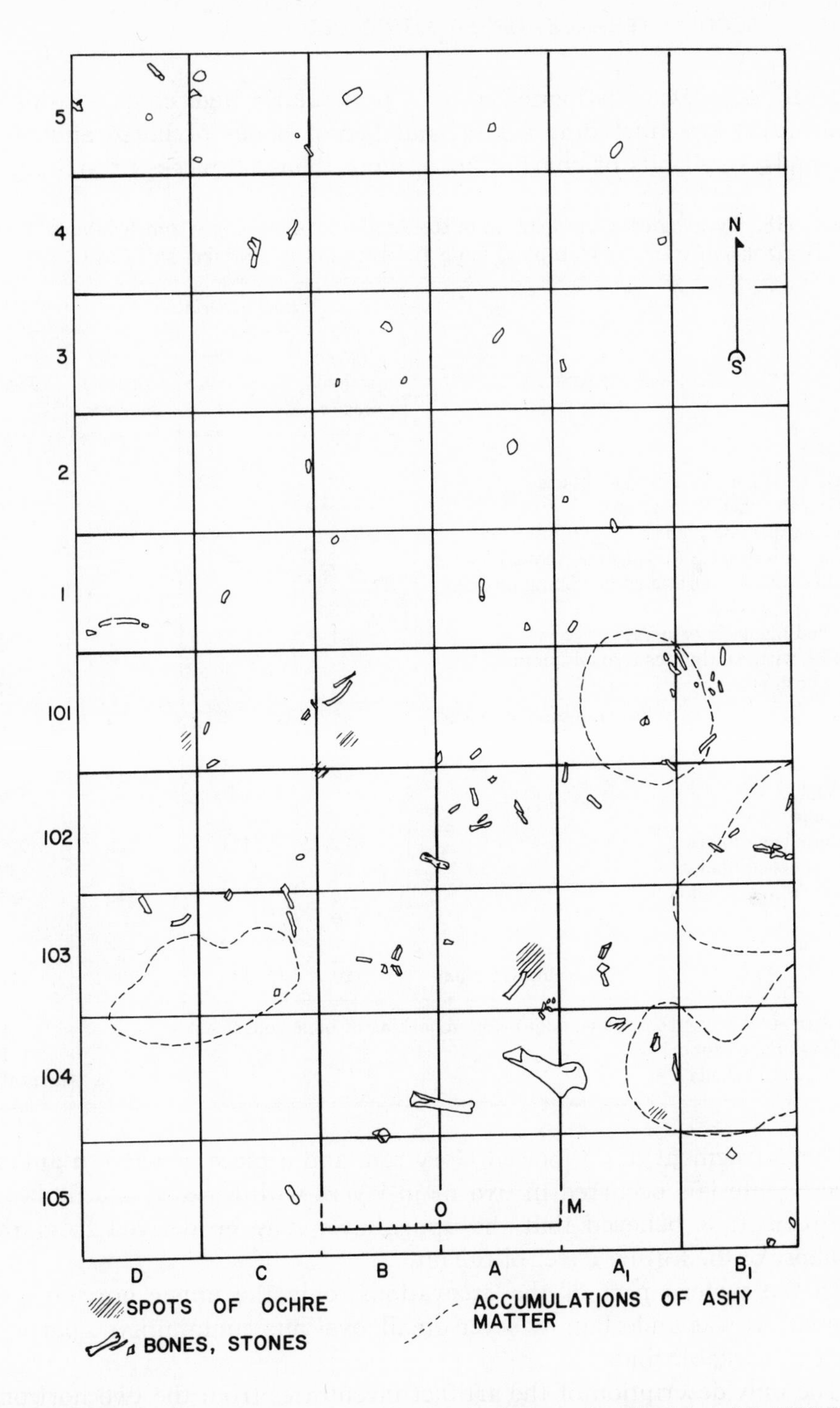

Figure 30. Plan of Kostenki XVII-Horizon 1 (redrawn after Boriskovskij 1963:Figure 81).

0.43 m. deep, was distinguished by a particularly high concentration of cultural debris, including a large number of bones of horse and other animals, small bits of charred bone, more than 200 pieces of artifactual

TABLE 18. Typological Composition of the Artifact Assemblage from Kostenki XVII-Horizon 1 (Critically Compiled from Information in Boriskovskij 1963:107ff.)

STONE ARTIFACTS	*Raw material*			*Total*
	Flint not available locally	*Locally available flint*	*Locally available quartzite*	
Burins	5	—	—	5
On the corner of a broken blade	(3)	—	—	(3)
On retouched truncations	(2)	—	—	(2)
End-scrapers on blades	13	—	4	17
Steep end-scrapers (atypical carinates)	2	—	—	2
Blades with some retouch or flaking on the ventral surface	3	—	2	5
Backed bladelets or points	1	—	—	1
Blades with continuous retouch on one or both edges	23	—	1	24
TOTAL retouched pieces	47	0	7	54
Cores	5	3	4	12
Blade				(10)
Flake				(2)
Unretouched flakes	372	111	529	1,012
Unretouched blades	13	1	18	32
Chips from retouch	273	1	349	623
Burin spalls	10	—	—	10
Nodules	—	3	—	3
TOTAL chipped stone	720	119	907	1,746
Sandstone tablets with notched edges (for smoothing of bone rods?)				1
Incised lumps of marl				1
Denticulated shells				several

stone, a fragment of an incised ivory rod, and a piece of worked antler. These materials occurred in two main layers with a nearly sterile layer between. It is believed that the upper layer may be derived from the collapse of the former cover of the pit.

In the eastern part of the excavations, only the upper horizon was present. It was underlain by seven small, oval pits containing no particularly remarkable finds.

The only description of the artifact inventories from the two horizons of Kostenki XVI treats them as if they were one; this composite description is summarized in Table 19.

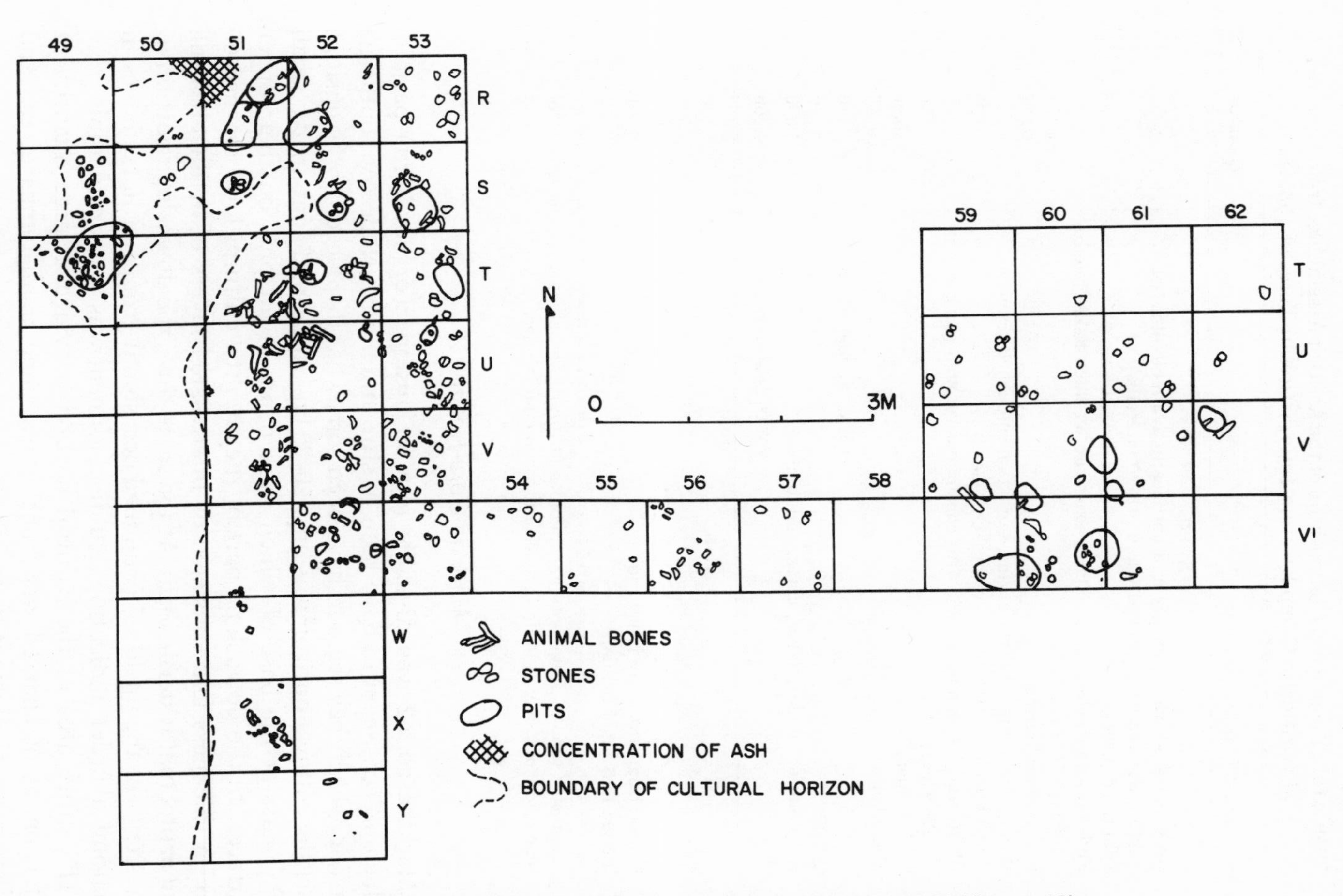

Figure 31. Plan of Kostenki XVI (redrawn after Tarasov 1961:Figure 12).

TABLE 19. Typological Composition of the Artifact Assemblage from Kostenki XVI (Critically Compiled from Information in Tarasov 1961:42–47)

Artifacts	*Quantity*
STONE	
(Raw material: ca. ⅔ locally and not locally available flint; ca. ⅓ locally available quartzite and other materials.)	
Splintered pieces	35
End-scrapers (including principally examples on thick flakes and on blades)	ca. 27
End-scraper/burins	some
Burins (including dihedral burins, burins on retouched truncations, and burins on the corners of broken blades)	25
Blades and fragments thereof with continuous retouch along one or both edges	30
Side-scrapers	some
Miscellanea	ca. 40[a]
TOTAL retouched pieces	ca. 180
Cores	ca. 10
Unretouched blades, flakes, chips, and lumps	ca. 4,300
TOTAL artifactual stone	>4,500
BONE	
Awls	2
Antler fragment with one end intentionally flattened and polished	1
Incised fragment of an ivory rod	1
Incised horse metapodials	2

[a] Mostly tabular fragments and pebbles of quartzite believed by the excavator to bear traces of use as grinding stones and/or hammerstones.

Markina Gora-Horizon 2

Markina gora-2 was divisible into an upslope (or northern) part, in which objects seem to have been in situ, and a downslope (or southern) part, in which they seem to have been somewhat displaced. In the upslope part the cultural horizon was only 20–25 cm. thick, and contained a small ashy mass at the base of which were bones burnt only on their upper surfaces. In the downslope part of the site, the cultural level reached 60 cm. in thickness and consisted of intercalated layers of artifact-bearing and artifactually sterile loam. At the same time, the downslope portion of the site (like the upslope) contained occasional groups of horse bones in anatomical order, indicating that displacement was not considerable.

The entire area of the cultural horizon provided a large quantity of small pieces of charred wood and bone, some small lumps of red and yellow mineral pigment, a considerable amount of animal bone (mostly fragmentary and belonging to horse), and a relatively large number of flint, quartzite, and bone artifacts. The typological composition of the artifacts is presented in Table 20. The outstanding features of the assemblage are the prominence of tools made on flakes (side-scrapers) and the absence of burins. Since burins are generally thought to have been important in the working and engraving of bone, their absence at Markina gora-2 may be regarded as particularly interesting. Not only are bone tools fairly numerous, but many of them also bear incised geometric patterns.

TABLE 20. Typological Composition of the Artifact Assemblage from Markina Gora-Horizon 2 (Compiled from Information in Rogachev 1957:77–81)

Artifacts	*Quantity*
STONE	
(Raw material: flint and quartzite)	
End-scrapers	>200
Splintered pieces	a few
Side-scrapers	many
Points on flakes	some
TOTAL retouched pieces	several 100
Cores (primarily flake)	several
Unretouched pieces	several 100
TOTAL artifactual stone	several 100
BONE	
Awls	several
Needles	several
Polishers	several
Retouchers (horse metapodials)	several

Kostenki XII-Horizon 1A

Kostenki XII-1A is believed to represent the continuation of the Kostenki-Streletskaya Culture of the lower humic bed. The materials are not thought to have been in situ, and no features have been reported from the site. The artifact inventory closely resembles those from the Kostenki-Streletskaya sites of the lower humic bed in consisting largely of side-scrapers. Five end-scrapers and a significant bifacially worked, triangular point were also found.

Anosovka II-Horizon 4, Kostenki VII-Horizons 1 and 2, and Kostenki I-Horizon 4

The materials from Anosovka II-4 are still in the process of analysis, and only limited information is available on them. The site is said to have provided fragmentary animal bones (some charred), several lumps of red pigment, charred bits of wood, and artifacts of locally available flint and quartzite. The artifacts included a splintered piece and a truncated blade. Kostenki VII-1 and 2 and Kostenki I-4 are the poorest of the upper-humic-bed sites. Neither horizon of Kostenki VII provided in situ materials or features. Horizon 2 was the poorer, supplying four burins, four end-scrapers (two of them fragmentary), and roughly thirty flakes and blades bearing some retouch. Horizon 1 yielded lumps of ochre and 700 flint and bone artifacts, including a series of end-scrapers, some retouched blades, a few cores, a bone needle fragment, and a fox canine with a hole drilled through the root. Kostenki I-4 contained mostly isolated bones of horse and mammoth and only a few flint and quartzite artifacts, which have never been described.

Summary

Among the features found in the upper humic bed, the most interesting were graves (at Markina gora-3 and Gorodtsovskaya) and traces of dwellings (at Tel'manskaya 2 and 3 and at Gorodtsovskaya). The artifact inventories of the upper humic bed are noteworthy for their diversity. Backed bladelets and points are prominent only in Tel'manskaya-2, being absent at most of the other sites. On the other hand, Gorodtsovskaya and Kostenki XII-1B are characterized by a large number of splintered pieces and by bone paddle-shaped shovels, while Markina gora-2 is notable for the absence of burins in company with a large number of flake tools and numerous bone artifacts. Kostenki XII-1A is outstanding for the presence of a triangular, bifacially worked concave-based point of the sort characteristic of the Kostenki-Streletskaya Culture prominently represented in the lower humic bed. It seems highly probable that some of the assemblages differ from one another because they are derived from different cultures. But it is also possible that some of the variability among assemblages is due simply to chance (particularly in the composition of small assemblages). And a portion of this variability may derive from the fact that bearers of a single culture likely did different things or different proportions of the same things at different sites and thus left behind different artifacts or at least different proportions of the same artifacts. Any attempt to sort out the various factors which may have led to differences among assemblages would require much more substantial qualitative and quantitative data than are currently available.

As in the lower humic bed, many collections in the upper bed contained a considerable number of pieces made of flint not obtainable locally. The significance of this fact is considered in detail in the final chapter.

chapter 9. Sites Overlying the Upper Humic Bed on the Second Terrace[1]

The loesslike loams overlying the upper humic bed have so far supplied thirteen sites (Fig. 8): Markina gora(= Kostenki XIV)-horizon 1, Kostenki I-horizons 1, 2 and 3, Tel'manskaya(= Kostenki VIII)-horizon 1, Kostenki IX, Anosovka I(= Kostenki X), Anosovka II(= Kostenki XI)-horizons 1A through 3, Kostenki II, and Borshevo III. For reasons which will become apparent, this chapter will also deal with Kostenki V-horizons 1 and 2 and Kostenki XIII. Further, for want of a better place to discuss it, the undatable site of Kostenki XVIII will be considered in an appended section to this chapter. The available information on the faunal assemblages encountered in the various sites is summarized in Table 21.

[1] With an appendix on Kostenki XVIII.

TABLE 21. Species Represented by Remains in Sites above the Upper Humic Bed on the Second Terrace*

Species	*Kostenki I-3* (*Lazukov 1957c:93–94*)	*Kostenki I-2* (*Lazukov 1957c:93–94*)	*Kostenki I-1* (*Lazukov 1957c:93–94*)	*Kostenki XIII* (*Bud'ko 1960*)	*Tel'manskaya-1* (*Lazukov 1957c:93–94*)	*Kostenki V-2* (*Rogachev 1957*)	*Kostenki II* (*Boriskovskij 1963:78*)	*Anosovka II-1, 2, 3* (*Rogachev 1953, 1957, 1961, 1962, 1966*)	*Markina gora-1* (*Rogachev 1957*)	*Anosovka I* (*Beregovaya 1960*)
Mammonteus primigenius (woolly mammoth)	4/?	X	XX	XX	145/3	X	> 30	X	X	X
Coelodonta antiquitatis (woolly rhinoceros)							1/1			
Equus caballus (wild horse)	49/?	X	XX		18/1		X	X		
Bos or *Bison* (wild cattle)					3/?					
Ovibos moschatus (musk ox)			X							
Cervus elaphus (red deer)	2/?		X							
Rangifer tarandus (reindeer)	69/?		+		7/1		X			X
Panthera spelaea (cave lion)			X		7/1		X			
Gulo gulo (wolverine)	15/?									
Ursus arctos (brown bear)			+				X			
Vulpes vulpes (ordinary fox)	6/?		X				X			
Vulpes cf. *corsac* (steppe fox)	8/?		35/?							
Alopex lagopus (arctic fox)	295/?		X	XX	30/6		X	X		X
Canis lupus (wolf)	> 3/?		XX	XX	302/5		2/?	X		
Lutra lutra (otter)			+							
Lepus sp. (hare)	32/?		28/?		78/7		X			
Marmota bobac (marmot)			X							
Spalax microphthalmus (European mole rat)	8/?		1/?		XX		X			
Allactaga jaculus (great jerboa)	5/?									
Citellus citellus (European suslik)	5/?									
Citellus rufescens (russet suslik)			X							

Species	Kostenki I-3 (Lazukov 1957c:93–94)	Kostenki I-2 (Lazukov 1957c:93–94)	Kostenki I-1 (Lazukov 1957c:93–94)	Kostenki XIII (Bud'ko 1960)	Tel'manskaya-1 (Lazukov 1957c:93–94)	Kostenki V-2 (Rogachev 1957)	Kostenki II (Boriskovskij 1963:78)	Anosovka II-1, 2, 3 (Rogachev 1953, 1957, 1961, 1962, 1966)	Markina gora-1 (Rogachev 1957)	Anosovka I (Beregovaya 1960)
Cricetus cricetus (ordinary hamster)	6/?		9/?							
Apodemus sylvaticus (forest mouse)							X			
Arvicola amphibius (water vole)	1/?									
Ellobius talpinus (mole vole)			X							
Rodentia indet.				X						
Aves (birds)			7/?							
Esox sp. (pike)							1/1			

* X = present; XX = abundant; + = rare; 0/0 = number of bones/number of individuals.

Once more, it is necessary to point out that the sites have been far from equally investigated and described. It is thus impossible at present to assign much significance to any differences apparent in the table.

Kostenki I-Horizon 3

Kostenki I-3 occurred between 2.20 and 2.60 m. from the surface in grey-brown, loesslike loam. The cultural horizon was unusually thick and contained hearths at different levels, which has led to the conclusion that at least three distinct occupations by people of the same culture are represented. The uppermost occupation is marked by debris in the upper 10–20 cm. of artifact-bearing loam. The middle occupation, occurring directly below the upper, contained two hearths (on squares A63 and b64 of Fig. 32). The lowermost or earliest occupation was the richest. It contained flints, fragments of animal bones, and lumps and spots of red ochre, all concentrated over an area of several square meters around one or two vague, irregular hearths (on squares α2 and α61 of Fig. 32). The concentration is believed to mark the location of an ancient dwelling. The ragged appearance of the hearths and the frequently inclined positions of artifacts and bone fragments suggest that the dwelling remains may not be entirely in situ.

Excavations directly below horizon 3 revealed a depression ca. 7 m. long, 0.9 m. wide, and 0.40–0.50 m. deep (squares A, B, C, 61–67 of Fig. 32). This depression is thought to represent the floor of a passageway into the ancient structure. The fill of the depression was sterile near the top, but contained artifacts typical for horizon 3 near the bottom.

The artifact inventory of Kostenki I-3 is summarized in Table 22. Among the shells used for the manufacture of the mollusc-shell "pendants" were those of two marine species encountered today (in fossil form) only on the Black Sea Coast. This fact, plus the over-all allure of the artifact inventory, has encouraged speculation about a possible relationship between Kostenki I-3 and the lowermost level of Syuren' I, an Upper Paleolithic cave site in the Crimea.

Kostenki I-Horizon 2

Kostenki I-2 occurred in the same grey-brown loam as Kostenki I-3, but higher, at a depth of only 1.50 to 1.80 m. from the surface. It contained no ochreous pigment and was marked only by the repeated occurrence of flint artifacts, fragments of bone, and pieces of rock in a 30 cm. thick band of loam. This band was separated by sterile layers from both Kos-

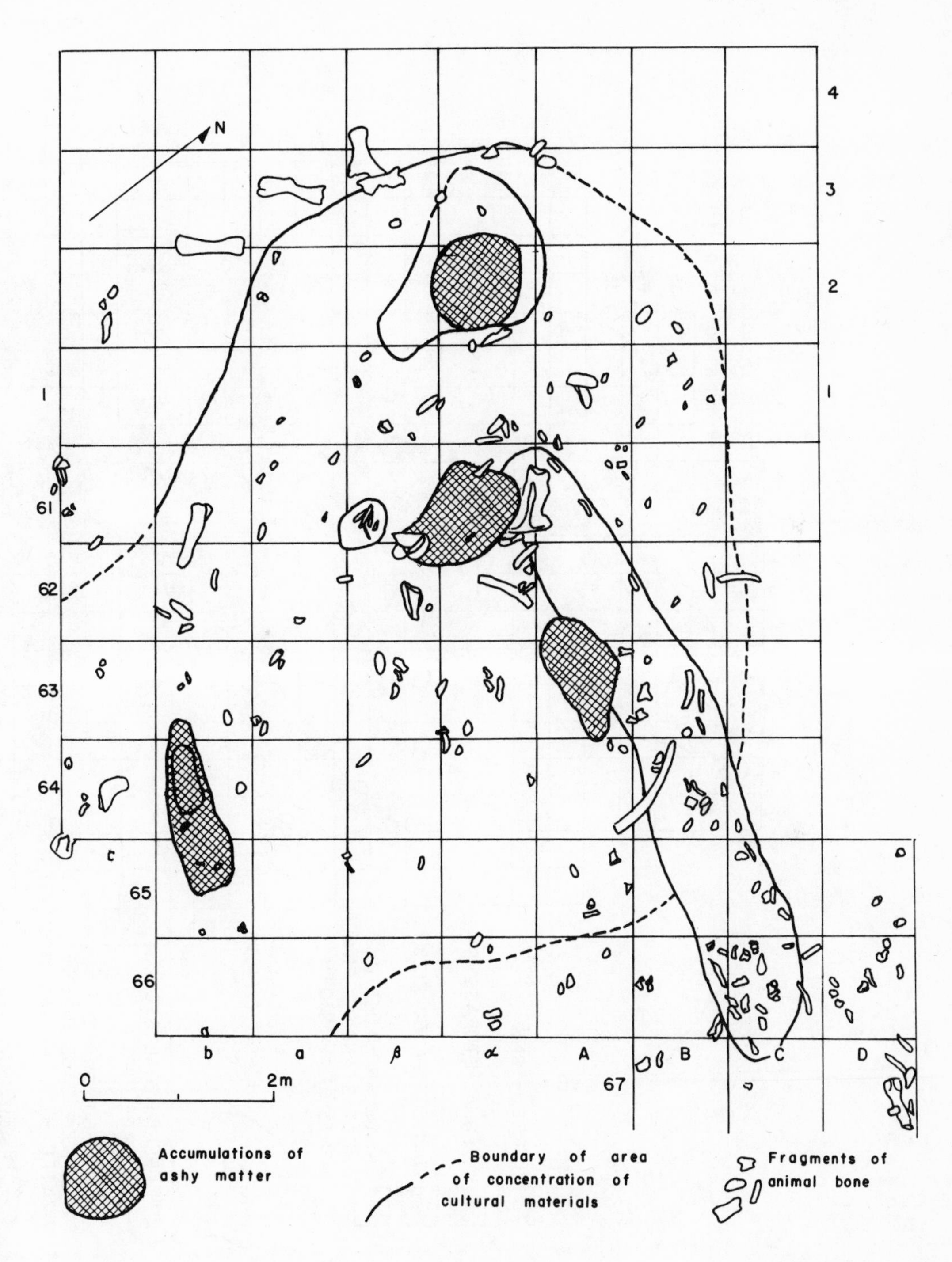

Figure 32. Plan of Kostenki I-Horizon 3 (redrawn after Rogachev 1957:Figure 31).

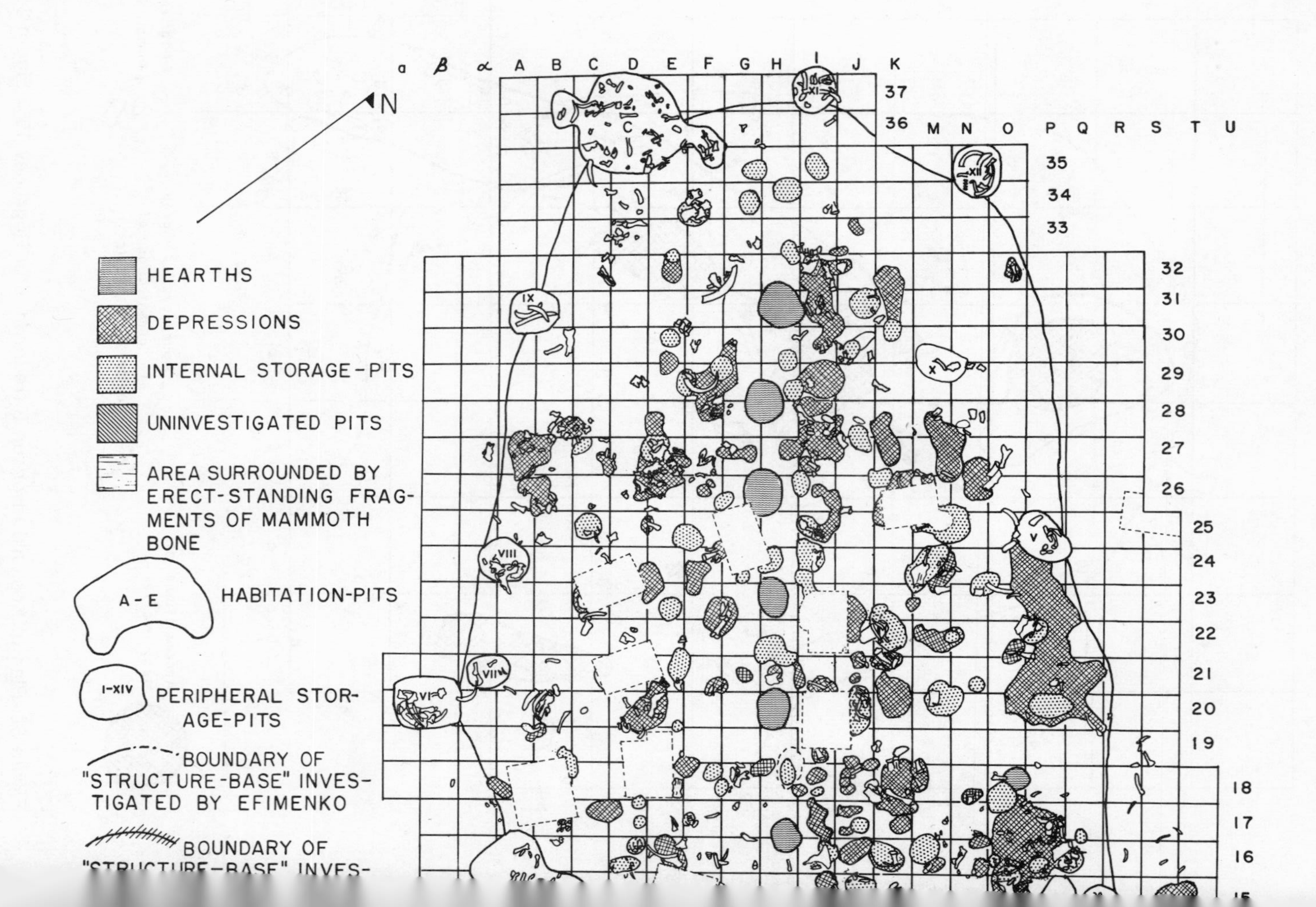

N
HEARTHS
DEPRESSIONS
INTERNAL STORAGE-PITS
UNINVESTIGATED PITS
AREA SURROUNDED BY ERECT-STANDING FRAGMENTS OF MAMMOTH BONE
A-E
HABITATION-PITS
I-XIV
PERIPHERAL STORAGE-PITS
BOUNDARY OF "STRUCTURE-BASE" INVESTIGATED BY EFIMENKO
BOUNDARY OF

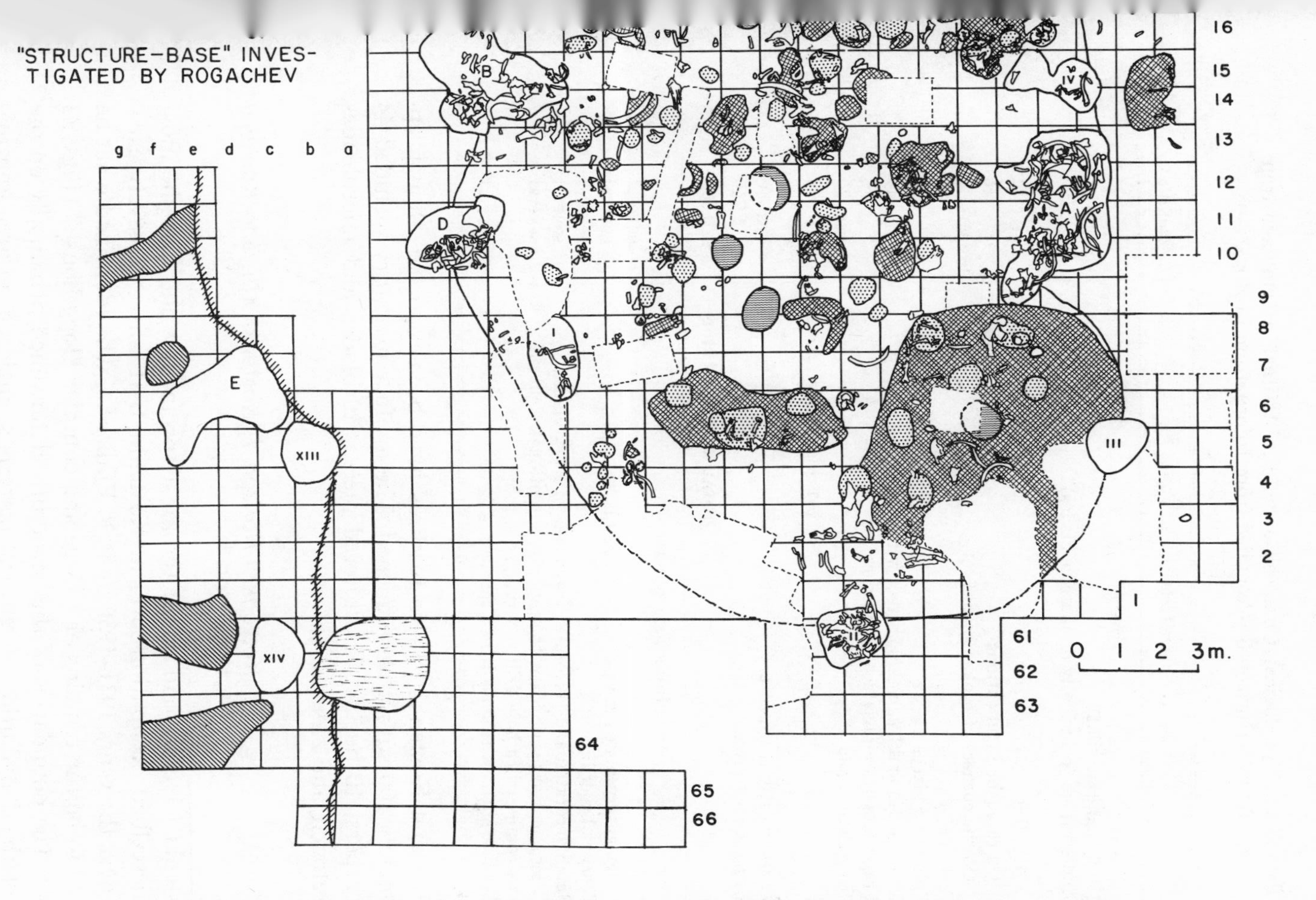

Figure 33. Plan of Kostenki I-Horizon 1 (redrawn after Efimenko 1958:Figures 6, 9, 18, and 29, and Rogachev 1957:Figure 3).

TABLE 22. Typological Composition of the Artifact Assemblage from Kostenki I-Horizon 3 (Compiled from Information in Rogachev 1957:30–34)

Artifacts	*Quantity*
STONE	
(Raw material: flint)	
End-scrapers (principally on massive blades)	> 20
Burins	ca. 40
Dihedral	(4)
On retouched truncations	(6)
On the corners of broken blades	(several)
Other	(?)
Splintered pieces	7
Microblades and fragments thereof with retouch	many
Fragments of unifacial leaf-shaped points	6
Nucleiform tools	ca. 20
TOTAL retouched pieces	> 200
Cores (mostly fragmentary)	ca. 50
Unretouched pieces	ca. 4,750
TOTAL artifactual stone	ca. 5,000
BONE AND SHELL	
Awls	several
Fragmentary bone rods ringed by incised lines	several
Ivory polisherlike tools	several
Small decorated and perforated fragments of ivory blades	several
Long bones of arctic fox with epiphyses intentionally cut off	several
Fox canines with hole drilled through the root	1
Mollusc shells with hole drilled through	several

tenki I-3 and Kostenki I-1. No features have been reported, though approximately 100 sq. m. were opened. The artifact inventory included 44 end-scrapers, 10 burins, 7 splintered pieces, 20 blades and microblades with retouch, and 27 small cores.

Kostenki I-Horizon 1, Kostenki XIII, and Kostenki V-Horizon 1

Kostenki I-1 is beyond doubt the most spectacular and also the most fully described occupation level at Kostenki I. It was extensively excavated over the years 1931–1936 by P. P. Efimenko, who identified what he believed to be the remains of a large and complex "long house" (Figs. 33 and 34). The boundaries of this structure, determined principally on the basis of the distribution of cultural materials, enclosed an area approximately 35 m. long and as much as 15–16 m. wide. Outside this area there

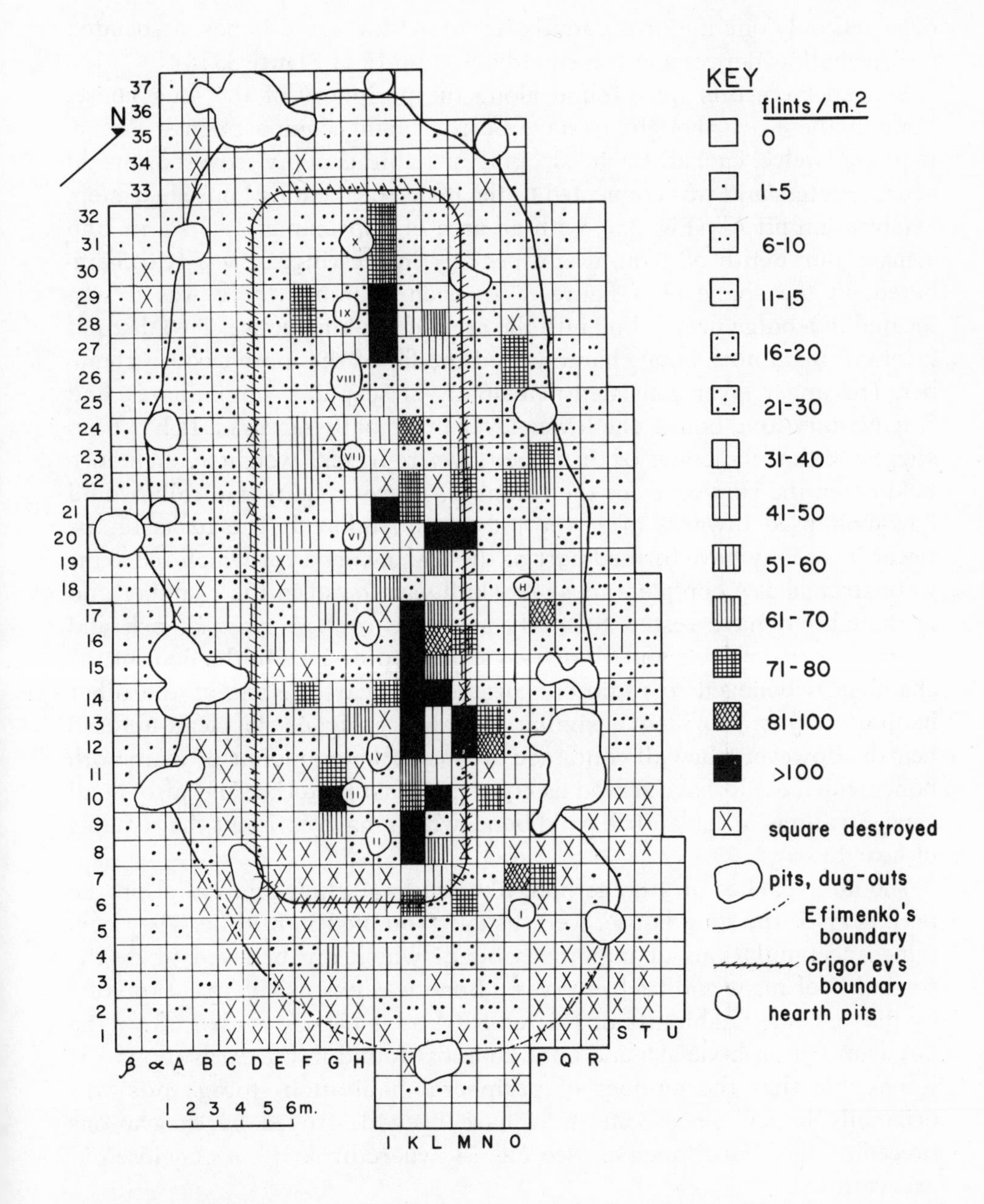

Figure 34. Distribution of Chipped Flint over the Area of Kostenki I-Horizon 1 (from Grigor'ev 1967: Figure 2).

occurred only one major accumulation of artifacts and bones, associated with a shallow depression (on squares S-T, 14–15 of Figure 33).

Sixteen large pits were found along the periphery of the long house. Four of these are thought to have been sleeping compartments, the remaining twelve, caches. Each "sleeping or habitation pit" covered several square meters and was connected to the inside of the long house by a step. "Habitation pit A" (Fig. 35), with an area of approximately 8 sq. m. and a maximum depth of 1 m., was especially interesting. It was two-chambered, in the shape of a figure 8. In each chamber there was a step located in a bulge protruding into the area of the long house. Two distinct layers of mammoth bone characterized the fill of the more eastern chamber. The upper layer consisted principally of scapulae, innominates, and fragmentary long bones, the lower layer principally of tusks. It has been suggested that the bones of the upper layer represent weights which once held down the skin cover of the chamber. These weights naturally would have collapsed inwards after the pit was abandoned. The tusks of the lower layer may have formed part of the framework over which the skins were stretched. A complete musk-ox skull was found in the chamber and is thought to have rested formerly atop the roof. A mass of ash and charred bone covering and filling two small depressions in the floor of the chamber is believed to represent an ancient hearth. None of the other habitation pits provided a similar double tiering or so clear a fossil hearth. However, they all contained a considerable amount of mammoth bone, which could have served as constructional material, and also small concentrations of ash and charred bone, which may represent the remains of hearths.

The large caches or storage pits, like the habitation pits found on the periphery of the long house, were usually rounded in outline. They contained accumulations of mammoth bones which are believed to be the remnants of meat and fuel reserves. (Bone was extensively used for fuel by the ancient inhabitants of Kostenki I-1 as is clearly evidenced by the large amount of bone ash and bone charcoal found in the excavations.) It is possible that the number of peripheral habitation/storage pits was originally larger, since some may have been destroyed by excavations preceding those of Efimenko (see Fig. 33, where broken lines enclose old excavations).

Careful investigation by Efimenko disclosed that a large portion of floor of the long house was covered by pits and depressions of various shapes and sizes and apparently of varying significance (see Fig. 33). The majority were round, oval, or subquadrangular in shape. Among the more

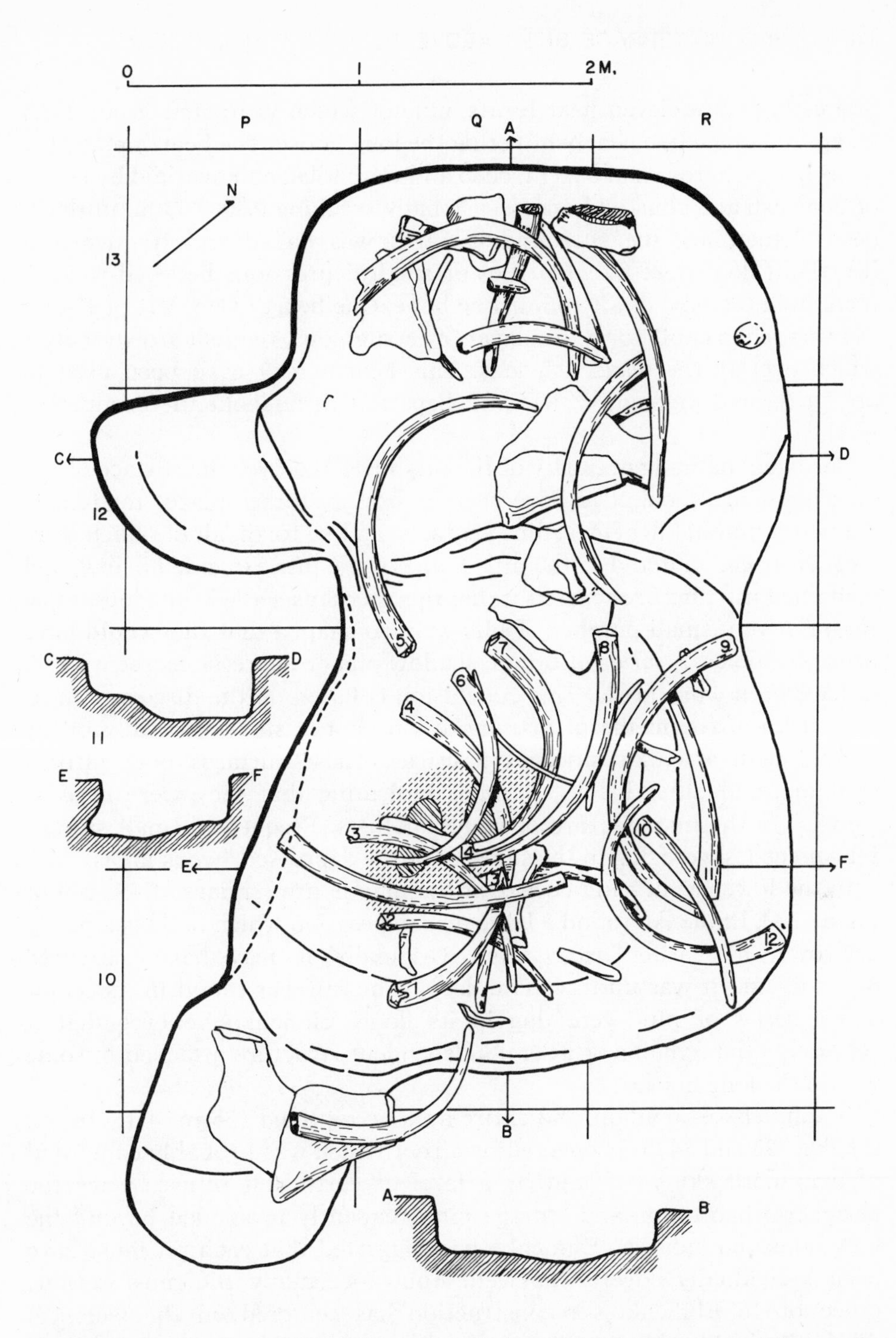

Figure 35. "Habitation Pit A" of Kostenki I-Horizon 1 (with ash accumulation on the bottom covering and filling two small depressions) (redrawn after Efimenko 1958: Figure 11).

interesting were eleven hearth pits, nine of which were strung out 2–2.5 m. apart along a line nearly bisecting the long house. The hearth pits were up to 1.10 m. across and 0.20 m. deep and were filled and overlaid by lenses of bone ash and charred bone occasionally reaching 0.30–0.35 m. in thickness. Sometimes, the surrounding earth was baked and frequently a hearth-pit floor bore irregularities or small depressions believed to have facilitated the flow of air to burning bone. One hearth (No. VII of Figure 34) was remarkable for a thin layer of ferruginous, reddish-brown matter which overlay the usual ash lens. This hearth may have been used to obtain the red pigment which was dispersed throughout the occupation level.

The overwhelming majority of the pits scattered over the surface of the long house are thought to have been caches or storage places for female statuettes, animal figurines, flint artifacts, and so forth, all of which were frequently encountered in the pits. Some of the pits expanded below, and contained ash and fire-scarred walls; they perhaps served for food preparation. A very small number of pits were so shaped that they could have been post holes. A series of broad, shallow pits or depressions seem likely to have been work areas. This conclusion is based on the discovery in or near them of fragments of mammoth long bones stuck vertically in the ground with articular surfaces upwards. These surfaces bore pitting, notching, and other marks, perhaps indicating that they were used as "anvils" in the manufacture of stone artifacts. Frequently small storage pits or caches were dug in the surfaces of the depressed "work areas."

In the lower right-hand corner of the long house (squares K–R, 2–9 of Figure 33), Efimenko found a large oval depression which had been partly destroyed by earlier excavations. Originally it may have measured 8m. × 6.5 m.; it was up to 60 cm. deep. A hearth was found in its center and a series of pits were dug in its floor. Efimenko believes that it represents the remains of a semi-independent structure attached in some way to the long house.

In Efimenko's opinion, the entire area he outlined (35 m. × 15–16 m.; see Figs. 33 and 34) was covered by a roof which was probably composed of mammoth skins overlaid by a level of earth and refuse. Since the peripheral habitation and storage pits frequently protruded beyond the long house boundaries, Efimenko has suggested that each pit must have been individually covered as well. Almost certainly the most serious objection to Efimenko's reconstruction has centered on the technical difficulties involved in covering such a large area. One commentator, S. N. Bibikov, has proposed that the features discovered by Efimenko represent a series of smaller structures scattered over the surface of the site. G. P.

Grigor'ev, who conducted a study of the distribution of flints in Efimenko's excavations, agrees that only one structure is represented, but believes that it covered a much smaller area than that suggested by Efimenko (Fig. 34). Actually, in spite of the extremely detailed description of the excavations published by Efimenko, no really definitive house reconstruction has been or perhaps can be offered. One problem in attempting any reconstruction is that large portions of the base of the supposed long house were destroyed by the relatively unsystematic excavations of some of Efimenko's predecessors. A second difficulty is that there has been extensive rodent disturbance. Efimenko makes no note of this problem, but so many flints were displaced upwards by rodents that Efimenko's predecessors spoke of an even higher-lying cultural horizon in the chernozem soil formed on the surface of the site. While it seems likely (in view of their contents) that a large number, if not the majority, of the pits and depressions described by Efimenko were dug by the ancient inhabitants of the site, one cannot help but wonder if some portion of them did not arise as a result of rodent activity. This possibility seems especially worth considering since these animals are known to favor soil previously disturbed by human occupation.

In 1951 and 1953, several meters to the south of the southern boundary of Efimenko's long house, A. N. Rogachev discovered the edge of a second, analogous phenomenon (see Fig. 33). Like Efimenko's feature, the one found by Rogachev had several large pits on or near its periphery. These pits included four thought to have been used for habitation (sleeping?) and three for storage. In addition, on squares touching the periphery of the new feature (b–*a*, 61–63 of Fig. 33), Rogachev found a series of erect-standing fragments of mammoth long bone in a rough circle ca. 2.75 m. in diameter. Rogachev's excavations were largely exploratory, and the majority of pits were only partly investigated. In its type composition, the artifact assemblage recovered by Rogachev was essentially identical to that gathered by Efimenko.

Much of the available information on the artifacts from Kostenki I-1 is summarized in Table 23 (see also Figs. 36–49). However, the extraordinary variety and richness of the assemblage, as apparent in the table, justifies a more detailed study. Among the stone artifacts, perhaps the two most interesting types are the so-called Kostenki knives (Fig. 37#1–5) and Kostenki points (Fig. 37#6–8). Kostenki knives, it will be recalled, are blades or flakes on which both ends have been truncated ventrally. Soviet prehistorians believe that these tools were cutting implements. The noted expert on prehistoric technology, S. A. Semenov, believes that the ends were trimmed to eliminate the natural concavity of the ventral surface (see Fig. 37#8). Kostenki points are a particular variety of shouldered points on which both the shoulder and the point are formed largely on the dorsal surface, the shoulder by abrupt retouch. Very frequently the point and/or the base of the stem bear ventral retouch as well. A study of Kostenki points under a binocular microscope has revealed that they often bear traces of repeated and prolonged use, leading analysts to suppose that they were actually knives (rather than projectile points).

The bone artifacts and "art objects" require more lengthy consideration. The so-called mattocks (Fig. 38#2 and 3) and chisel-like tools consist of sections of mammoth tusk on which one end has been beveled to form a sort of massive spatula; the other end remains rounded and relatively thick. It has been suggested that the spatulate ends of the mattocks were used to dig the various sorts of pits discovered in the excavations; the thicker, rounded ends would then have been placed in a haft. The chisel-like tools differ from the mattocks in being smaller and in bearing geometric decoration on their thicker ends (Fig. 39#14 and 15).

The "large stabbing or thrusting weapons" consisted of four objects classified variously as a boar-spear (ivory), a dagger (ivory), and spears (1 bone, 1 ivory). The "dagger" is a pointed object fashioned on a flat, narrow, ivory flake (blade). The "boar-spear" consists of a 0.75 m. long, thin rod of ivory with one end broken off. One of the two "spears" is apparently the midsection of a longer rod-shaped artifact, the other is a rodlike ivory point, decorated on its entire length by notches and incised lines.

The baton with a sphere-shaped head (Fig. 40#1) is a wandlike ivory object, 44.5 cm. long. It is made up of two principal parts—a more or less flat "body" with some thickening at the base and a sphere-shaped "head." Another small prominence or bump is found on the body a short distance below the head. The over-all appearance and especially the forward inclination of the head, found also on a number of female statuettes from the site (see below), indicate that the baton could even be a highly stylized human figure.

The "shaft straightener" is a T-shaped fragment of reindeer antler with a large, artificially fashioned hole at the junction of the two principal parts of the T (Fig. 38#1). Although objects like this have frequently been interpreted as status symbols ("batons de commandement"), some prefer to interpret them as shaft straighteners or thong stretchers.

The egg-shaped objects (Fig. 39#6) are both made of ivory. The better preserved of the two narrows at its thicker end and takes on a cylindrical shape. The joint between the cylindrical and the larger egglike sections is decorated by what may be a carved representation of a cord. Each object

TABLE 23. Typological Composition of the Artifact Assemblages from Kostenki I-Horizon 1 and Kostenki XIII

Artifacts	*Kostenki I-1 (Efimenko 1958: 209–409; Rogachev 1957:26–28)*	*Kostenki XIII (Bud'ko 1960)*
STONE	Raw material: chiefly flint not available locally; also locally available flint and quartzite.	Raw material: chiefly flint not available locally; also locally available flint and quartzite.
Blades or sections of blades with double inverse truncation (= "Kostenki knives")	many	some
Shouldered points (= "Kostenki points")	several	some
Leaf-shaped points (all fragmentary)	several	?
Borers	several	?
Burins (dihedral, on the corners of broken blades, on retouched truncations, nucleiform)	many	many
Backed blades and points	some	some
End-scrapers (several varieties)	many	many
End-scraper/burins	some	?
Side-scrapers	some	?
Blades and fragments of blades with continuous retouch along one or both edges	some	some
Miscellanea	some[a]	some
TOTAL retouched pieces	several 100	90
Unretouched flakes and blades	several 1,000	several 100
Cores	a few	some
TOTAL chipped stone	several 1,000	963
Retouchers (slate)	several	—
BONE		
Mattocks	ca. 4	—
Chisel-like tools	2	—
Large stabbing or thrusting weapons	4	—
Baton with sphere-shaped head	1	—
Shaft straightener	1	—
Egg-shaped objects	2	—
Polishers	ca. 18	—
Whole	(5)	—
Fragmentary	(13)	—
Polisherlike objects	ca. 5	—
Points, awls, and needles (?) (mostly fragmentary)	many	1(?)
Headbands	several	—
Pierced and modified animal teeth	many	1
Indescript artifacts	several	—

TABLE 23. (*Continued*)

Artifacts	*Kostenki I-1 (Efimenko 1958: 209–409; Rogachev 1957:26–28)*	*Kostenki XIII (Bud'ko 1960)*
FEMALE FIGURINES (marl and ivory)		
Whole	6	—
Fragmentary	ca. 70	1(?)
Large portions of figures	(7)	—
Torso only	(17)	—
Heads only	(23) (?)	1 (?)
Amorphous	(20)	—
Parts of seated figures	(3)	—
MEDALLIONS (marl)	10	
ANIMAL FIGURINES (marl and bone)		
Whole figures	ca. 16	—
Mammoth (?)	(10)	—
Indeterminate	(ca. 6)	—
Heads only	ca. 62	—
Lion or tiger	(2)	—
Bear	(1)	—
Wolf	(1)	—
Indeterminate carnivores	(6)	—
Rhinoceros	(1)	—
Horse	(1)	—
Goat	(1)	—
Toad	(1)	—
Birds	(11)	—
Indeterminate animals	(10)	—
Anthropomorphic	(7)	—
Roughouts	(20)	—
PENDANTS (marl), mostly fragmentary	several	—
ENGRAVINGS ON ROCK	4	—
ENGRAVINGS ON BONE	4	—

[a] Principally objects thought to have been used to chop hard materials. The group includes some discoid pieces, some objects called adzes (or chisels), some others labeled tranchets, and most interestingly, a large piece called an axe (Fig. 36A). This "axe" is made on a flint nodule and is ca. 12 cm. long, 4.5 cm. wide, and 2.5 cm. thick in the middle. It was worked bifacially into a nearly oval shape. The narrower end bears a massive burin, the broader end the supposed axe edge. Running back from this edge on both surfaces are a large number of striations (Fig. 36B), perhaps indicating that the tool was used to chop wood.

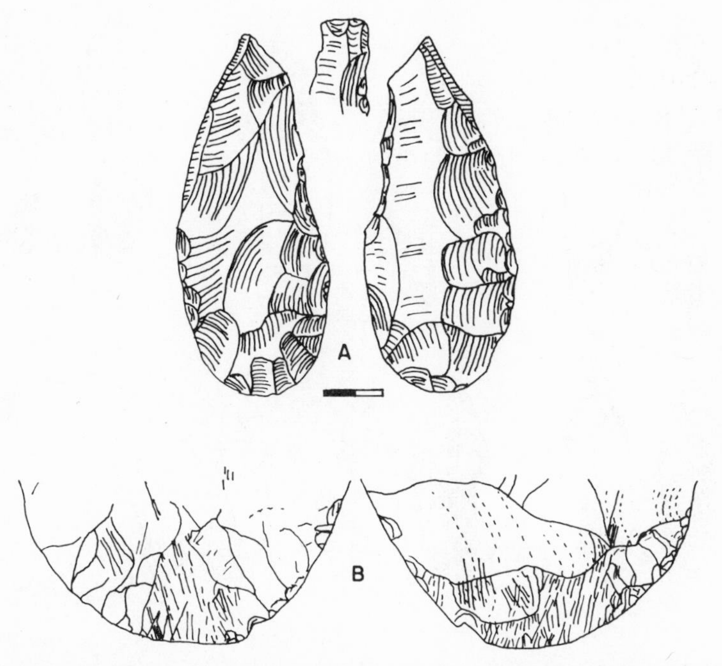

Figure 36. "Flint Axe" from Kostenki I-Horizon 1 (redrawn after Efimenko 1958:Figure 95, and Semenov 1964:Figure 58). A. "Flint axe"; B. Striations on both surfaces of the "axe blade" (magnified 4 times).

has a small pointed protuberance at its narrower end. One of the objects was found with this protuberance stuck in the ground.

The "polishers" are typical of artifacts referred to by this name. They are made on longitudinally split ribs of a large animal (horse?) and are usually almost parallel-sided, with one end fashioned into a kind of convex spatula. The surface of this "working end" often bears indentations or notches thought to have originated when the piece was used as a support in an activity such as the cutting of tendons by flint tools. More intriguing than the polishers are the set of several superficially similar but more elaborate artifacts shown in Fig. 41#15–19. With the exception of one made of ivory, these objects were likewise made on split ribs of a large animal and possess a rounded, spatulate working end. However, unlike the polishers, they are usually not parallel-sided, but tend to narrow away from the working end, while the other end is specially fashioned and decorated. Generally, the decorated end consists of a small, flat, rounded head with two pairs of symmetrically placed indentations. Adjacent to the head along the edges of the body and sometimes on the periphery of the head itself are found small, incised, parallel lines or crosses. Like the surfaces of the polishers proper, the surfaces of the working ends of the

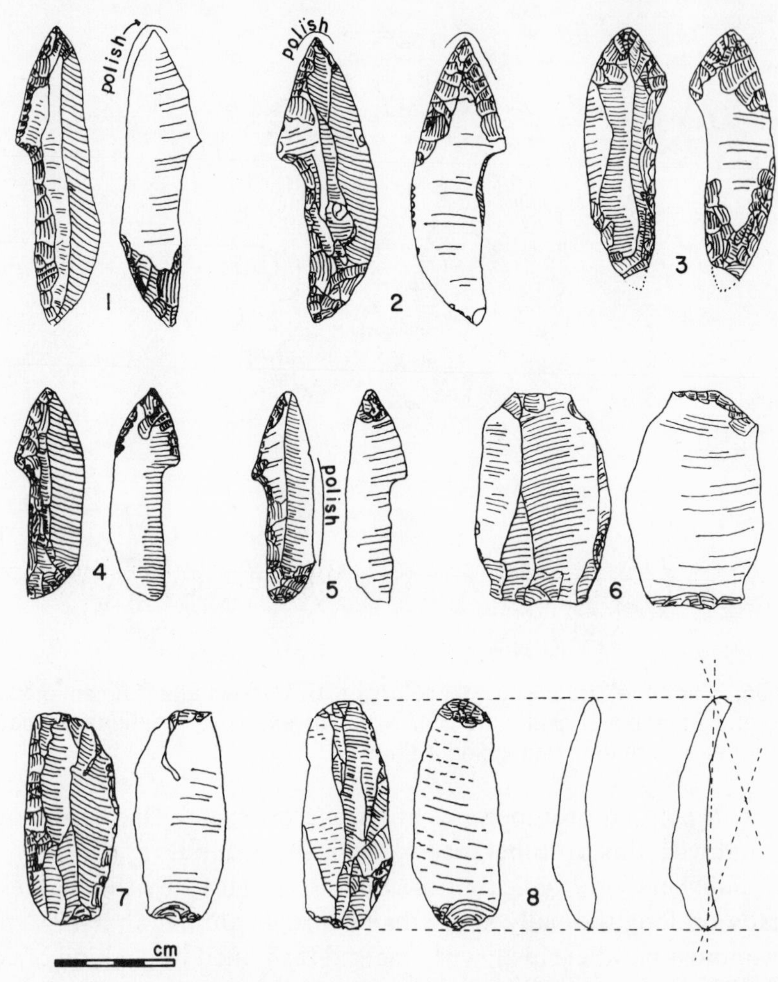

Figure 37. Stone Artifacts from Kostenki I-Horizon 1 (redrawn after Efimenko 1958: 231, 240, and 241, and Semenov 1964:65).

artifacts just described are often partly covered with incisions and indentations, perhaps indicating something about their use.

Among the points, awls, and needles (the presence of these latter is not certainly established since no intact pieces with eyes were recovered) were two enigmatic objects. The first is a 23 cm. long ivory rod, the upper part of which is carved, perhaps to represent a human figure (Fig. 40#3). The second is a 5.3 cm. long, pointed object resembling a nail with an asymmetrically placed head (Fig. 40#2).

The so-called headbands (Fig. 39#2,4,5,8,10–12) include a group of fragmentary artifacts, usually of ivory, which resemble the rounded working ends of polishers. However, in distinction from the polishers, each

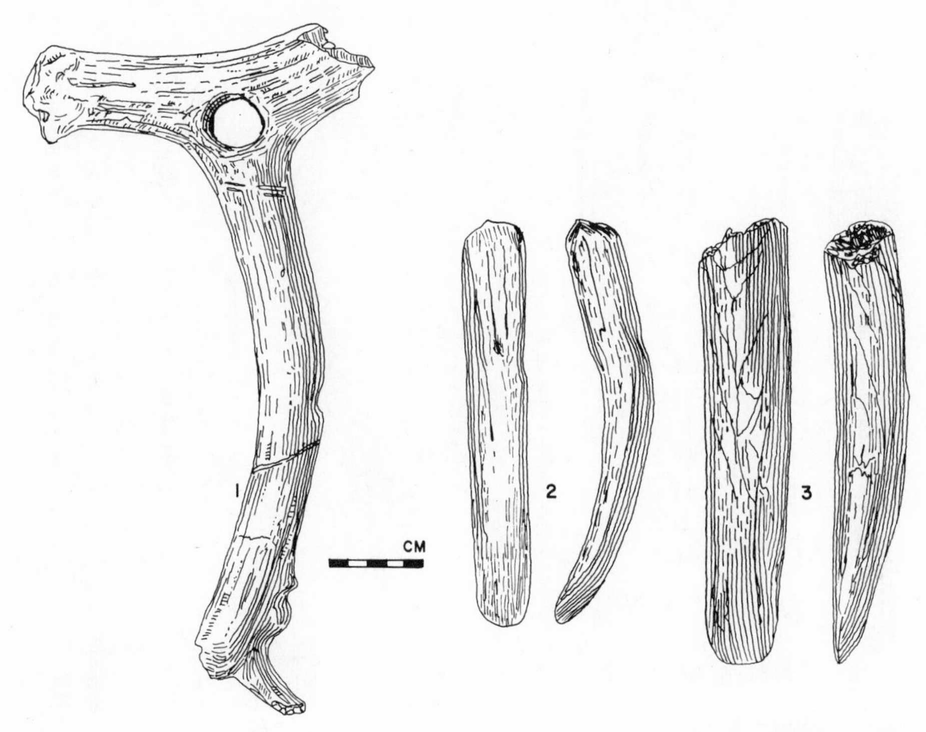

Figure 38. Bone Artifacts from Kostenki I-Horizon 1 (redrawn after Efimenko 1958: 293, 300).

headband fragment is pierced by a hole drilled or cut through, and usually bears some decoration, for example, incised crosses (a common motif in Kostenki I-1). Wolf and arctic fox canines predominate among the pierced and modified animal teeth. Most commonly, a tooth has a small hole drilled through the root. In a few cases the root has been removed in whole or in part. In one case, a fragment of wolf canine was used to manufacture a small polisherlike tool.

In addition to the bone artifacts which have been described (all listed in Table 23), Kostenki I-1 provided a relatively large number of unique and enigmatic objects. One which deserves special mention is a small, flat piece of ivory decorated around its margins with incised crosses and grossly suggesting the head of an animal (Fig. 41#13). Also found were a series of fragments of tusks and of other bones (especially ribs) which apparently had been fashioned as blanks for some of the artifacts described above. These fragments were accompanied by a large number of bone fragments exhibiting indentations, notches, incisions, and other marks evidently derived from human activity. In this regard, it is worthwhile to recall the earlier cited fragments of mammoth long bones, found

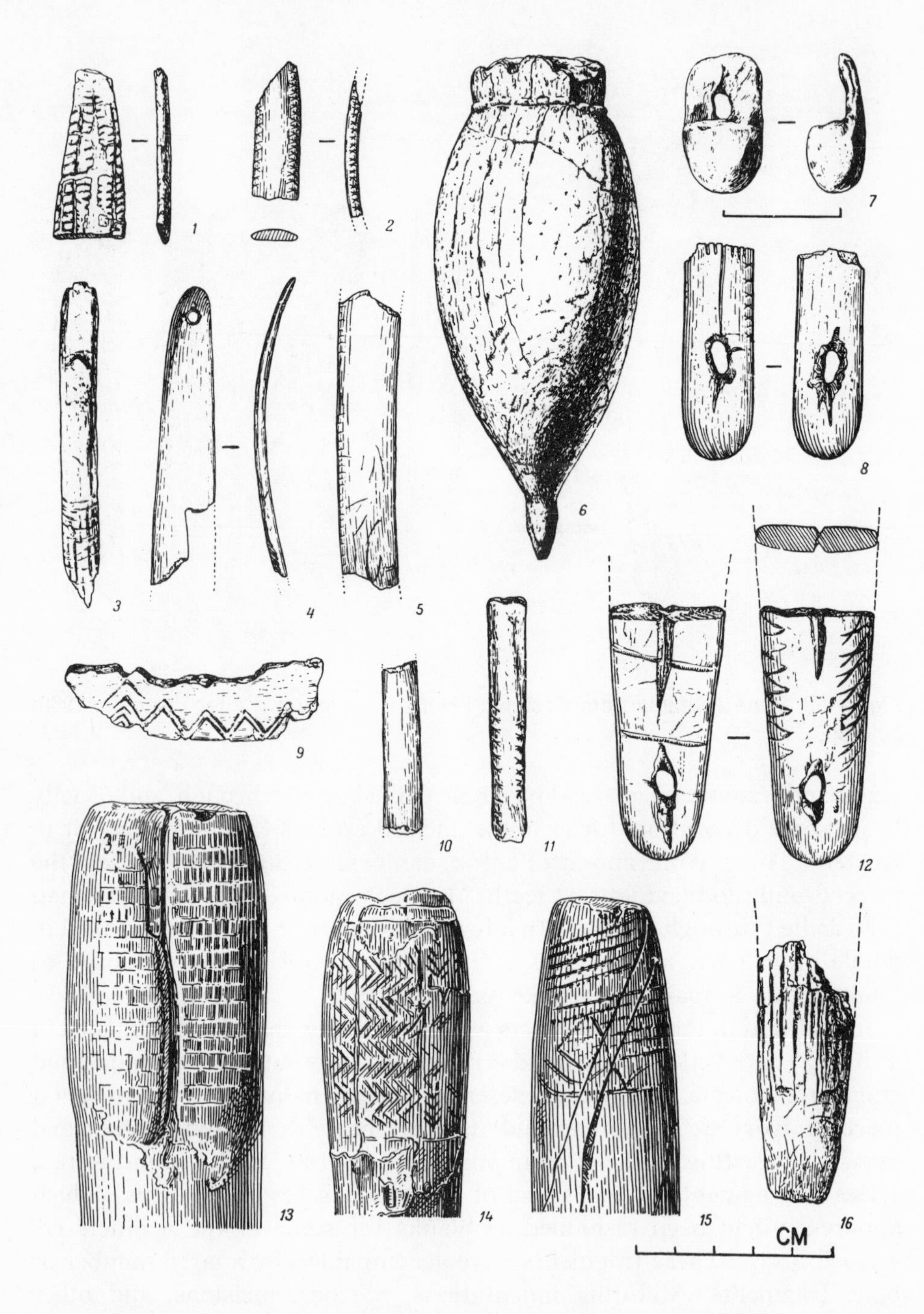

Figure 39. Sculpted and Incised Bone Artifacts from Kostenki I-Horizon 1 (from Abramova 1962:Plate XVIII).

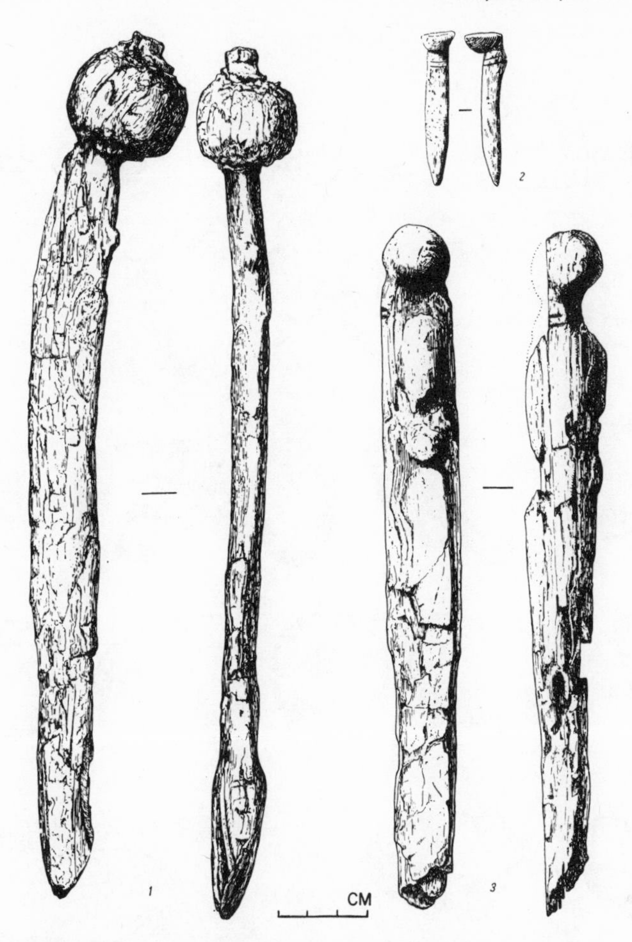

Figure 40. Sculpted Anthropomorphic Artifacts from Kostenki I-Horizon 1 (from Abramova 1962:Plate XI).

stuck in the ground with articular surfaces upwards. These surfaces often bore dents, notches, and other marks, which may indicate that they were used as anvils or small tables in some kind of activity.

No artifacts from Kostenki I-1 have prompted more excitement than the series of female figurines, including six almost whole examples and a large number of fragments. Virtually all the fragments and two of the nearly whole examples are made of locally available impure limestone, commonly known as marl. The other four almost whole examples are of ivory. While marl was clearly the more popular material, the ivory statuettes are more spectacular and will be considered first.

The four ivory figurines (Figs. 42 and 43) range in their present state from 9 to 16 cm. high. Three are missing their heads, apparently deliberately knocked off by the ancient inhabitants of the site. Like a number of

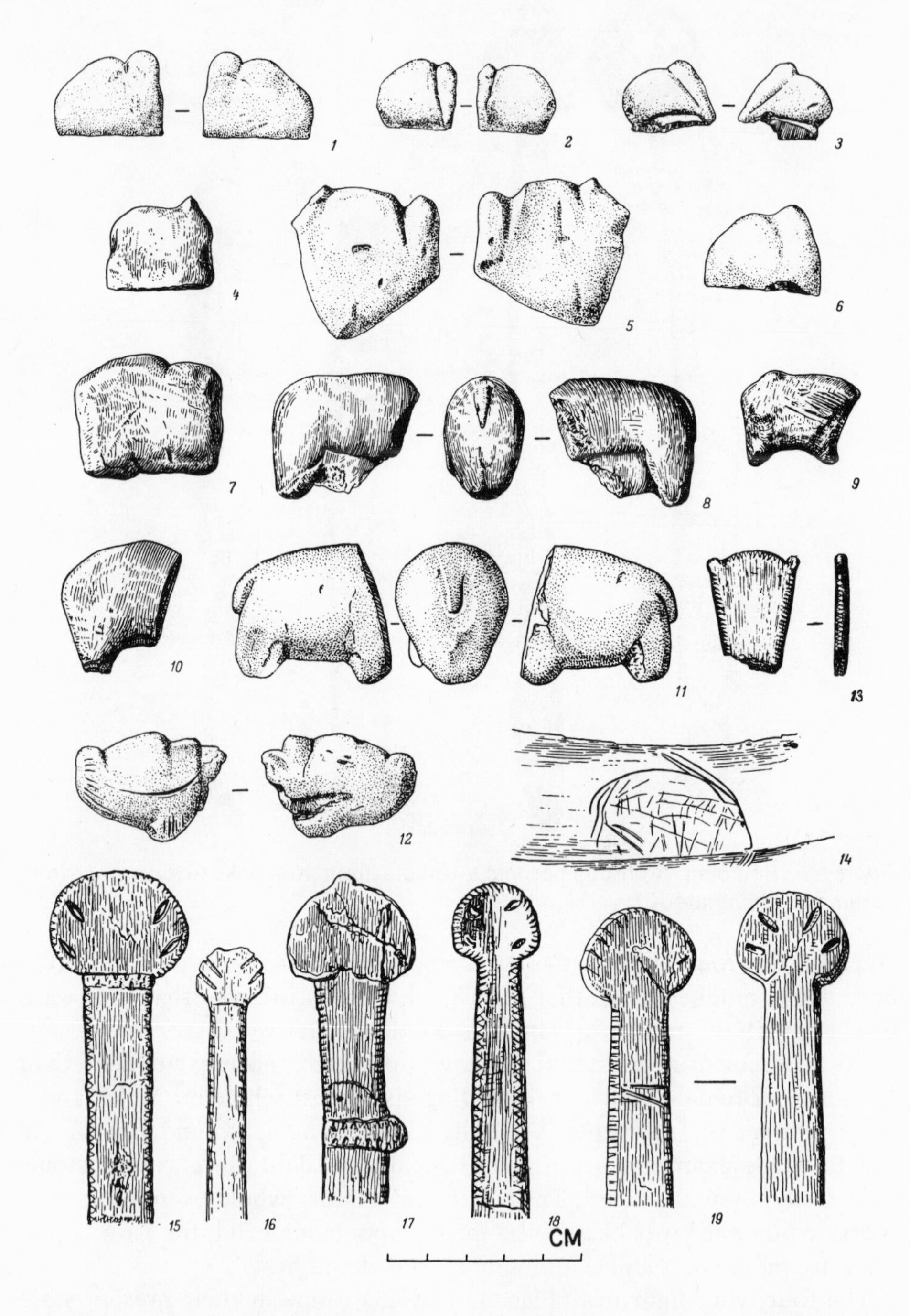

Figure 41. Animal Figures, Engraving, and Polisherlike Artifacts from Kostenki I-Horizon 1 (from Abramova 1962:Plate XIV).

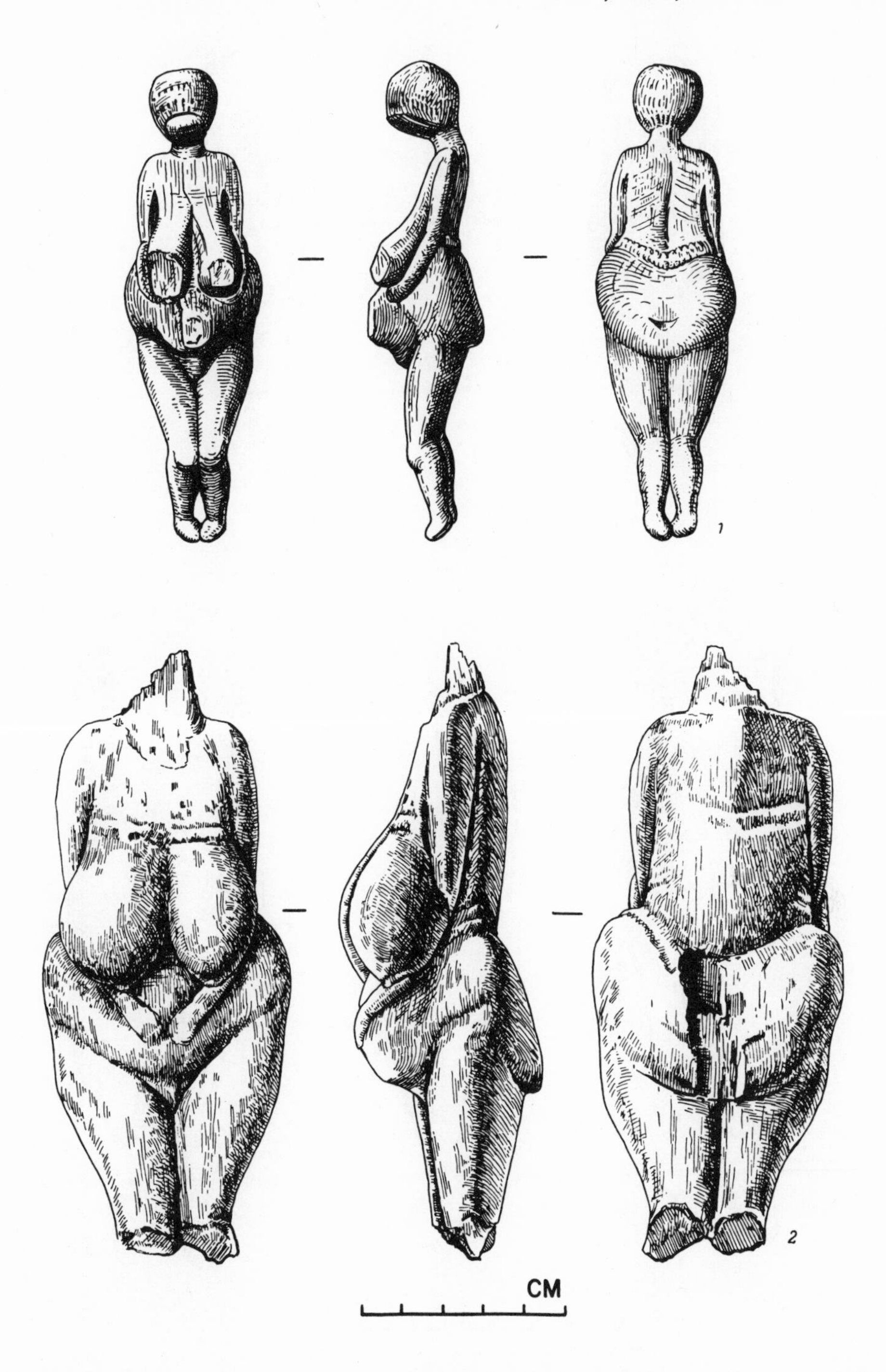

Figure 42. Female Statuettes from Kostenki I-Horizon 1 (from Abramova 1962: Plate III).

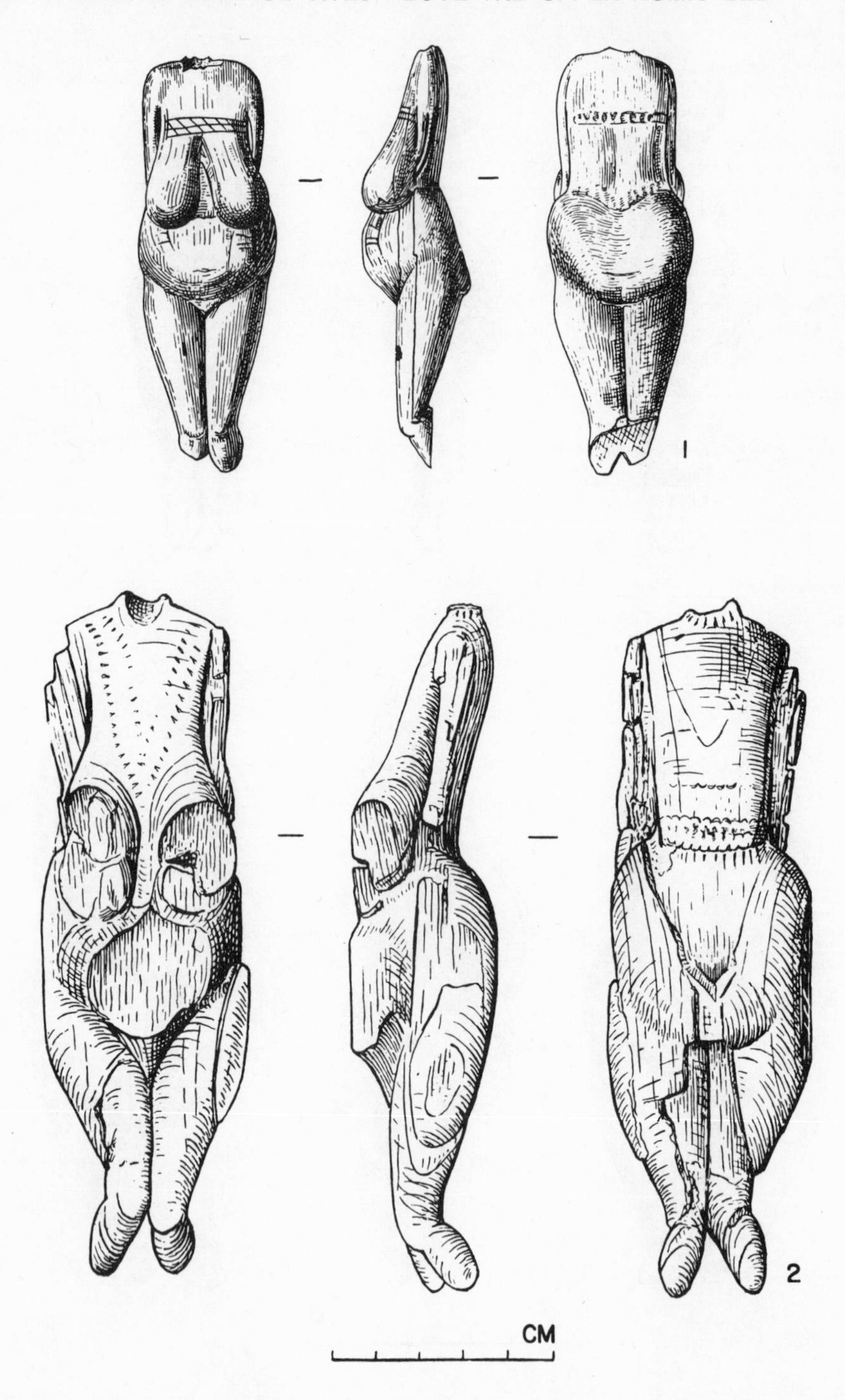

Figure 43. Female Statuettes from Kostenki I-Horizon 1 (from Abramova 1962: Plate II).

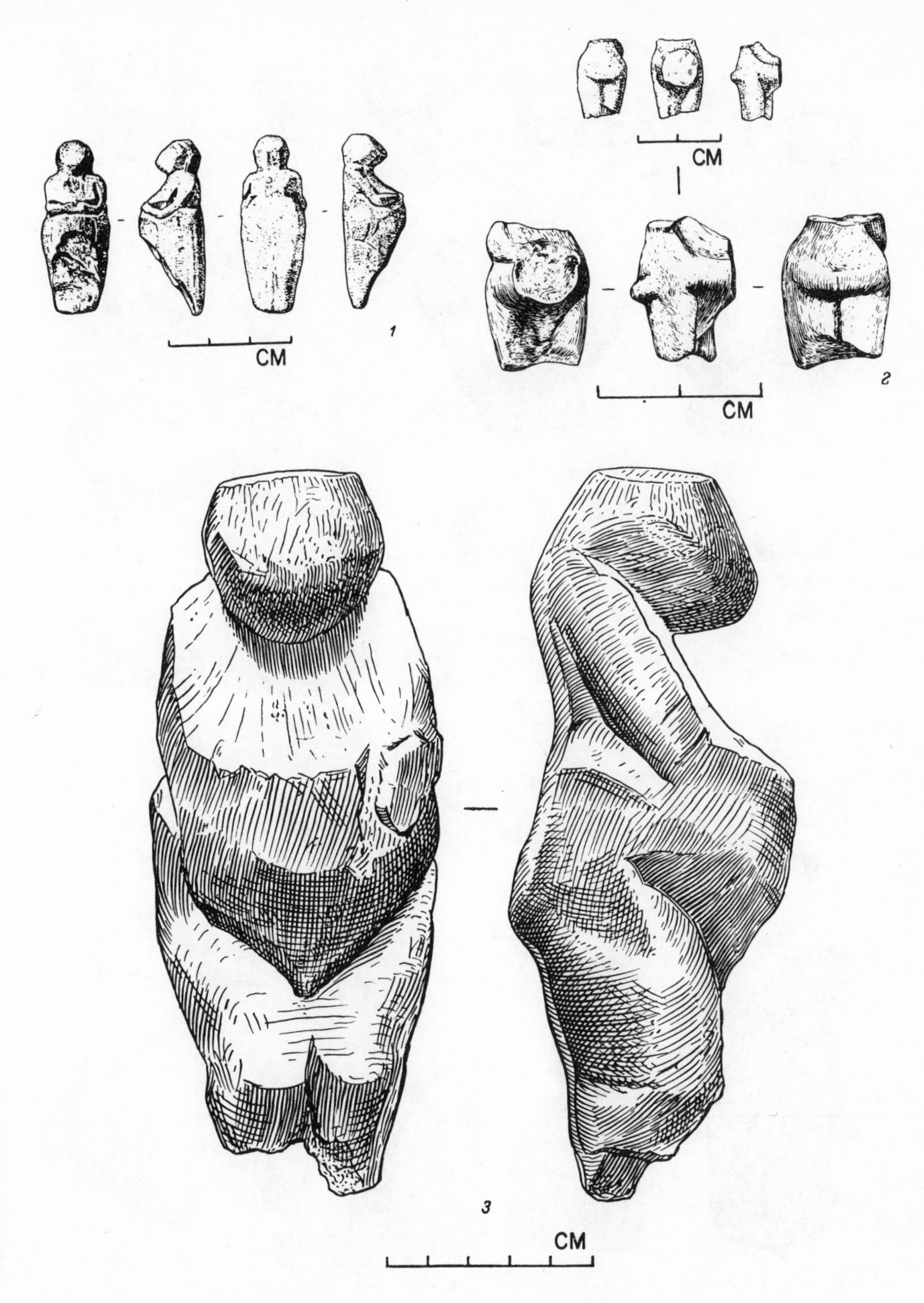

Figure 44. Female Statuettes from Kostenki I-Horizon 1 (from Abramova 1962: Plate V).

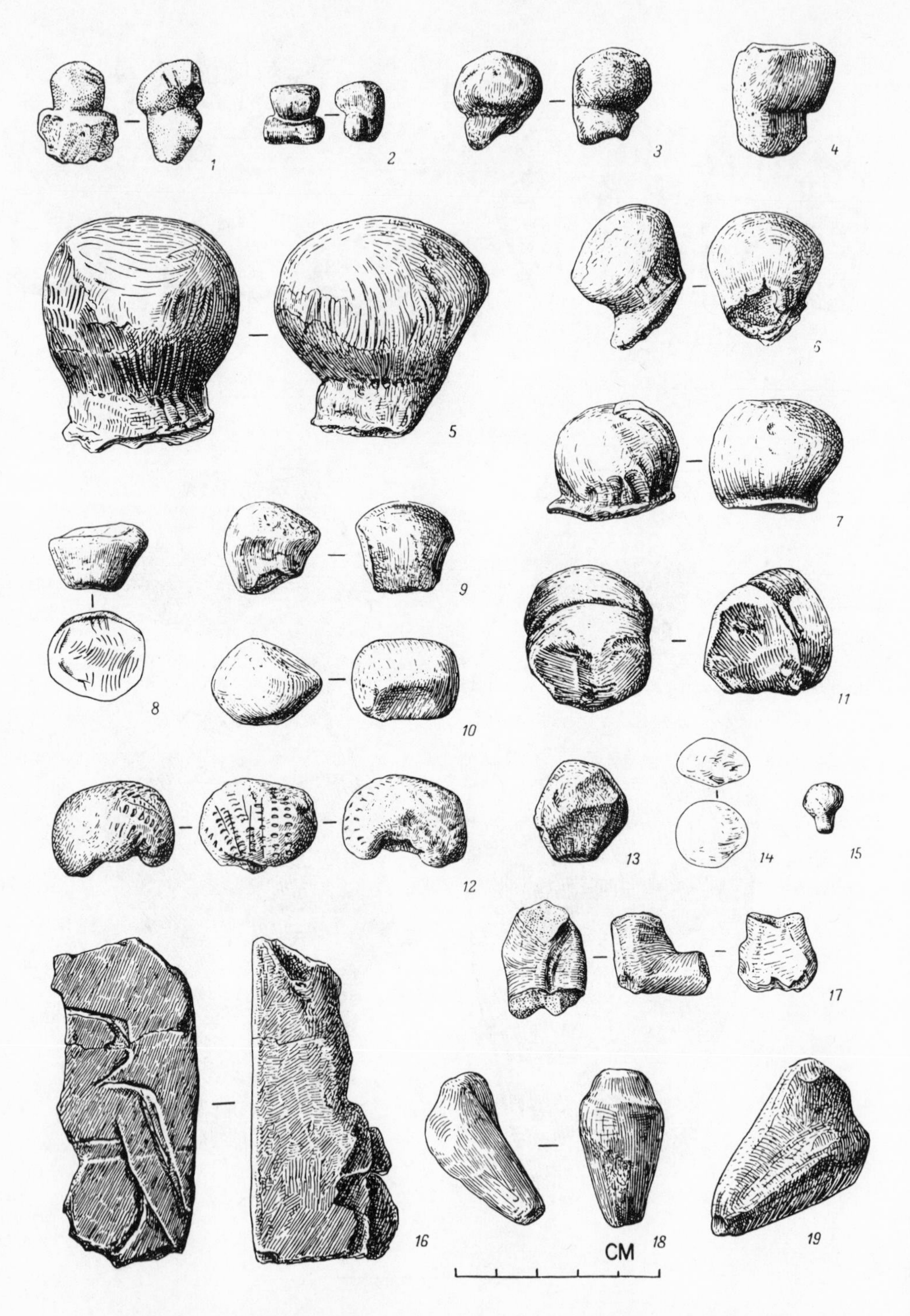

Figure 45. Figurine Heads and Fragments and Engraving from Kostenki I-Horizon 1 (from Abramova 1962:Plate IX).

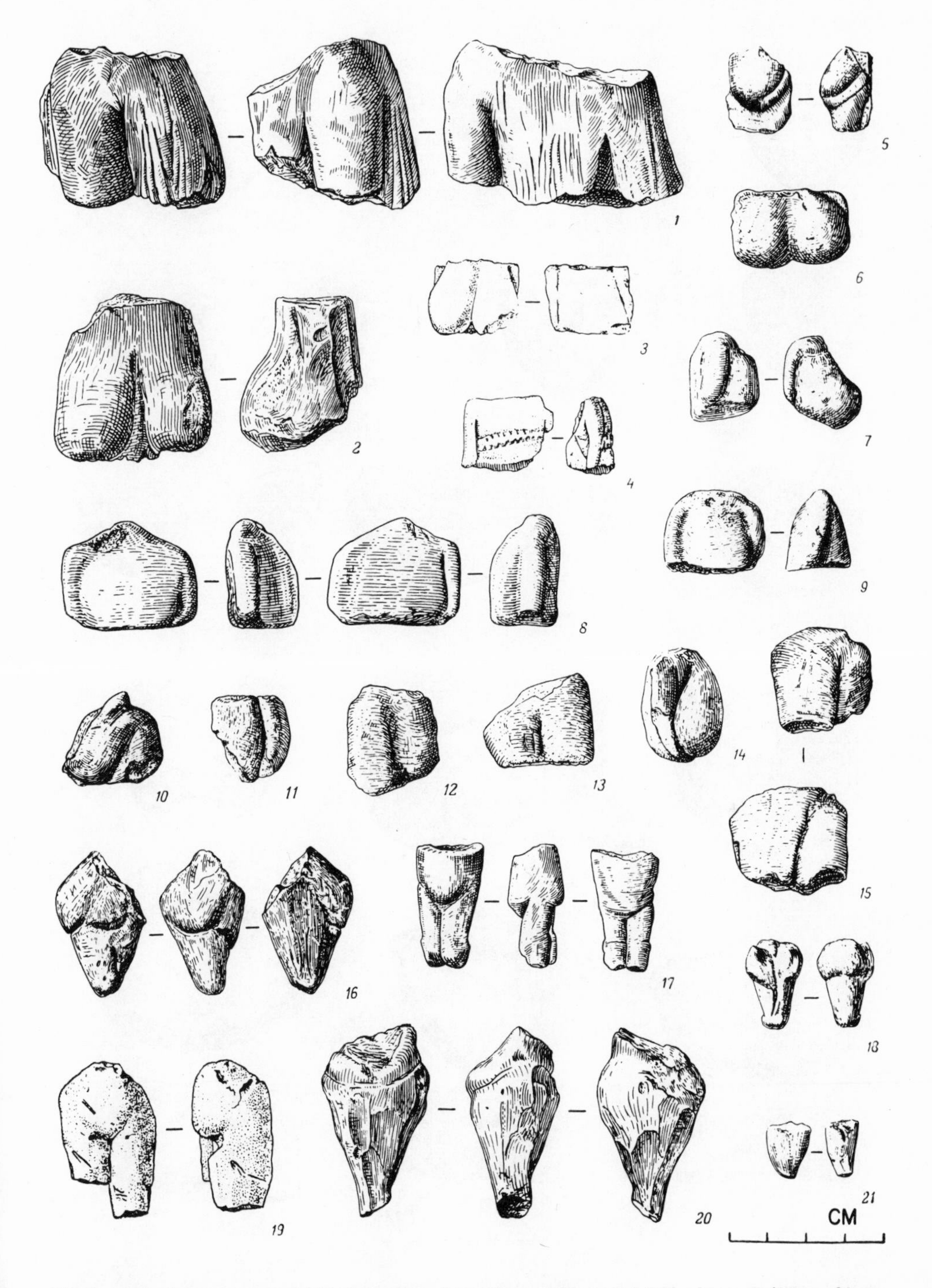

Figure 46. Fragments of Female Figurines from Kostenki I-Horizon 1 (from Abramova 1962:Plate VIII).

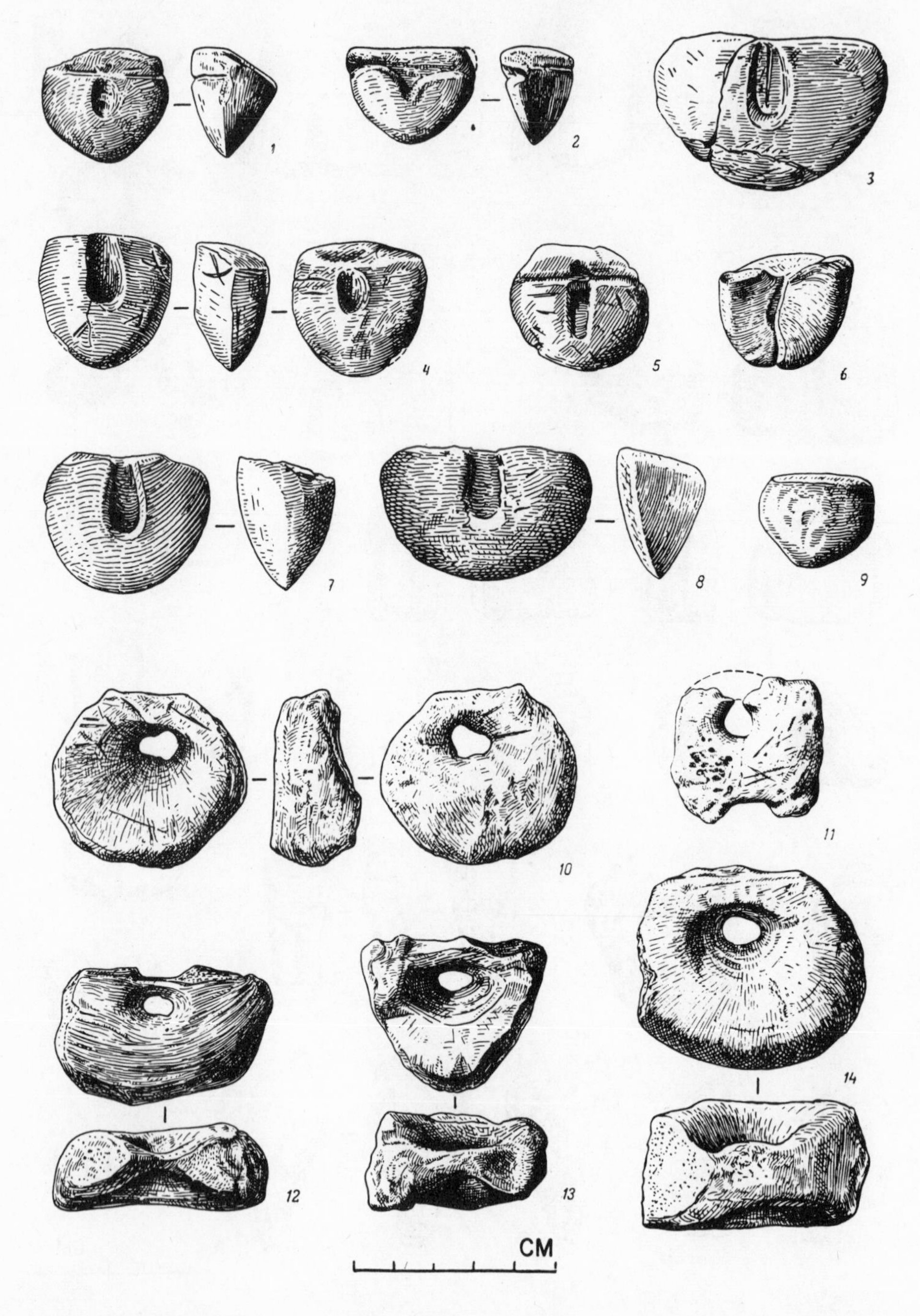

Figure 47. "Medallions" and "Pendants" from Kostenki I-Horizon 1 (from Abramova 1962:Plate XIII).

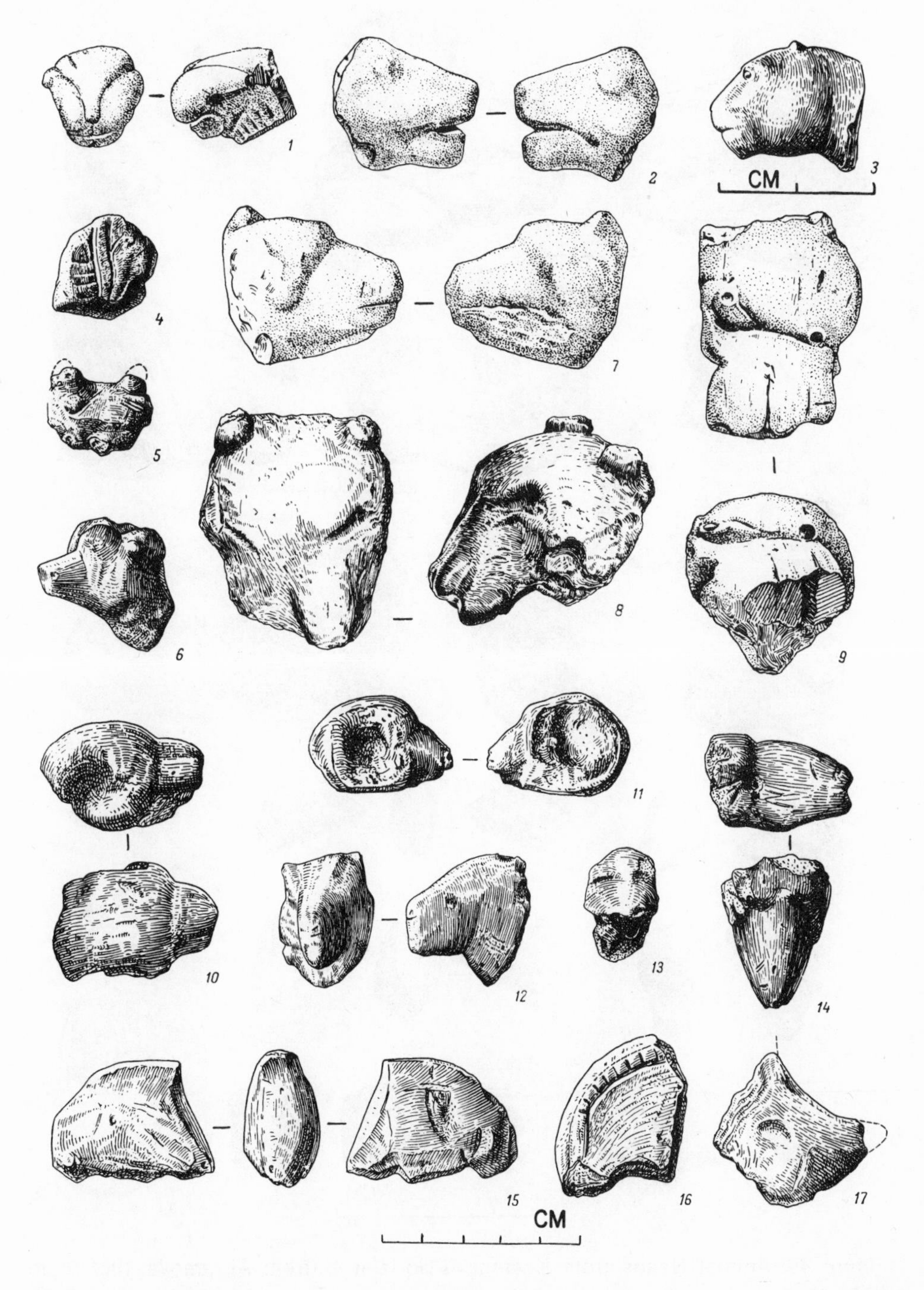

Figure 48. Animal Heads from Kostenki I-Horizon 1 (from Abramova 1962:Plate XVI).

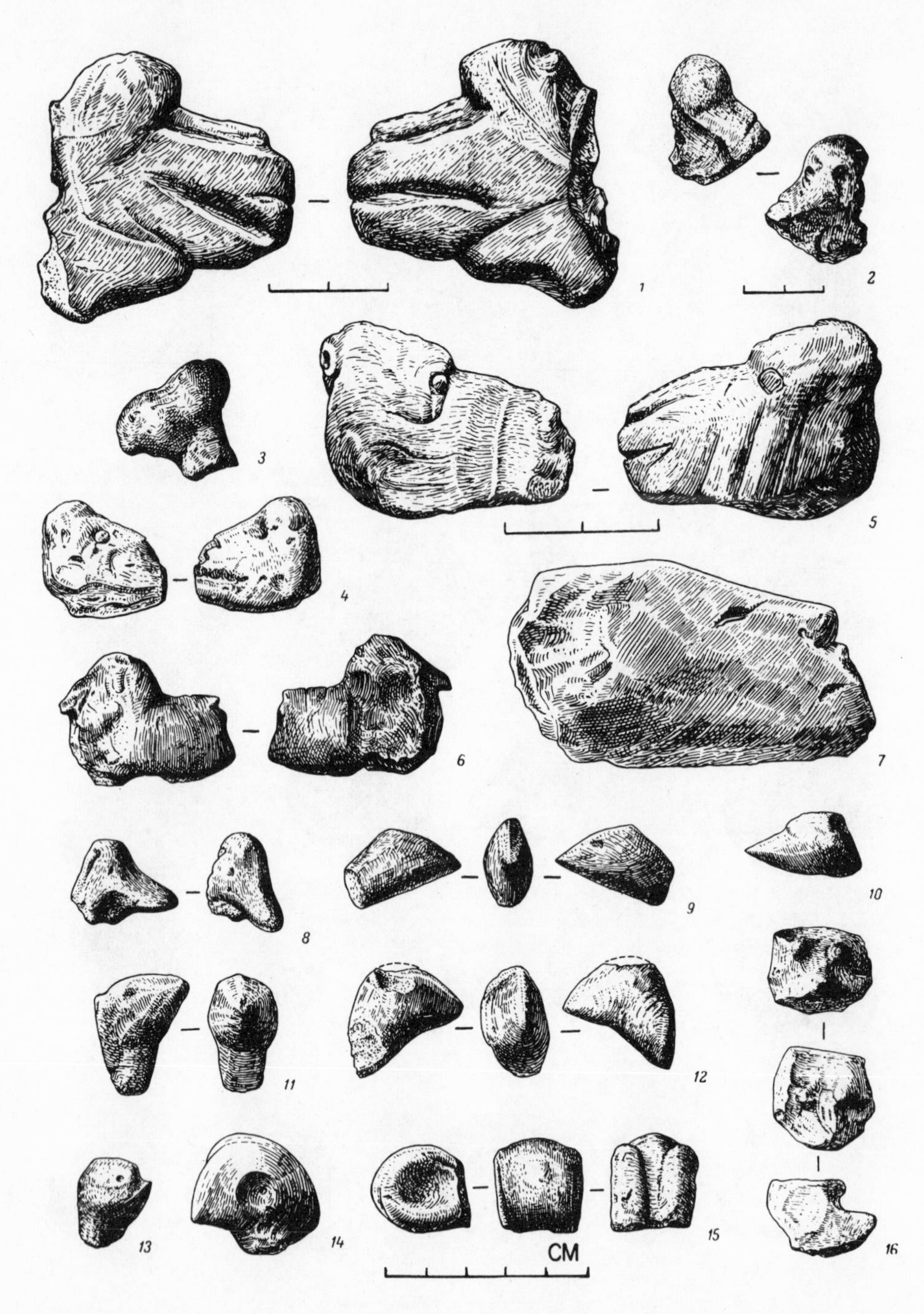

Figure 49. Animal Heads from Kostenki I-Horizon 1 (from Abramova 1962:Plate XII).

widely publicized statuettes from Upper Paleolithic sites elsewhere in Europe, the ivory ones from Kostenki I are characterized by exaggerated, pendulous breasts and large stomachs. Further, the pelvis-thigh region is relatively broad, though the protrusion of the buttocks is not particularly marked. The arms are pressed tightly to the body and the thighs tightly to one another. Little attention was paid to the rendering of the hands and feet. All four figurines exhibit some surface decoration, in two cases especially in a zone running above the breasts and around the back. Decoration on the head of the single figurine which has a head perhaps represents hair. There is no hint of a face.

The two nearly whole marl figurines differ strongly from the ivory ones and from one another. The first is a rather crude-looking statuette (Fig. 44#3), 17.5 cm. high, which was glued back together from a series of fragments. Maybe it was intentionally destroyed by the former inhabitants of the site. While it does perhaps bear a certain over-all resemblance to the ivory figurines, it is not so clearly female. The second almost complete marl statuette (Fig. 44#1) is a tiny (4.2 cm. high), stout, rather stylized human figure whose resemblance to a woman is clearly questionable. In addition to numerous supposed fragments of marl figurines (Table 23 and Figs. 44#2, 45#1–7, and 46), sixteen small spherelike marl objects were isolated which resemble figurine heads, but which were evidently manufactured separately (Fig. 45#8–15). By and large they lack a fracture which could establish previous attachment to a larger piece. Finally, ten lumps of marl were discovered which may have served as blanks for statuettes.

Besides the figurines, another group of marl artifacts with supposed sexual significance has been identified. These objects have been called "medallions" (Fig. 47#1–8). Each one roughly resembles a lens cut in half along one of its diameters. On one convex side of each half-lens is fashioned an oval depression, placed medially, with one end touching the flat edge of the object. These artifacts have been interpreted as schematic representations of the lower half of the female torso—the lower part of the stomach, the genital region, and the upper part of the thighs. Three supposed blanks or roughouts for such medallions were also found.

Among the animal figurines (Fig. 41#1–12) are roughly ten small marl objects thought to depict mammoths, at least in outline (Fig. 41#1–7). The basal parts of many of these objects are smooth and flat enough to be stood up. At least two of them (Fig. 41#1 and 2) are convincing representations; the remainder require varying amounts of imagination for their recognition as mammoths. A fair amount of imagination is also required for identification of many of the so-called animal heads of marl (Figs. 48 and 49).

The final category of marl artifacts to be considered is that of "pendants" (Fig. 47#10–14). Most of these objects were fragmentary. The few whole examples consisted of variously shaped (most often rounded) marl lumps with an off-center hole through the thinnest portion.

Of the eight engravings on rock (marl tablets) and bone, only two seem worth mentioning. The first, on marl (Fig. 45#16), may portray a part of the outline of a woman with pendulous breasts similar to those on some of the figurines. The second, on bone (Fig. 41#14), may depict a musk ox.

In summary, it seems clear from what has been preserved that the ancient inhabitants of Kostenki I-1 possessed an extraordinarily rich material culture.

Flint artifacts similar to those of Kostenki I-1 have been found on the surface and in test pits at a number of points in the general vicinity of the site, most prominently at Kostenki V-1 and at Kostenki XIII. The materials from Kostenki V-1 have never been thoroughly described, but at least some details are available on what was found at Kostenki XIII. It will be recalled that this site occurred in grey-brown loam overlying the Third (rather than the Second) Terrace. However, there is no reason to suppose that it is geologically older than sites in the grey-brown loam overlying the Second. The artifact inventory, set forth in Table 23, is plainly not as rich as that of Kostenki I-1, particularly in bone objects. But the presence in both sites of Kostenki knives and Kostenki points certainly implies a genetic relationship between them.

In addition to artifacts, the cultural horizon of Kostenki XIII contained much animal bone (often charred) and, in places, red ochre. The area exposed by excavations (18 sq. m.) was too small to allow a definitive statement about the features which may be present, but at least two pits with interesting contents were revealed. The first was notable for the large amount of wolf remains (often in anatomical order) which it contained, the second for the presence of skeletal remains (sometimes in anatomical order) of no less than six arctic foxes as well as bones of a number of other animals.

More interesting than Kostenki XIII are sites far distant from the Kostenki-Borshevo region which contain materials like those of Kostenki I-1. Shouldered points of the Kostenki type have been found as far away as Austria and Czechoslovakia. And at Avdeevo on a small tributary of the Sejm River, 40 km. from Kursk and approximately 210 km. northeast of Kostenki (see Map 1, p. 27) is a site whose contents are virtually identical to those of Kostenki I-1. Not only has Avdeevo provided the same kinds of bone and stone artifacts, but excavations there exposed a large area surrounded and covered by various sorts of pits and depressions in exactly the same manner as at Kostenki I-1. The great similarity —indeed, near identity—between Avdeevo and Kostenki I-1 has led Soviet investigators (especially A. N. Rogachev) to formulate the "Kostenki-Avdeevo Culture," which includes at very least Kostenki I-1, Avdeevo, and Kostenki XIII.

Tel'manskaya-Horizon 1 and Kostenki V-Horizon 2

The principal excavations in Tel'manskaya-1 were conducted in 1937 by P. P. Efimenko. He uncovered a rounded depression 5.20–5.60 m. across and bounded for the most part by vertical walls. From the walls the floor dipped gently towards the center (depth near the walls 0.35–0.50 m., near the center 0.70 m.) (Fig. 50). It has been suggested that the depression marks the base of a former structure. The entrance is believed to have been on the west since the western margin of the depression was sloping rather than vertical. Also, the only significant quantity of cultural debris outside the depression was found on the western edge.

The thickness of the cultural level filling the depression averaged 0.30–0.50 m. It extended markedly outside the depression only to the west and southwest. Inside, squares immediately adjacent to the walls were generally the poorest in finds and also the most weakly colored (by red ochre and ash found throughout the artifact-bearing loam). The discovery of a number of objects (large mammoth bones, artifacts, and so forth) at odd angles may indicate that they were originally outside or above the depression and fell or slid in after the collapse of the roof. The roof is thought to have rested on a low earthen wall, evidence for which was found on the surface immediately surrounding the depression.

Efimenko's investigation of the floor of the depression revealed a roughly circular accumulation of charred bones and ash, 0.75–0.80 m. across, occurring slightly off-center in a shallow (0.15–0.20 m. deep) bowl-shaped pit. This has been interpreted as the remains of a hearth. It was apparently eroded after the ancient dwelling was abandoned, since a thin layer of grey ashy matter was deposited to the south and west of it.

Approximately 2.25 north, 2.00 northeast, and 1.75 m. east of the hearth, Efimenko discovered three so-called storage pits dug into the floor of the depression. These pits were round in outline, varying from 0.35 to 0.55 m. across, and from 0.20 to 0.23 m. deep. They contained materials typical for Tel'manskaya-1. Subsequent excavation beneath the western half of

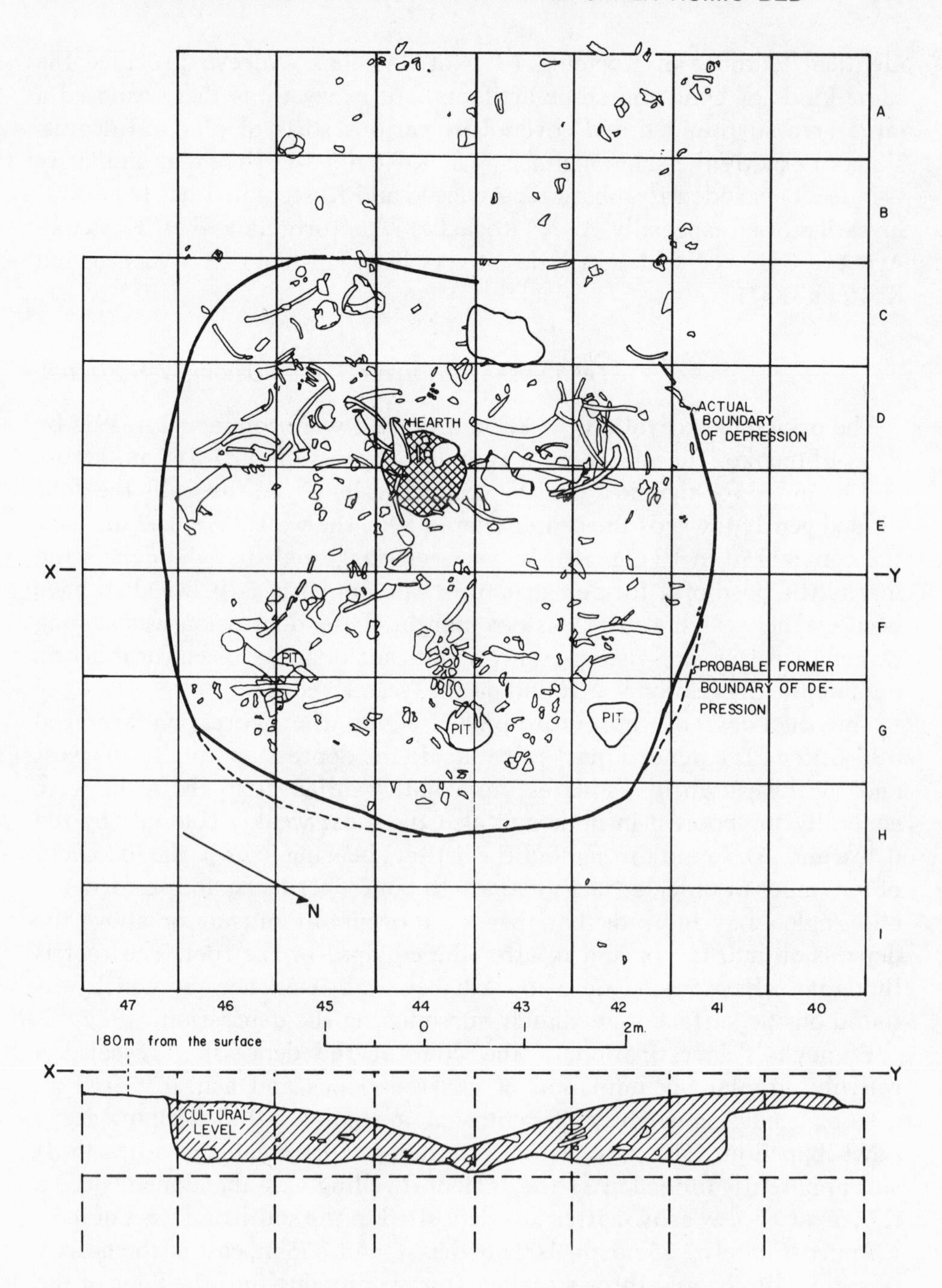

Figure 50. Plan and Profile of Tel'manskaya-Horizon 1 (redrawn after Efimenko and 8 and 10).

the depression by A. N. Rogachev (investigating lower-lying cultural levels) disclosed four more storage pits. Two of these were partially overlaid by the hearth mass. However, they did not contain any special concentrations of ashy material and, in Rogachev's opinion, were filled before the hearth came into use. One of them expanded below to become broad and flat on the bottom (diameter at the level of the floor of the depression 0.50 m., diameter on the bottom 1.15 m.; maximum depth 0.96 m.). Further, its fill was laminated: thin layers containing bone fragments and artifacts alternated with nearly sterile layers. Curiously, the fill also provided a number of pieces of charred wood, completely absent in the hearth and in the remainder of Tel'manskaya-1. The second pit partially overlaid by the hearth was oval (0.80 × 0.45 m.) with vertical walls reaching a depth of 0.55 m. Cultural debris were scattered throughout its fill.

The remaining two pits discovered by Rogachev each lay a little over a meter from the hearth (to the southeast and south respectively). One was only partly investigated, but was probably roundish (ca. 0.50 m. across) and deep (0.96 m.). The second was oval (0.55 × 0.30 m.) and shallow (0.15 m.). Both pits contained stone and bone artifacts, animal bones (including some charred), fragments of ferruginous concretions, and other objects typical for Tel'manskaya-1 in general.

The faunal remains of Tel'manskaya-1 constitute an interesting feature. Careful study revealed that the different mammalian species tended to be represented by different classes of skeletal parts: for example, wolf largely by vertebrae and bones of the paw; arctic fox by skull fragments, jaws, and teeth; hare by noncranial bones of various sorts; and mammoth principally by foot and ankle bones. This phenomenon very likely reflects differential utilization of different animals by the ancient inhabitants. Of particular interest is the relatively large number of skeletal parts (phalanges, metacarpals, and metatarsals) of wolf paws, frequently found in at least partial anatomical order. Since paws are often removed with the pelt during skinning, the evidence at Tel'manskaya may indicate considerable use of wolf pelts. One use to which mammoth was put may be implied from the abundance of charred hunks of mammoth bone in the hearth pit: quite possibly this bone (or more precisely its organic components) served as fuel.

The artifact inventory found in Tel'manskaya-1 is summarized in Table 24. It presents a very striking contrast with the inventory of Kostenki I-1. Not only are Kostenki points and Kostenki knives absent, but there are no end-scrapers or backed blades, and bone artifacts are comparatively rare. Further, there are no figurines in marl and bone. On the other hand, there

TABLE 24. Typological Composition of the Artifact Assemblage from Tel'manskaya-Horizon 1 (Critically Compiled from Information in Efimenko and Boriskovskij 1957:207–229 and Rogachev 1957:45–47)

Artifacts	*Efimenko excavations*	*Rogachev excavations*	*Total*
	Raw material: mostly flint not available locally; also locally available quartzite.		
STONE			
Side-scrapers	> 70	many	> 70
Leaf-shaped points	135	59	194
Whole	(35)	(18)	(53)
Fragments	(ca. 100)	(41)	(141)
Burins	ca. 140	30	ca. 170
On the corners of broken blades	(ca. 30)		
Dihedral	(ca. 50)		
On retouched truncations	(ca. 25)		
Flat burins	(ca. 35)		
Blades with continuous retouch along one or both edges	some	some	some
Miscellanea	> 25[a]	?	
TOTAL retouched pieces	several 100	several doz.	several 100
Cores	ca. 15	few	
Burin spalls	ca. 170	?	
Unretouched flakes, blades, and debris	several 100	several 100	several 1,000
TOTAL artifactual flint	ca. 4,200	ca. 2,000	ca. 6,200
BONE			
Awls and points	8	1	9
Polishers	4	several	4+
Pierced arctic-fox teeth	3	—	3
Ivory pendants	2	1	3
Miscellanea	3[b]	some	

[a] Four bifacial discs, approximately six so-called chopping tools, and approximately fifteen nucleiform objects.

[b] A flat, rectangular piece of bone with a small hole in one end, and two small long bones with their epiphyses carefully cut off. One of these was decorated by incised, parallel grooves, running from end to end over the whole surface of the object.

is a very high frequency of side-scrapers and, more significantly, of leaf-shaped points, which most frequently recall laurel leaves (Fig. 51#1–3). Retouch tends to be concentrated on their ends on both the dorsal and ventral surfaces; however, relatively often it passes along one or both lateral edges and sometimes it nearly covers one or both surfaces. At least twelve points were distinguished by the presence of a weakly expressed stem (Fig. 51#4–6). Many examples were polished at the point and along the edge, indicating prolonged use. Soviet investigators are thus inclined

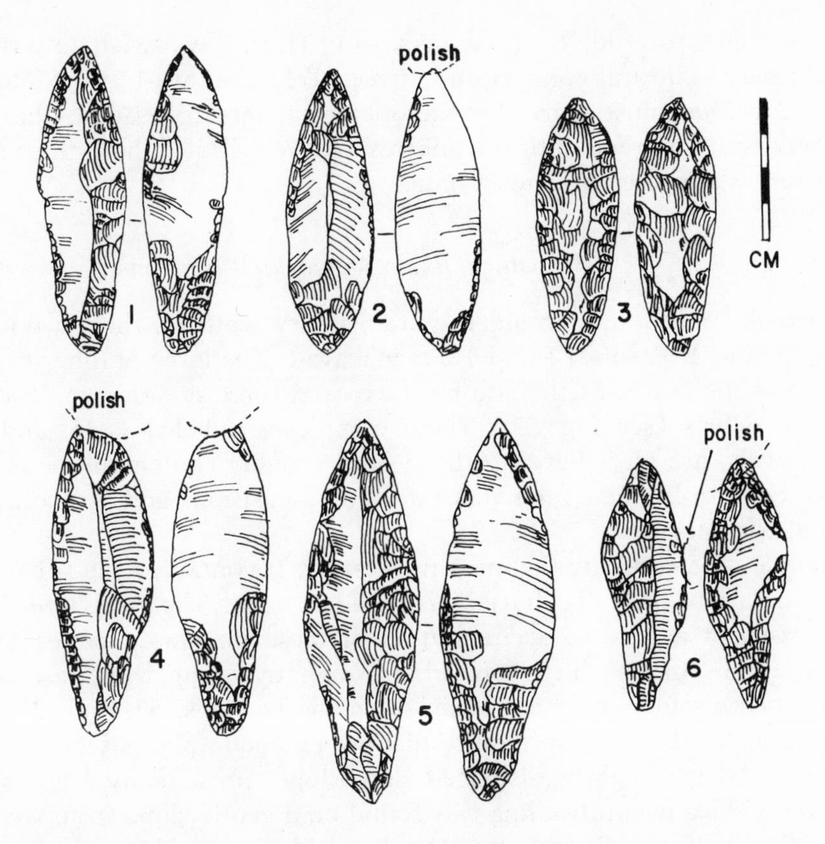

Figure 51. Leaf-Shaped Points from Tel'manskaya-Horizon 1 (redrawn after Efimenko and Boriskovskij 1957:Figures 14 and 15).

to regard them as cutting tools rather than projectile points.

Among all the other Kostenki-Borshevo sites, only Kostenki V-2 has provided an artifact assemblage said to be closely similar to that of Tel'manskaya-1. This assemblage contained 70 flints, including two side-scrapers, 2 dihedral burins, 9 blades with continuous retouch along one or both edges, a fragment of a leaf-shaped point, and 56 unretouched blades and flakes. No features were found. Since Kostenki V-1 (discussed above) contained artifacts similar to those of Kostenki I-1, a genuine relationship between Kostenki V-2 and Tel'manskaya-1 may well indicate that Tel'manskaya-1 antedates Kostenki I-1.

Outside the Kostenki-Borshevo region, artifacts resembling those from Tel'manskaya-1, especially leaf-shaped points, have been found far to the west, in Poland. Here they are probably best known from Nietoperzowa Cave at Jerzmanowice, where they have been radiocarbon-dated to 38,160±1250 B.P. (Gro-2181), an age which stratigraphic evidence indicates is much too old for Tel'manskaya-1. Thus, if we wish to assume some kind of cultural connection between Tel'manskaya-1 and Nietoperzowa Cave, we must deny the Nietoperzowa date or assume that the leaf-points are extremely time-transgressive. Which, if either, alternative is correct is at present indeterminate.

Kostenki II and Anosovka II-Horizon 1A

Kostenki II has also provided extraordinary features, though not the same kind as Kostenki I-1 and Tel'manskaya-1. The large number of pits and excavations dug at the site have exposed three major complexes of cultural debris (see Fig. 52). These complexes, labeled I, II, and III respectively, are all believed to have been roughly contemporaneous, as indicated both by their relative stratigraphic positions and by their artifactual contents.

Complex I is certainly the most interesting. It contained the ruins of a structure as well as the burial of an adult man. The ruins consisted principally of a lenslike accumulation of large mammoth bones up to 0.50–0.60 m. thick, which formed a rough oval approximately 8 m. across north-south and 6.5 m. across east-west (Figs. 52 and 53). The boundaries of the oval were quite distinct except in places where a few bones had been slightly displaced downslope, presumably because of erosion. (The ancient dwelling was found on a gentle slope from west to east.) Some difficulty in investigating the ruins occurred because portions of them had been disturbed by early, relatively unsystematic excavations and by pits dug by local farmers.

At least twenty-eight animals were represented by the more than 2,000 whole and fragmentary mammoth bones making up the oval concentration. The bones included whole examples or fragments of approximately 100 ribs, 40 tusks, a large number of limb bones, 50 scapulae, 14 pelves, 140 vertebrae (including some in anatomical order), and a number of teeth and skulls. The different classes of bone were not evenly distributed within the concentration. Rather, tusks occurred mostly in the western part, bones of extremities in the northeastern part, and skulls and mandibles in the southern part. All the large bones are believed to have served in some way as construction material. It is thought that the majority reached their present positions as a result of the inward collapse of the walls and roof. Many exhibit damage and fractures which could have occurred during such a collapse. A few, found in vertical or inclined positions, had actually been driven or dug into the ground—in particular, long bones on the margins of the oval. Along the northeast (that is,

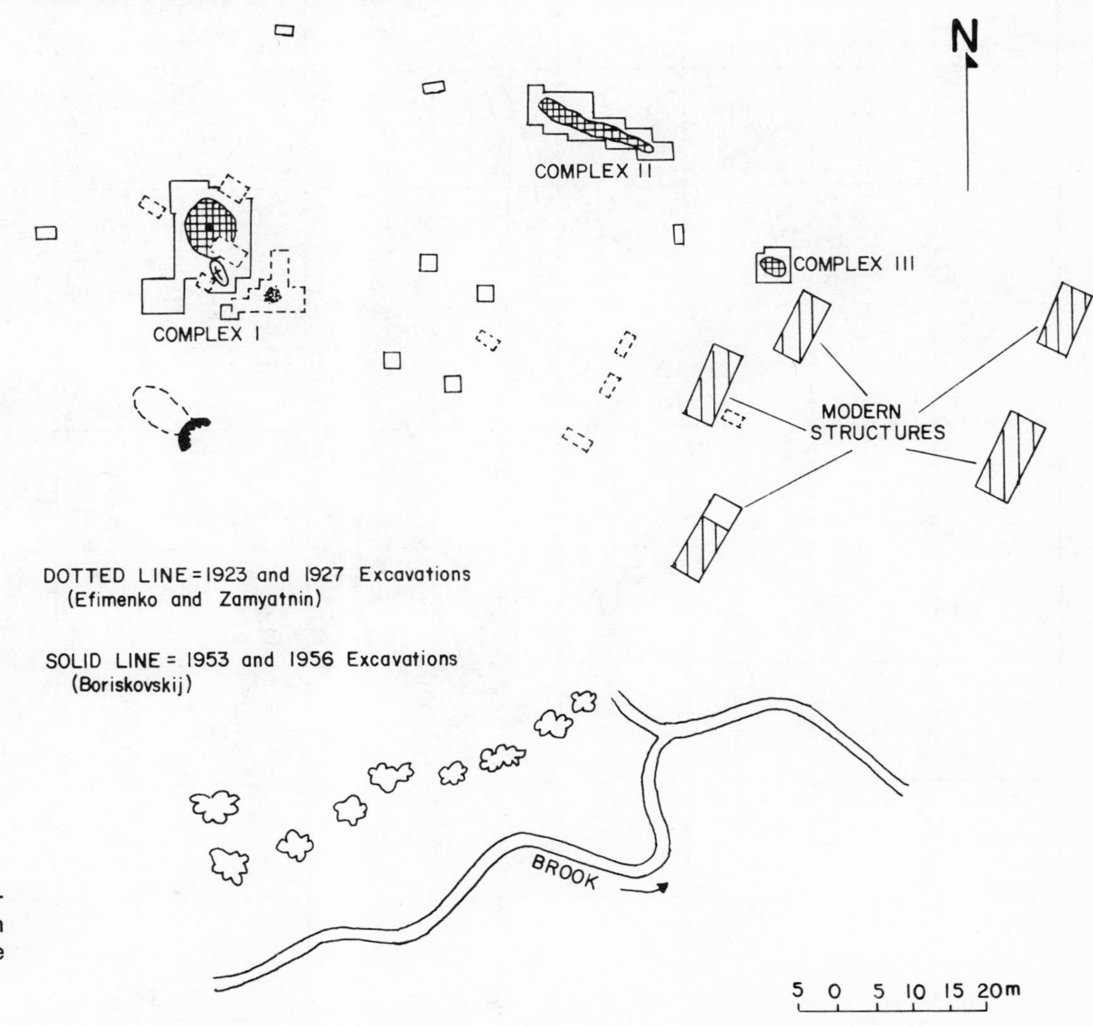

Figure 52. Plan of the Excavations at Kostenki II (redrawn after Boriskovskij 1963:Figure 47).

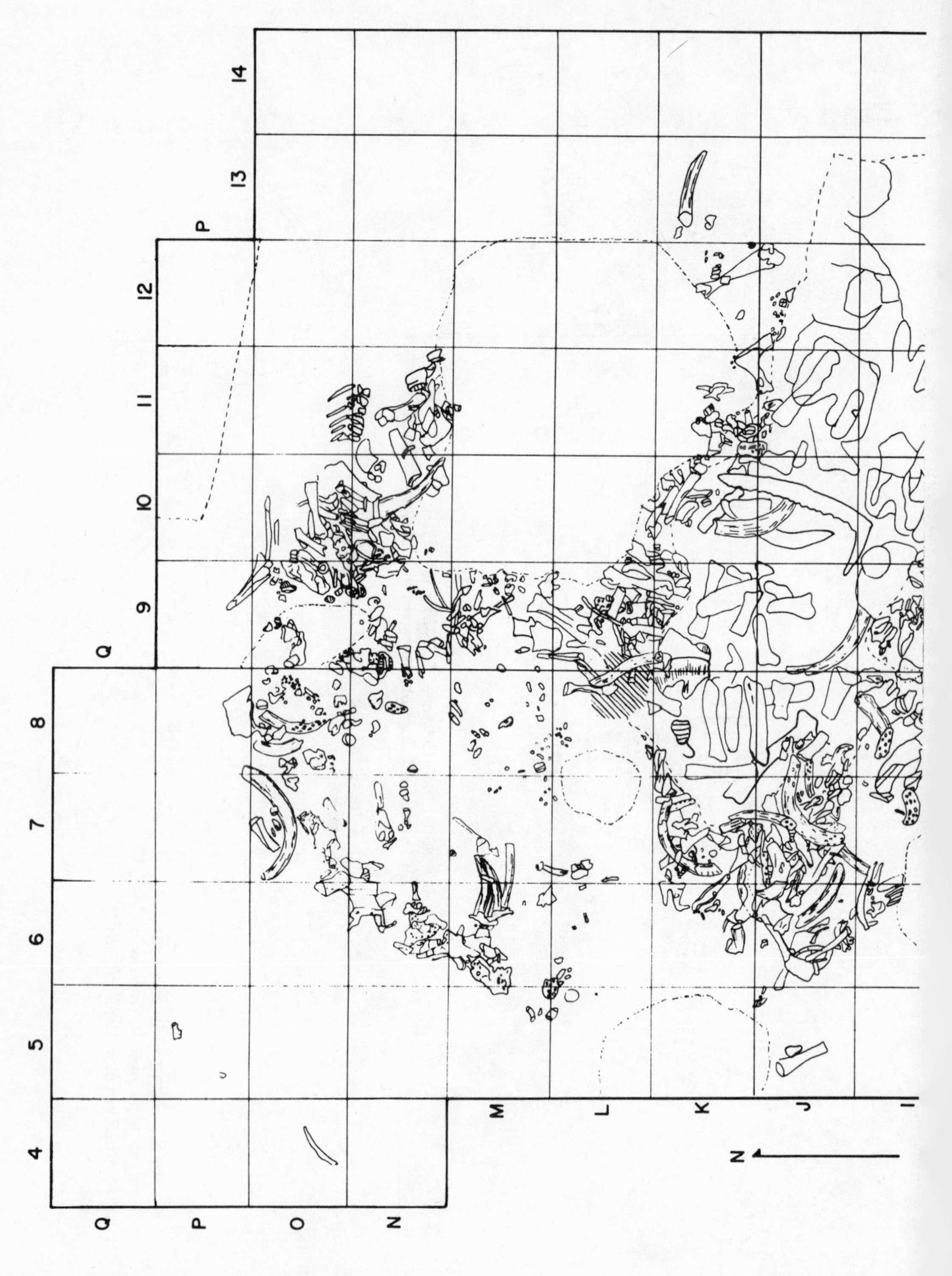
4
5
6
7
8
9
10
11
12
13
14
Q
P
O
N
M
L
K
J
I
N

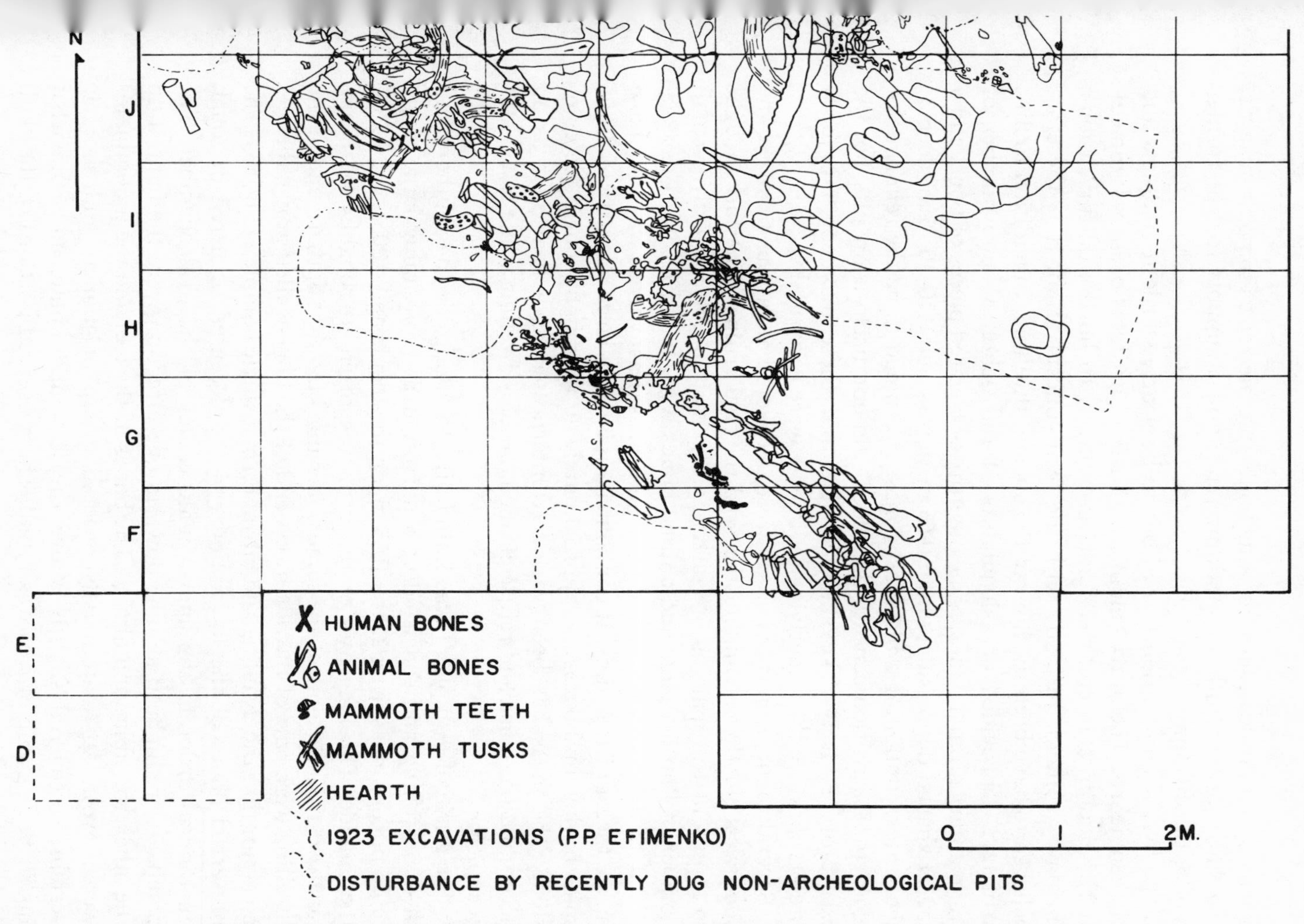

Figure 53. Complex I of Kostenki II (Redrawn after Boriskovskij 1963:Figure 5).

downslope) margin, a series of long bones, inclined so as to point inwards, may have formed both a containing fence and a support for the former roof of the dwelling.

The oval accumulation turned out to be nearly sterile in artifacts and kitchen debris. The overwhelming majority of artifacts occurred immediately below in a 10 cm. thick dark-grey layer. In horizontal dimensions, this layer coincided exactly with the oval concentration. It is therefore believed to have been the floor of the ancient dwelling. In addition to flint artifacts, it provided occasional bits of red ochre, a large number of fragmentary animal bones, some quantity of charred pieces of bone, and a saucer-shaped depression, about 0.65 m. across and 0.10–10.15 m. deep at the center, containing a black ashy mass presumed to be the remnants of a hearth. Excavation beneath the "floor" did not disclose any pits, but the excavator (P. I. Boriskovskij) believes that these may not have been preserved, since the underlying sediments were very sandy.

Several vague, thin spots of ash were uncovered at various points to the southwest, northwest, and northeast of the oval "ruins." They are thought to represent the remains of ephemeral open-air fireplaces. Only a small number of flint artifacts and animal bones were found in direct association with them. A large, round (3–3.5 m. across) ashy mass was found 5–6 m. southeast of the ruins. It contained a relatively large quantity of flints, some broken-up bones, and approximately 40 thoroughly burnt pieces of stone. The mass has been variously interpreted as a hearth or as an accumulation of ash and refuse cleaned out of a dwelling while it was still occupied.

The grave of Complex I was found directly alongside the southern end of the dwelling and consisted of a narrow oval (containing large mammoth bones) measuring 2.20 × 0.55 m. on the inside and 4.00 × 1.50 m. on the outside. The long axis of the oval was oriented roughly southeast-northwest. Since some of the same bones marking the southern end of the dwelling were part of the northwest end of the bone-walled grave, there is no doubt that the dwelling and burial form a single complex (Fig. 53). The preserved bones of the lower limbs of the deceased occurred in rough anatomical order in the approximate center of the oval chamber. The patellae were highest; sloping down in one direction were the femora, in the other, the tibiae and fibulae. The bones of the feet and the innominates were lowest. An anatomically ordered group of lumbar and thoracic vertebrae occurred slightly above the left innominate, and somewhat higher yet a group of ribs was found. The preserved portions of the skull and the upper limb skeleton lay outside the burial chamber 1.5 m. and more to the northwest. The arrangement of the different bones at the time of discovery has been taken to indicate that the deceased was buried in a sitting position facing southeast, with legs crossed and pressed to the chest. The lower part of the body was covered with earth, but the upper part was allowed to protrude above the surface within the bone-walled chamber. (The chamber was covered by a perishable roof which long ago disappeared.) Subsequently, the upper part of the body was disturbed by scavengers, and some of the bones were significantly displaced from their original positions. No objects which could be called grave goods were found in the burial chamber, nor was there any measurable amount of pigment present.

Complex II was located approximately 50 m. east-northeast (= downslope) of Complex I and consisted chiefly of a strip of mammoth bones oriented northwest-southeast. It was 14 m. long, 1.5–1.7 m. wide, 0.20–0.25 m. thick (Figs. 52 and 54). The stratigraphic circumstances were entirely analogous to those of Complex I. Since the artifact inventories coming from the two complexes were closely similar, it is even possible that they were part of the same settlement.

The bones making up the strip of Complex II belonged almost exclusively to mammoth; only a few very rare pieces were derived from other animals (woolly rhino, horse, arctic fox, and wolf). More than 800 fragmentary and whole bones of mammoth were identified, coming from at least five individual animals. Although the same skeletal parts were represented as in Complex I, they occurred in distinctive frequencies. In particular, ribs formed the most numerous category (more than 300 were found), while other bones—those of extremities, vertebrae (some in anatomical order), teeth, tusks, and skull fragments—were relatively much less numerous than in Complex I.

None of the bones making up Complex II were found driven or dug into the ground (as was common in Complex I); rather, the majority occurred in the same plane as the strip as a whole, with approximately the same dip to the southeast (= downslope) and the same orientation (northwest-southeast). The only exceptions were a few ribs oriented more or less perpendicular to the strip.

It is curious that small pieces of charred bone were frequently found in the general mass composing the strip, while flints and bits of red pigment were almost entirely absent. Most of the flint artifacts associated with Complex II were recovered either directly above the strip or just beyond its northwest end, near a series of thin (2–5 cm.), irregular, and diffuse spots of ashy matter. It is thought that these ashy spots may have been

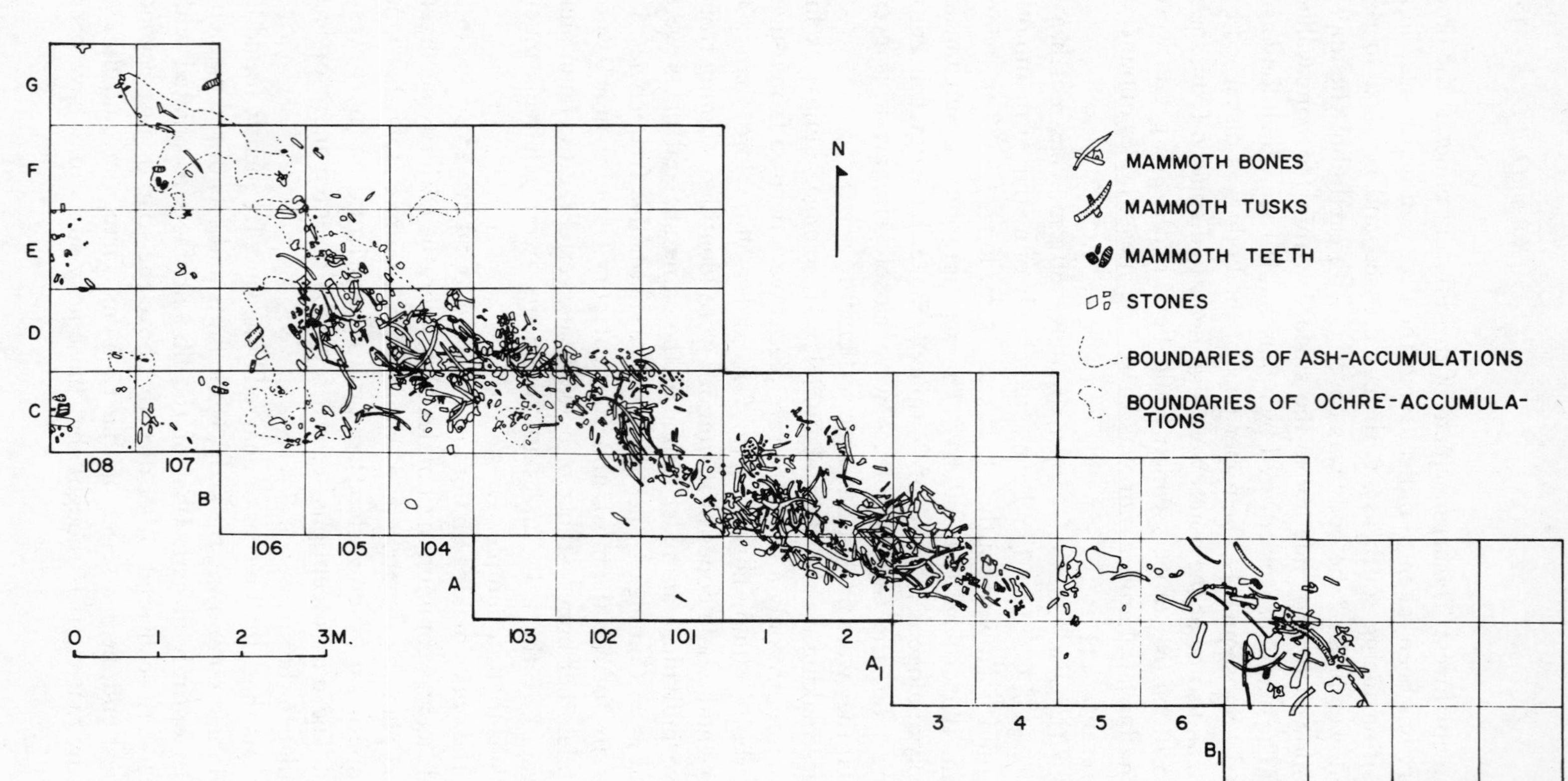

Figure 54. Complex II of Kostenki II (redrawn after Boriskovskij 1963:Figure 41).

redeposited from a short distance upslope (= northwest), although they could not have been moved far since they contained unsorted burnt stones (5–10 cm. across) and small fragments of burnt bones.

The occurrence of most of the artifacts slightly above and/or outside the limits of the bone strip may indicate that the bones were located in a hollow, though no hollow was apparent during excavation. The hollow may have formed a depository for constructional material or fuel.

Complex III was located roughly 70 m. to the east of Complex I and 20 m. to the southeast of Complex II in approximately the same stratigraphic circumstances. Its most prominent feature was a nearly circular accumulation of bones, about 1.40 m. across, consisting principally of fragments of mammoth ribs and teeth (Fig. 55). Some fragmentary ribs of a smaller animal, possibly wolf, were also present. Only a few bones were burnt, although the entire accumulation was located directly on a vague, irregular, 1–2 cm. thick, ashy spot. Investigation of this spot showed that it was in turn composed of two smaller, more intensively colored spots, each occurring in an irregular dish-shaped depression 2–4 cm. deep at center. A small number of mammoth bones (some charred) and several flint artifacts lay beneath the large spot, and a few other mammoth bones occurred to the northwest of it above the bone accumulation. Inexplicably, Complex III was relatively rich in flint artifacts.

The artifact inventory of Kostenki II is summarized in Table 25. It is clear from the table that the frequencies of different kinds of raw materials and of different tool types varied significantly from complex to complex. This variation probably reflects, in an as yet indeterminable fashion, the different meanings of the complexes. It is also apparent from the table that the assemblage of Kostenki II contrasts strongly with those of Kostenki I-1 and Tel'manskaya-1. The Kostenki knives and Kostenki points of Kostenki I-1 as well as the leaf-shaped points of Tel'manskaya-1 are completely absent from Kostenki II; at the same time splintered pieces (virtually absent at Kostenki I-1 and Tel'manskaya-1) abound. The bone-artifact inventory is not particularly large, but is interesting for the presence of the so-called stylized human figurine (Fig. 56). If indeed the interpretation of these rodlike objects is correct, they are quite unique among the Upper Paleolithic human statuettes of Europe and are more reminiscent of such objects from the Late Pleistocene of Siberia.

Only one other site in the loesslike loam overlying the upper humic bed has provided materials said to resemble closely those from Kostenki II. This site is Anosovka II-1A. During excavation of this horizon, A. N. Rogachev encountered an accumulation of more than 400 nearly intact mammoth bones, including tusks, skulls, mandibles, scapulae, pelves, long bones, and foot bones. These bones belonged to at least thirty individual

TABLE 25. Typological Composition of the Artifact Assemblage from Kostenki II (Critically Compiled from Information in Boriskovskij 1963)

Artifacts	*Complex I*		*Complex II*	*Complex III*	*Total*
	"Dwelling"	*Hearth to the south-east of the "dwelling"*			
STONE					
Raw material[a]					
Flint not available locally	ca. 1,750	ca. 595	ca. 100	ca. 880	ca. 3,325
Locally available flint	ca. 900	ca. 300	ca. 300	ca. 187	ca. 1,687
Locally available quartzite	ca. 100	ca. 65	ca. 10	ca. 33	ca. 208
Slate	ca. 50	ca. 40	—	—	ca. 90
Splintered pieces	ca. 140	ca. 70	4	17	ca. 231
Burins	ca. 110	ca. 49	5	11	ca. 175
On retouched truncations	(ca. 25)	(8)	(1)	(4)	(ca. 38)
Dihedral	(ca. 35)	(15)	(2)	(7)	(ca. 59)
On the corners of broken blades	(ca. 35)	(17)	—	—	(ca. 52)
Nucleiform	(ca. 15)	(2)	(2)	—	(ca. 19)
Other	—	(7)	—	—	(7)
End-scrapers	ca. 30	ca. 19	5	4	ca. 58
End-scraper/burins					some
Backed blades and fragments thereof	3	2	—	1	6
Blades with retouch along one or both edges and fragments thereof	ca. 70	ca. 62	2	5	ca. 139
TOTAL retouched pieces	ca. 366	ca. 206	16	ca. 38	ca. 631
Cores (mostly blade)	55	34	1	ca. 11	ca. 101
Burin spalls	ca. 110	35	25	30	ca. 200
Unretouched blades	ca. 350	ca. 160	15	70	ca. 595
Unretouched flakes and chips	ca. 1,800	ca. 565	ca. 340	ca. 920	ca. 3,625
TOTAL artifactual stone	ca. 2,800	ca. 1,000	ca. 410	ca. 1,100	ca. 5,310

BONE					
Awls	7				7
Fragmentary projectile points	5				5
Polisher	1				1
Flat fragments of bone with incised decoration	2				2
Stylized human figurine	1				1

[a] All the retouched pieces but 3 were made of flint (the chopping tool of Complex I and one of the retouched pieces of Complex II were of quartzite; Complex I also provided a crude slate burin).

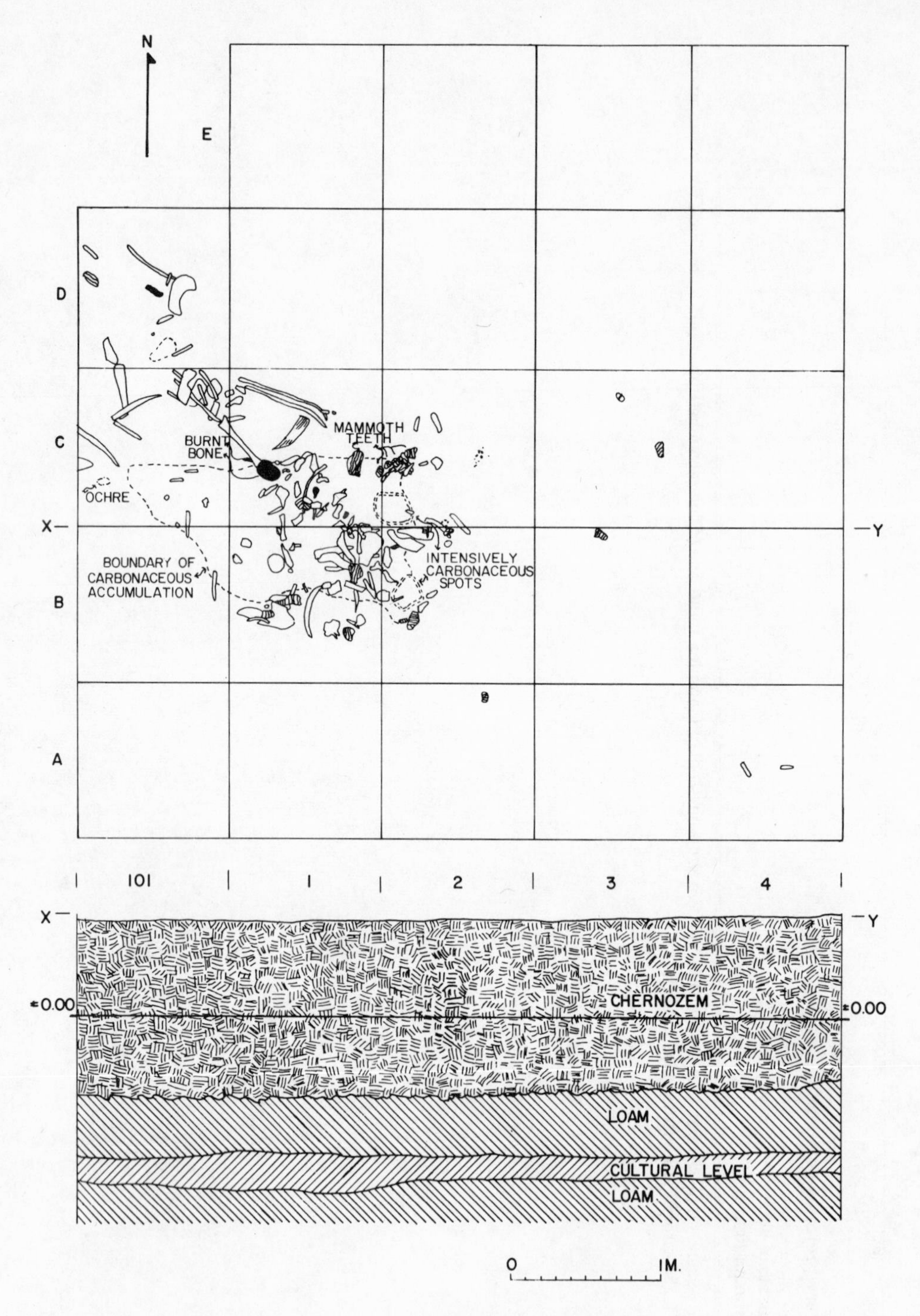

Figure 55. Complex III of Kostenki II (redrawn after Boriskovskij 1963: Figures 48 and 49).

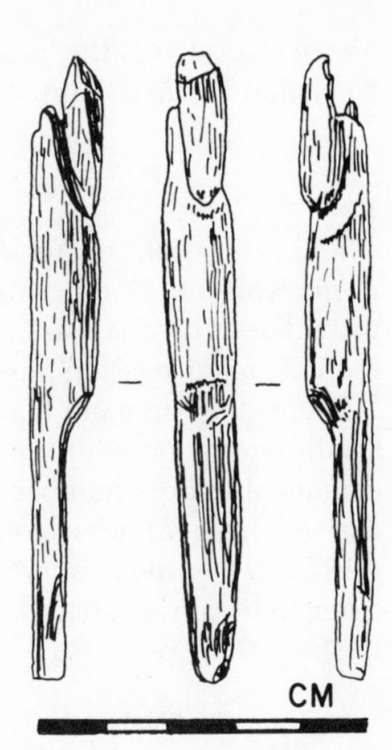

Figure 56. Anthropomorphic Figure from Kostenki II (redrawn after Abramova 1962: Plate XXII).

animals. Unfortunately, the accumulation had been partly destroyed by recent economic activity, and at this writing it has not been fully described in print. It is possible to say, however, that most of the bones occurred in a ring enclosing a slightly depressed area with an uneven floor. Bone splinters (= "kitchen debris"), flint artifacts, lumps of red pigment, and a large quantity of small bits of charred bone were concentrated near the center of the ring. Charred bone occurred particularly in an ashy, carbonaceous spot believed to represent an ancient hearth and in a small pit on the floor of the depressed area. The ring and the depressed area have been interpreted as the remains of an ancient structure in which the large bones served as constructional elements. Different kinds of bones predominated in different parts of the ring and some of the bones looked as if they had fallen onto others from above. Further, bones and parts of bones lying nearer the surface tended to be much more poorly preserved than those occurring deeper, which presumably reflects later burial.

Five pits were found immediately outside the ring of bones. They were filled with more large mammoth bones and with varying quantities of cultural debris (charred bone, bone splinters, and flints) and are assumed to have been functionally related to the ancient structure.

The artifact inventory of Anosovka II-1A is summarized in Table 26.

Above all else, it is the large number of splintered pieces at this site which has led to its close comparison with Kostenki II.

Anosovka II-Horizons 3, 2, and 1B

The excavations of Anosovka II-3, 2, and 1B are among the most recent in the Kostenki-Borshevo region, and the materials recovered are still in the process of analysis. As a result, the available information is very limited and discussion must necessarily be brief.

The most prominent feature exposed in Anosovka II-3 was a hearth in a small depression with burnt stones on the bottom. A shallow pit nearby contained a large number of wolf bones, partly in anatomical order and derived from at least four individual animals. The artifact collection (Table 27) is most interesting because it includes a bifacially worked, triangular, concave-based point of the kind typical for the Kostenki-Streletskaya Culture.

TABLE 26. Typological Composition of the Artifact Assemblage from Anosovka II-Horizon 1A (Compiled from Information in Rogachev 1961:87 and 1962a:13)

Artifacts	*Quantity*
STONE	
(Raw material: principally flint, some quartzite)	
End-scrapers	5
Burins	11
Nucleiform	(6)
Other	(5)
Blacked blades and points	19
Splintered pieces	48
Side-scrapers	2
Blades with continuous retouch on one or both edges	20
TOTAL retouched pieces	105
Cores	20
Unretouched blades and microblades	280
Unretouched flakes	1,640
TOTAL artifactual stone	> 2,000
Lumps of hematite (pigment) with clear traces of wear on the edges	some
BONE	
Points	1
Pendants	1

TABLE 27. Typological Composition of the Artifact Assemblage from Anosovka II-Horizon 3 (Compiled from Information in Rogachev 1962a and 1966)

Artifacts	*Quantity*
Raw material	
Flint	400
Quartzite	6
Other	37
Leaf-shaped points with retouch on the ventral surface only	2
Fragments of blades with retouch on the ventral surface only	5
Fragments of blades with both ventral and dorsal retouch	2
Pointed ends of leaf-shaped points (retouch on the dorsal surface only)	4
Burins	14
Dihedral	(3)
On retouched truncations	(7)
Other	(4)
End-scrapers	8
Bifacially worked, triangular, concave-based point	1
TOTAL retouched pieces	36
Unretouched pieces	ca. 360
TOTAL chipped stone	> 400
Retouchers (slate)	5
Tabular pieces of quartzite with worn surfaces	some
Sphere-shaped sandstone grinding stones	some

The immediately overlying horizon, Anosovka II-2, was considerably richer. It appeared in profile as a dark lens, up to 20–25 cm. thick, containing no less than 13,000 pieces of artifactual flint (including more than 500 retouched pieces), at least 5,500 fragments and splinters of animal bones, 1,730 pieces of ferruginous sandstone and hematite (= a source of pigment?), 596 lumps of marl (including 160 artifacts and 12 lumps with traces of working), and a huge mass of charred fragments of bone (total weight 19 kg.). The finds were concentrated around two ashy, carbonaceous masses, one of which occurred in a small pit 70 cm. across and 6–7 cm. deep. The entire lens and its contents are believed to have accumulated on the floor of an ancient structure. Some large mammoth bones standing on the approximate periphery of the lens are thought to have been used to construct the building.

The artifact inventory of Anosovka II-2 is presented in Table 28 (Fig. 57). Its outstanding features are the great variety of backed and truncated

TABLE 28. Typological Composition of the Artifact Assemblage from Anosovka II-Horizon 2 (Compiled from Information in Rogachev 1961:89, 92, and 1962b)

Artifacts	*Quantity*
STONE	
(Raw material: principally flint not available locally)	
Backed points	
Whole	65
Without truncation of the base	(19)
With straight truncation of the base	(32)
With oblique truncation of the base	(14)
Fragments of the pointed (= distal) end	20
Backed bladelets	
Whole	67
Without truncation of either end	(38)
With truncation of the distal end	(14)
With truncation of the proximal end	(3)
With truncation of both ends	(12)
Fragments	126
Truncated blades, sometimes with edges backed	
With straight truncation	
Whole	7
Fragmentary	12
With convex truncation	
Whole	11
Fragmentary	7
End-scrapers	3
Double	(1)
On fragments of blades	(2)
Burins	ca. 100
On retouched truncations	(57)
Dihedral	(16)
Other	(ca. 27)
Splintered pieces	16
Borers	1
Indeterminate fragments of tools	70
Blades (mostly fragmentary) with continuous retouch along one or both edges	97
TOTAL retouched pieces	> 500
Cores	16
Unretouched pieces	ca. 12,500
TOTAL artifactual stone	> 13,000
BONE	
Awls and fragments thereof	several
"Clasps"	2[a]
MARL	
Stylized animal figurines	
Mammoth	15
Whole	(12)
Fragmentary	(3)

TABLE 28. (*Continued*)

Artifacts	*Quantity*
Stylized animal figures (*Continued*)	
Rhinoceros	5
Whole	(2)
Fragmentary	(3)
Indeterminate animals	18
Whole	(7)
Fragmentary	(11)
Hemispheres	59
Whole	(49)
Fragmentary	(10)

[a] Awl-shaped objects (Fig. 57#26, 33) on each of which the thicker end was carved into what might be construed as a head, in one case much more detailed than in the other and conceivably that of a wolf.

pieces and the series of stylized marl animal figurines (Fig. 57#1–23). These latter were small (18–35 mm. long, 14–22 mm. high, and 11–20 mm. wide) and had flat bases. They were accompanied by a series of marl hemispheres of even smaller dimensions (9–12 mm. in diameter, 6–15 mm. in height) (Fig. 57#24–34). One of these hemispheres had a hole drilled through it to make a "bead" (Fig. 57#25).

Cultural debris at Anosovka II-1B were concentrated around a small ashy spot. At least 300 flint artifacts were found, including no less than 42 retouched pieces. These artifacts are said to be indistinguishable by raw materials or types from those of the underlying horizon, Anosovka II-2.

Markina Gora-Horizon 1, Kostenki IX, and Borshevo III

The remaining sites are characterized by contents which are meager and/or undescribed. Markina gora-1 contained no noteworthy features except for some small concentrations of mammoth bones. The small collection of artifacts is said to include a few end-scrapers, three burins, a fragmentary shouldered point, some blades with continuous retouch along one or both edges, and at least four cores. Kostenki IX provided some bone fragments, charcoal, and a tiny collection of flints including a few end-scrapers, some fragments of backed blades, and a small quantity of blades with continuous retouch along one or both edges. In contrast, Anosovka I (= Kostenki X) contained both a large amount of animal bone and a moderately large assemblage of flint artifacts. However, these remain completely undescribed in print. Finally, Borshevo III, the poorest of all the Second Terrace sites, has yielded only a very small number of flints in association with some animal bones.

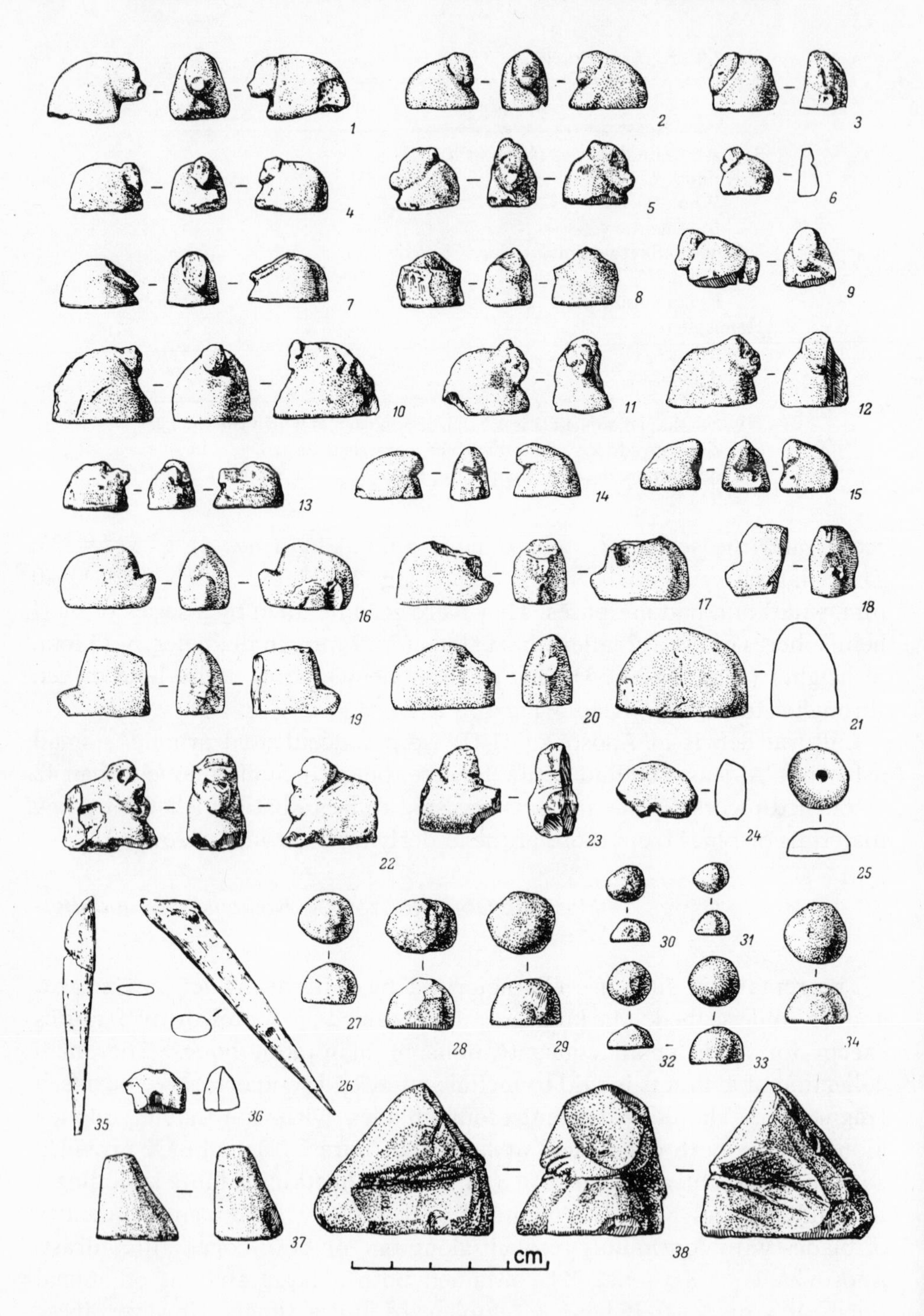

Figure 57. Art Objects from Anosovka II-Horizon 2 (from Abramova 1962:Plate XXIII).

Summary

From the information presented in this chapter it is clear that there are sites in the colluvium above the upper humic bed which possess far more spectacular features and far richer artifact assemblages than any of the sites in the humic beds. This may be largely a reflection of more recent occupation and the increased likelihood for preservation of features with little or no dispersal of debris. But it is tempting to suppose that the richness of the sites reflects at least in part more permanent settlements and perhaps also larger social groups, which in turn could be linked to an increase in the quantity of herbivorous game resulting from an increase in the amount of grazing land.[2] It is conceivable also that more permanent settlements could result from advances in hunting technology. This topic will be considered again in the final chapter.

Besides the spectacular nature of the features, their variety is also striking. Thus at Kostenki I-1, there are the supposed remnants of an immense "long house," flanked and outlined by a series of great pits. The floor of the long house is dotted by a large number of small pits and depressions of various kinds. On the other hand, at Tel'manskaya-1, excavations exposed the remains of a "round house" represented by a large, nearly circular depression filled with cultural debris. And at Kostenki II and Anosovka II-1A, supposed structural remnants were encountered in the form of huge, roughly oval masses of mammoth bones. Finally, at Kostenki I-3 and Anosovka II-2, evidence for former structures may be seen in the rather sharply restricted horizontal distribution of cultural remains in the excavations. The artifact assemblages from the different sites are no less varied than the features. Kostenki I-1 is characterized by Kostenki knives and Kostenki points in combination with a rich and varied bone and marl artifact inventory. Tel'manskaya-1 by contrast is unique in containing distinctive leaf-shaped points in company with a large number of side-scrapers and few or no end-scrapers and backed blades. Kostenki II and Anosovka II-1A are marked by high percentages of splintered pieces, absent or nearly absent at the other sites. And Anosovka II-3 is distinctive for a great abundance and variety of backed and truncated pieces. It seems highly likely that much of the variation described is to be traced to the occupation of the different sites by peoples of different cultures; but the possibility cannot be ruled out that some of the variation reflects occupation by the same people engaged in different activities and thus leaving behind different material remains. In

[2] It will be recalled that the scant pollen evidence available suggests a decrease in forestation while the deposits above the humic beds were accumulating. Presumably this decrease was accompanied by an increase in herbaceous steppe or tundra.

this connection, it would be useful to know the ages of the sites relative to one another, but this question can be approached only very tentatively at the moment, since we must rely either on isolated radiocarbon dates and/or on reported but as yet incompletely documented resemblances among artifact inventories. Of particular importance is the supposed resemblance between the assemblages of Kostenki I-1 and Kostenki V-1 on the one hand, and between those of Tel'manskaya-1 and Kostenki V-2 on the other. These resemblances plus the available radiocarbon dates (Table 3) allow us to suggest tentatively the following chronological sequence (from older to younger): Tel'manskaya-1, Anosovka II-2, Kostenki I-1, Kostenki II, and Anosovka II-1A. The significance of the variation in features among these sites will be taken up again in the final chapter. The implications of the occurrence in them of flint not available locally will also be considered there.

Kostenki XVIII, an Appendix

It will be recalled that Kostenki XVIII is totally unique in intruding into the Upper Cretaceous sands that form the degraded surface of the Third (= 35–40 m.) Terrace of the Don. It is further unique in having supplied nothing but human and animal bones. No artifacts are known from it. Although the bones establish beyond doubt the late Würm age of the site, the peculiar geological situation and the lack of artifactual associations presently rule out the possibility of dating it relative to other Kostenki-Borshevo localities.

The principal feature of Kostenki XVIII is a grave. Unfortunately, both the grave and its contents had been disturbed shortly before the excavations, and its exact horizontal extent was therefore indeterminate. The human remains were found roughly 1 m. from the surface, establishing a minimum figure for the original depth of the grave. The position and arrangement of the remains suggest that the deceased was buried on the left side with the knees bent, face directed southwest, top of the head northwest. Absolutely no pigment or artifacts were found in association with the skeleton, but it was covered by three distinct layers of mammoth bones. The lowest level consisted of two fragments of scapulae, the middle layer of a series of long bones, and the uppermost layer of a number of long bones and fragmentary tusks. All efforts to find a nearby occupation site with which to link the grave were unsuccessful. However, excavation directly alongside revealed a second ancient pit on whose bottom lay an accumulation of mammoth bones. And a test excavation in the Upper Cretaceous sands 10–15 m. from the grave provided some additional bones of Pleistocene mammals, though not certainly derived from cultural activity. A second test excavation located nearby in the colluvial loam overlying the sands exposed an ancient two-chambered pit containing fragments of approximately ten mammoth femora and a small quantity of charred bone and red ochre (pigment). At present, however, there is no reason to link this finding with the grave.

chapter 10. Sites on the First Terrace

Eleven sites are commonly spoken of as First Terrace sites. These are: Kostenki IV-horizons 1 and 2, Kostenki III, Kostenki XXI, Kostenki XIX, Borshevo I, Borshevo II-horizons 1, 2, and 3, Streletskaya I, and Rudkino. The available information on the faunal remains from these sites is presented in Table 29. As before, it is necessary to realize that the various sites have been excavated and described to very different extents, and thus it is pointless at present to speculate on the possible meaning of variation among the faunal assemblages given in the table.

Kostenki IV-Horizon 2

The excavations of Kostenki IV were conducted in two principal units located 15–20 m. apart (Fig. 58). Unfortunately, in the northern unit, where both cultural levels were abundantly represented, the first occurred directly on top of the second, frequently with little or no sterile sediment between. In several areas, the materials of the two horizons were thus

TABLE 29. Species Represented by Bones in First Terrace Sites[a]

Species	*Kostenki IV-southern excavation (Rogachev 1955:17–18)*[b]	*Kostenki IV-northern excavation (Rogachev 1955:17–18)*[b]	*Kostenki XIX (Boris-kovskij 1963:130)*	*Kostenki III (Lazukov 1957c: 93–94)*	*Borshevo I (Lazukov 1957c:93–94)*	*Borshevo II-3 (Lazukov 1957c:93–94)*	*Borshevo II-2 (Lazukov 1957c:93–94)*	*Borshevo II-1 (Lazukov 1957c:93–94)*	*Kostenki XXI (Praslov 1964)*
Mammonteus primigenius (woolly mammoth)	211/4	113/5	X	XX	XX	XX	X		X
Coelodonta antiquitatis (woolly rhinoceros)	X	1/1			X				X
Equus caballus (wild horse)	179/4	120/3	X	X	XX	XX	XX	593/8	X
Bos sp. (*Bison priscus?*) (wild cattle)	3/1		X				X	4/1	
Cervus elaphus (red deer)		3/1		X	X				
Alces alces (elk)								7/1	
Rangifer tarandus (reindeer)	63/4	4/1			X	X		41/4	
Saiga tatarica (saiga antelope)	2/1	7/1	X						
Sus scrofa (wild boar)	?								
Panthera spelaea (cave lion)	7/1	49/3		X					
Lynx lynx (lynx)					X				
Gulo gulo (wolverine)	1/1	2/1				X			
Ursus arctos (brown bear)	2/1	2/1							X

Vulpes vulpes (ordinary fox)		1/1				X		X	
Alopex lagopus (arctic fox)	5/2	1/1	X	X					
Canis lupus (wolf)	63/4	76/3	X	X	X	X		59/2	X
Martes foina (beech marten)					X				
Lepus sp. (hare)	> 3387/68	789/22		X		XX		29/2	
Marmota bobac (marmot)		2/1							?
Spalax microphthalmus (European mole rat)	X	X							
Allactaga jaculus (great jerboa)			X						
Lagurus lagurus (sagebrush vole)			X						
Citellus rufescens (russet suslik)	X		X						
Cricetus cricetus (ordinary hamster)	X	X							
Microtus oeconomus (northern vole)			X						
Microtus arvalis (continental field vole)			X						
Elobius talpinus (mole vole)	X								

[a] X = present; XX = abundant; 0/0 = number of bones/number of individuals.

[b] It was generally impossible to separate the faunal remains from the northern excavation into two collections, one for each of the occupation horizons. All that can be said is that the remains of *C. antiquitatis* and most of those of *P. spelaea* belonged to horizon 1. On the other hand, those of *C. elaphus* were derived exclusively from horizon 2. Most animals were clearly represented in both horizons. It may be assumed that the faunal remains gathered in the southern excavation belonged nearly altogether if not entirely to horizon 2 (in this excavation, horizon 2 was by far better represented).

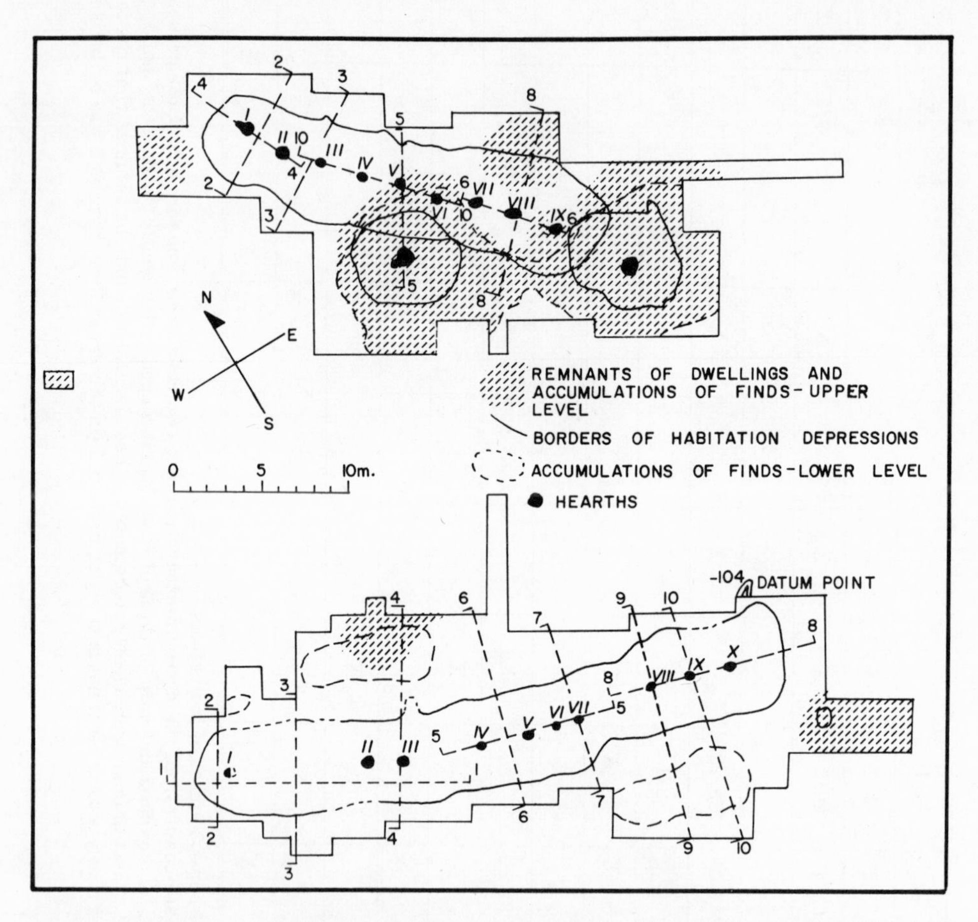

Figure 58. Plan of Kostenki IV-Horizons 1 and 2, Showing Locations of Profiles (redrawn after Rogachev 1955:Figure 3).

completely mixed. Luckily, in places where the horizons were distinguishable in profile, they were characterized by different varieties of flint and also by different types of artifacts. This allowed at least partial separation of mixed materials.

In each of the major excavation units, the cultural remains of the second horizon turned out to be heavily concentrated in a long hollow or depression regarded as marking the spot of an ancient structure. Both depressions were oriented with their long axes roughly upslope-downslope. Perhaps this position facilitated drainage around them. The depression found in the more southern excavation unit was 34 m. long and averaged 5.5 m. in width (Fig. 59). Its floor sloped gently downward from the edges, reaching a maximum depth of 40 cm. and averaging 20–30 cm. Its loamy fill was colored red by ochre and contained a large quantity of artifacts and animal bones. Two low earthen ridges 10 cm. high at maximum ran transversally across the floor, dividing the depression into three sections—an eastern (ca. 14 m. long), a central (ca. 9 m. long), and a western (ca. 10.5 m. long). Each section is believed to have been the floor of a separate room in the ancient structure.

A series of round, bowl-shaped pits, 55–65 cm. in diameter and 5–13 cm. deep were found strung out along the midline of the depression. All were filled by black ashy matter and were almost certainly hearths. They were not evenly spaced, but seemed to form three groups corresponding to the three sections. The western section contained three pits; possibly two others were destroyed by early, relatively unsystematic excavations. Four were found in the central section and three in the eastern. In addition, the western end of the eastern section contained a pit on a line with the hearth pits and with the same form, but without the typical black ashy fill. This pit is presumed to represent a hearth which was abandoned much earlier than the others. Microscopic analysis of samples of the ashy material from various hearths revealed numerous small fragments of charred bone. Further, the ash turned out to be strongly weathered, probably as a result of exposure to the elements before burial.

Besides the hearth pits, 52 other small pits were found in the depression, scattered over its entire surface. Four of these, all in the western section, may have been post holes. Three of them were round, the fourth oval. They varied from 15–28 cm. in diameter and from 15–25 cm. in depth. Their fills were essentially sterile and only weakly colored compared to the fill of the depression as a whole. The remaining pits were mostly round, measured 30–50 cm. in diameter, and had straight walls and flat bottoms, 15–35 cm. deep. They were filled with loam reddened by ochre and packed with cultural debris in about the same density as the rest of the occupation horizon. Most of them have been interpreted as storage pits or caches. A few pits contained extraordinary amounts of red ochre and numerous bones of hare (especially bones of the paw). It has been suggested that these pits were used for the coloring and tanning of hare skins.

The distribution of cultural debris within the depression presents an interesting picture. A strip of loam running down the center, 50–100 cm. from the edges, was both richest in finds and most darkly colored. It was interrupted only between the central and western sections by a 60 cm. wide strip of weakly colored loam. Near the edges of the depression finds became scarce and coloration was much less intense. The excavator, A. N. Rogachev, believes these facts are explained by the assumption that the former structure was covered by a gabled roof whose eaves nearly

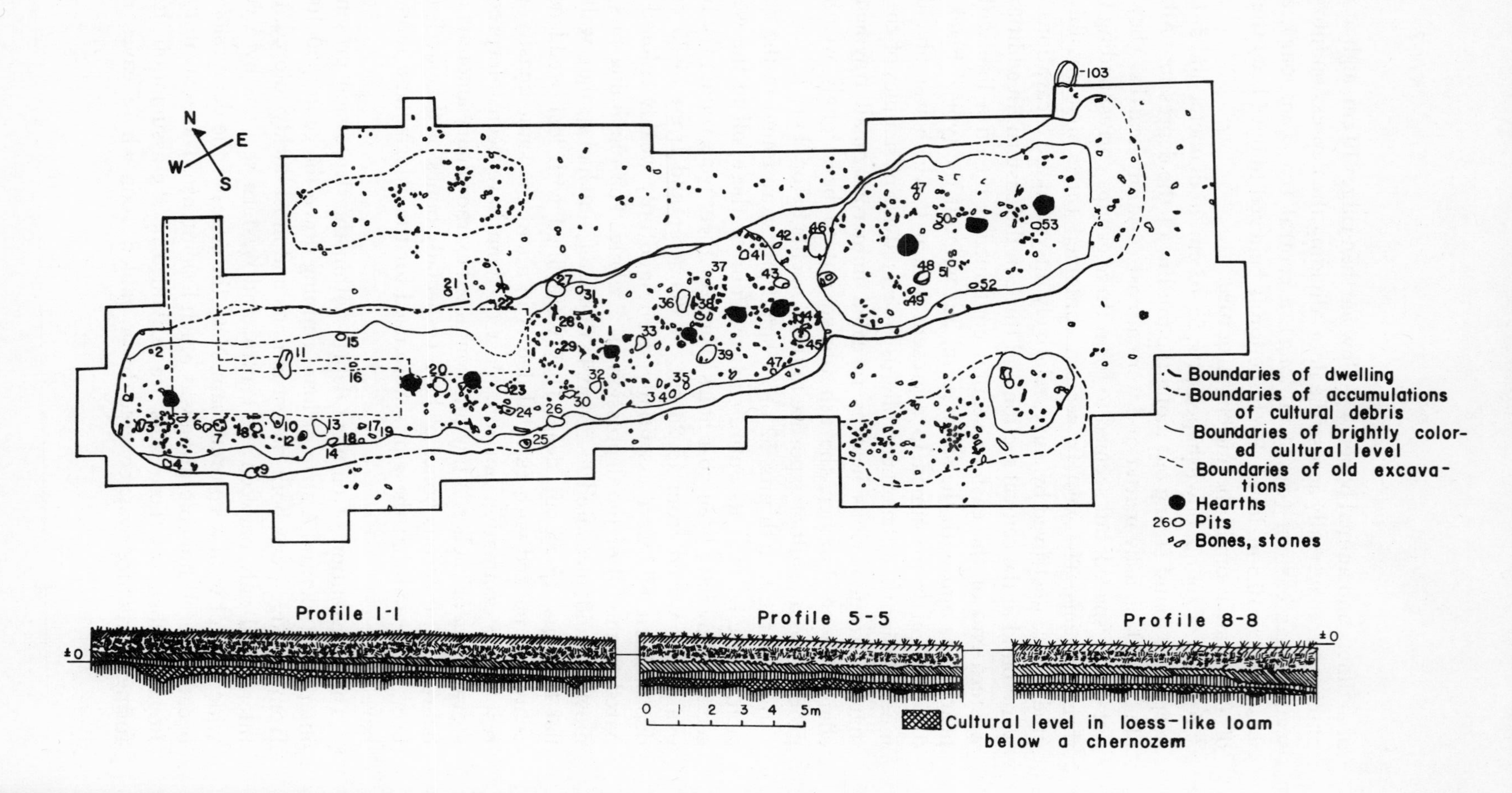
N
E
W
S
-103
Boundaries of dwelling
Boundaries of accumulations of cultural debris
Boundaries of brightly colored cultural level
Boundaries of old excavations
Hearths
26 Pits
Bones, stones
Profile 1-1
Profile 5-5
Profile 8-8
±0
±0
0 1 2 3 4 5m
Cultural level in loess-like loam below a chernozem

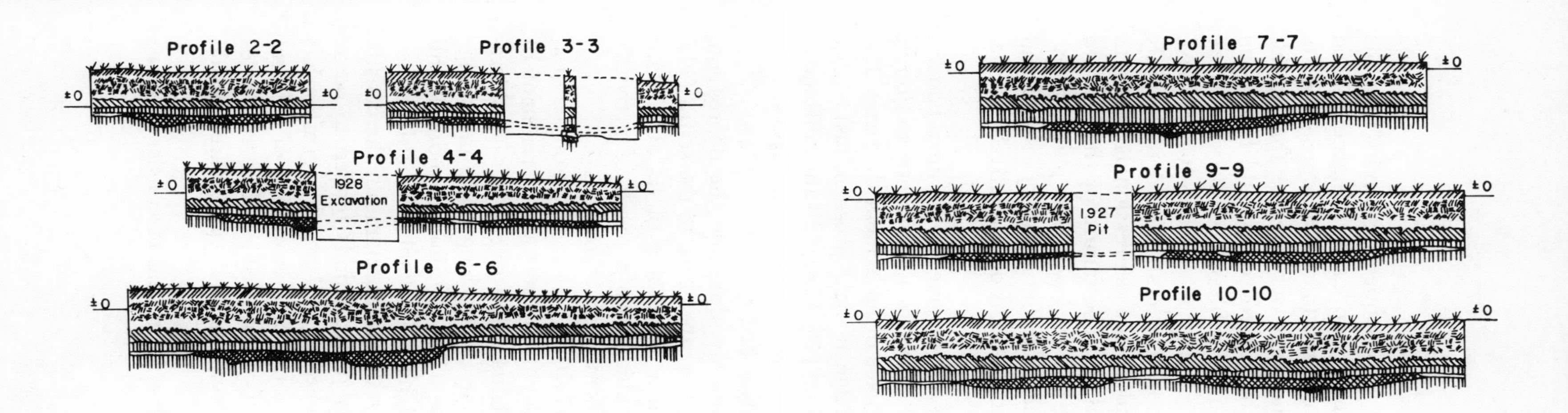

Figure 59. Plan and Profiles of Kostenki IV-Horizon 2, Southern Excavation (redrawn after Rogachev 1955b: Figure 29). Numbers 1-1, 2-2, 3-3, etc., refer to profiles shown in Figure 58.

touched the sides of the depression. As a consequence, activity near the sides was restricted, and less cultural debris and less ochre accumulated there. In the few places where brightly colored loam did approach quite closely to the sides of the depression, the sides were steeper than usual; thus the space between the floor and the gabled roof would have been greater. Further circumstantial evidence for gabling may be seen in the arrangement of the hearths along the midline, where they would have been farthest from any part of the roof. The distribution of brightly colored fill right up to the western end of the depression is taken to indicate that a vertical wall was built there. The failure of the loam to reach the eastern end may indicate that a sloping wall was placed there. The 60 cm. wide strip of weakly colored loam between the central and western sections is thought to mark the position of a relatively permanent partition.

A small concentration of chipped flints and fragments of animal bone in weakly colored loam near the northeast corner of the western section of the depression is believed to cover the place of an ancient doorway. The presence of a small ledge or step on the edge of the depression just at this point provides support for this conclusion. (On Figure 59 the concentration is marked by a dotted bulge in the northern edge of the depression.) No other possible doorways have been suggested.

Two small, independent concentrations lay alongside the depression. One of these occurred 2 m. to the north, the other 2 m. to the south (Fig. 59). The one to the south was found in a depression of its own. Both concentrations are believed to have originated as a result of activities conducted immediately adjacent to the former structure.

The second long depression, located 17–20 m. to the north of the first, was closely similar in form and is thought to represent a remnant of essentially the same kind of gabled long house. However, it was considerably smaller than the first, measuring only 23 m. long with an average width of 5.5 m. and a depth of 20–35 cm. (Fig. 60). Furthermore, its fill contrasted sharply with that of its neighbor in displaying only minor horizontal variations in the intensity of red coloration and in the density of cultural materials. Sections relatively poor in finds tended to occur along the midline. This grouping is believed to indicate that erosion has occurred along the length of the depression. The distribution of cultural remains slightly beyond the downslope (= southeast) end corroborates this interpretation (in general, cultural remains were very rare outside the depression).

Like the first depression, the second has been said to consist of three parts. However, no earthen ridges were found as dividers, and the rationale for partition has never been made clear. Careful examination of the edges failed to reveal any points where entrances are likely to have been located, with the possible exception of the approximate midpoint of the northern side.

Also like its neighbor, the second depression contained a number of pits dug in the floor. These included one series of nine, 50–100 cm. across and 5–15 cm. deep, running along the midline and assumed to be hearth pits because of their black ashy contents. Smaller pits, filled with the same ashy material and thought to have been used in food preparation, were found directly alongside three of the hearth pits. Twenty-five additional pits, ranging from 20 to 40 cm. across and scattered at random over the surface of the depression, have been interpreted as caches. In fourteen of these the concentration of red ochre near the bottom was particularly intense. Frequently the same pits contained enigmatic black-patinated flint pebbles and perforated mollusc shells.

It is only in their size and in the string of hearths down the center that the two features from Kostenki IV-2 resemble the supposed long house of Kostenki I-1. The area of the Kostenki I-1 dwelling was surrounded by twelve great pits and was not depressed. This difference, in combination with marked differences between the artifact assemblages of Kostenki I-1 and Kostenki IV-2, makes it unlikely that the two sites were derived from a single culture, though there is no reason to suppose that they are very far apart in time.

The artifact assemblage of Kostenki IV-2 is summarized in Table 30 (see also Fig. 61). The variety and abundance of backed blades and points is considered its outstanding feature. The so-called Gravette points (Fig. 61#1 and 2) are at best marginal examples of this artifact type insofar as it is possible to judge from the available illustrations of intact pieces. Figure 61#3 shows awl-like points or flint awls, which are relatively small blades with one edge backed and the other sufficiently retouched at its upper end to form a point with the backed edge. In some cases at least, these pieces may be Gravette or even Font-Yves points. Microscopic examination revealed that several examples were worn at the tip.

Among the bone and shell artifacts, the perforated shells of *Neritina* sp. are of special interest. They tended to occur in groups, and at least one group was found in close association with some pierced wolf teeth (Fig. 61#10–14). The ensemble (shells plus wolf teeth) may well represent the remains of a composite necklace. Friction with a cord is inferred from polishing apparent on the edges of the holes through the shells. Dark red

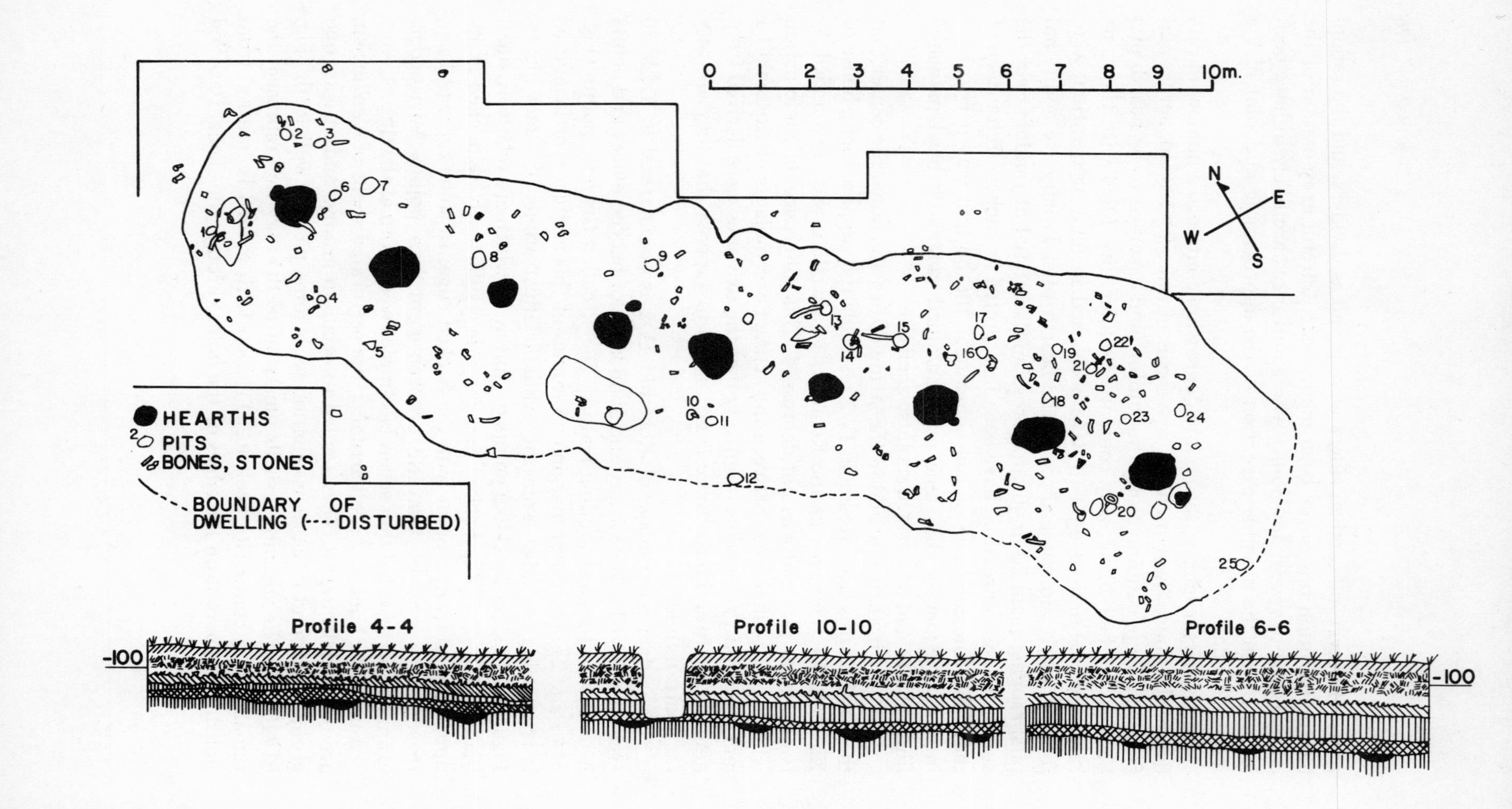
0 1 2 3 4 5 6 7 8 9 10m.
N
E
W
S
HEARTHS
PITS
BONES, STONES
BOUNDARY OF DWELLING (---- DISTURBED)
Profile 4-4
Profile 10-10
Profile 6-6
-100
-100

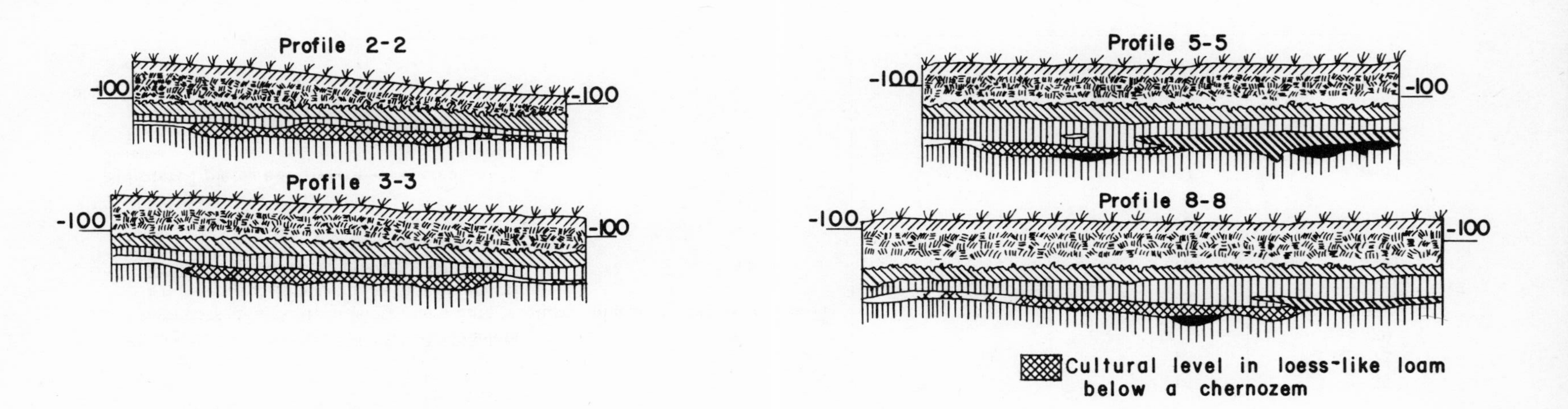

Figure 60. Plan and Profiles of Kostenki IV-Horizon 2, Northern Excavation (redrawn after Rogachev 1955b: Figure 31). Numbers 1-1, 2-2, 3-3, etc., refer to profiles shown in Figure 58.

TABLE 30. Typological Composition of the Artifact Inventory of Kostenki IV-Horizon 2 (Compiled from Information in Rogachev 1955:116ff.)

Artifacts	*Southern excavation unit*	*Northern excavation unit*	*Total*
STONE	Raw material: mostly flint	Raw material: mostly flint	
Backed bladelets and points			
Backed bladelets without truncations	60	27	87
Backed bladelets with truncation of the upper end	34	14	48
Backed bladelets with truncation of the lower end	42	10	52
Backed bladelets with truncation of both ends	30	16	46
Denticulate backed bladelets			
Whole	18	7	25
Fragmentary	50	25	75
Gravette points			
Whole	9	8	17
Fragmentary	54	18	72
Awl-like points or flint awls			
Whole	15	15	30
Fragmentary	54	18	72
Shouldered (= partially?) backed bladelets			ca. 50
Fragments of backed bladelets and points (exclusive of fragments already listed)	472	612	2,084
Fragments of upper ends without truncation	(173)	(37)	(210)
Fragments of upper ends with truncation	(164)	(79)	(243)
Fragments of bases without truncation	(320)	(104)	(424)
Fragments of bases with truncation	(215)	(84)	(299)
Fragments of midsections	(600)	(308)	(908)
Splintered pieces and fragments thereof	546	660	1,206
Burins	118	40	158
Burins on the corners of broken blades			(32)
Burins on retouched truncations			(27)
Dihedral burins			(14)
Other			(85)

End-scrapers and truncated blades	155	57	212
Blades and flakes with retouch (mostly fragmentary)	ca. 1,358	1,518	ca. 2,876
TOTAL retouched pieces	ca. 3,852	ca. 2,990	ca. 7,842
Cores and fragments thereof (all blade)	161	88	249
Unretouched pieces	ca. 34,000	ca. 18,900	ca. 51,900
TOTAL artifactual stone	ca. 38,000	ca. 22,000	ca. 60,000
Small pieces of sandstone and slate with pitted, flatter surfaces (= anvils?)			8
Hammerstones			2
Slate retouchers			2
Axelike objects of sandstone and slate			3
BONE AND SHELL			
Awls			32
Whole			(10)
Fragmentary			(22)
Polishers (all fragmentary)			9
Chisel-shaped tools			1
"Spear points"			1
Miscellaneous bone artifacts			several
Arctic-fox, wolf, and reindeer teeth, each with a hole drilled through the root			9
Shells of *Paludina diluviana*, each with a hole drilled through			2
Shells of *Neritina* sp., each with a hole drilled through	5	108	113

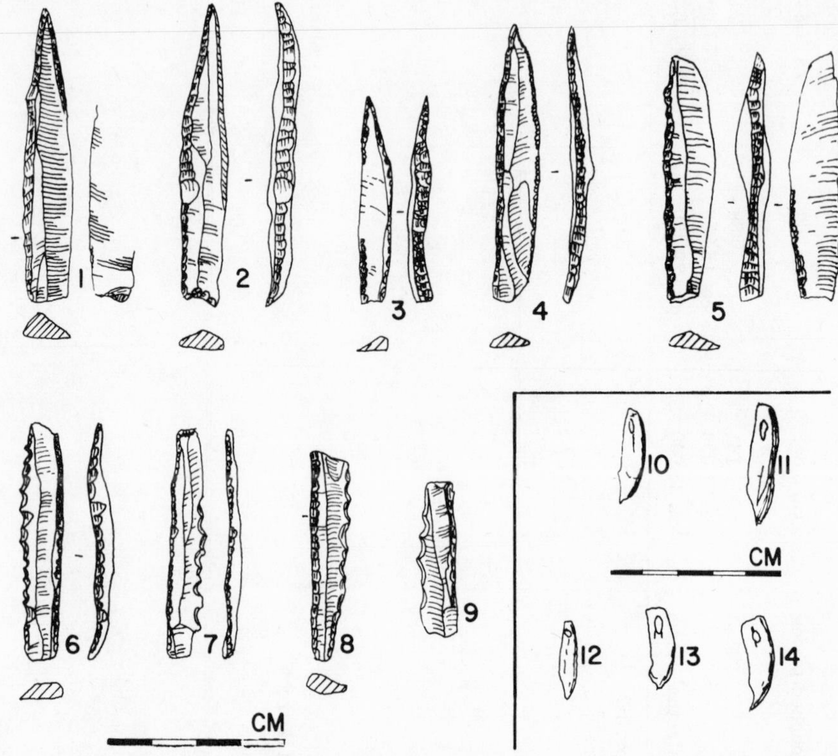

Figure 61. Artifacts from Kostenki IV-Horizon 2 (redrawn after Rogachev 1955b:Figures 37, 38, 39, and 43).

pigment, caked inside the shells, is considered a remnant of the body paint of the former owner(s).

No cultural remains entirely comparable to those of Kostenki IV-2 are known from any other site in the Kostenki-Borshevo region.

Kostenki IV-Horizon 1

The first horizon of Kostenki IV contrasts markedly with the second both in features and in artifacts. All the important features and the majority of the artifacts came from the northern excavation unit (Fig. 58). Here the excavators encountered two relatively well-defined round depressions located approximately 6 m. apart (Fig. 62). Each is regarded as the remnant of a long-abandoned structure. They are of about equal size, the western one having a diameter of approximately 6 m. with a maximum depth of 50 cm., the eastern one a diameter of 6–6.5 m. with a depth of 30–40 cm. Each was filled by ochreous, dark-red loam containing considerable quantities of cultural debris. Debris-containing, colored loam was not confined to the depressions, however, but spilled 1–2 m. and sometimes farther beyond their boundaries. This spilling has been explained as being in part a result of erosion in the direction of the Don and a nearby ravine (that is, to the east and southeast) and in part a result of the fact that the former structures probably covered areas larger than the depressions. Especially thick concentrations of cultural materials were found immediately to the southwest of each depression. It is here that ancient doorways may have stood.

A series of interesting features were encountered within each depression. A roughly oval (2.5 × 1.5 m.) mass of black ashy matter in the center of the western depression turned out to cover and fill eight pits (Fig. 63, left). The largest one, toward the center of the oval, was bowl-shaped, with a diameter of 80–110 cm. and a maximum depth of 10 cm. The entire complex is regarded as the remains of a hearth used in food preparation. A similar set of six ash-filled pits was found in the eastern depression (Fig. 63, middle). Here, however, they were not covered by a single ashy mass. The central and largest one was oval, measuring 1.00 × 1.10 m. across, and reached 10 cm. depth. The five peripheral pits do not seem to have existed simultaneously, since one of them occurred nearly entirely within the loamy fill of the depression, while the others penetrated beneath its floor.

Both round depressions contained yet further pits, some of which are thought to be the result of rodent activity. Others, however, contained considerable quantities of cultural debris or were filled by intensely colored loam and have been interpreted as caches. One group of caches in the eastern depression was particularly interesting since the pits overlapped one another in a way which suggests that they were dug at different times (Fig. 63, right).

In addition to fragmentary animal remains and to stone and bone artifacts to be discussed below, each depression contained some large sandstone slabs and some accumulations of smaller pieces of nonartifactual stone. Both the slabs and the smaller pieces tended to occur near the edges of the depressions well above their bottoms. Sometimes the slabs were found in peculiar, inclined positions. It is therefore supposed that the slabs and the smaller pieces of rock served as constructional material. The same may be true of some occasional large fragments of mammoth bone and tusk. (In this context, it is interesting to note that a small bank of earth, 5–9 cm. high and 40–50 cm. wide, girdled the southern margin of the eastern depression; this feature is regarded as having provided support for the ancient roof.) Atop the fill of the western depression were

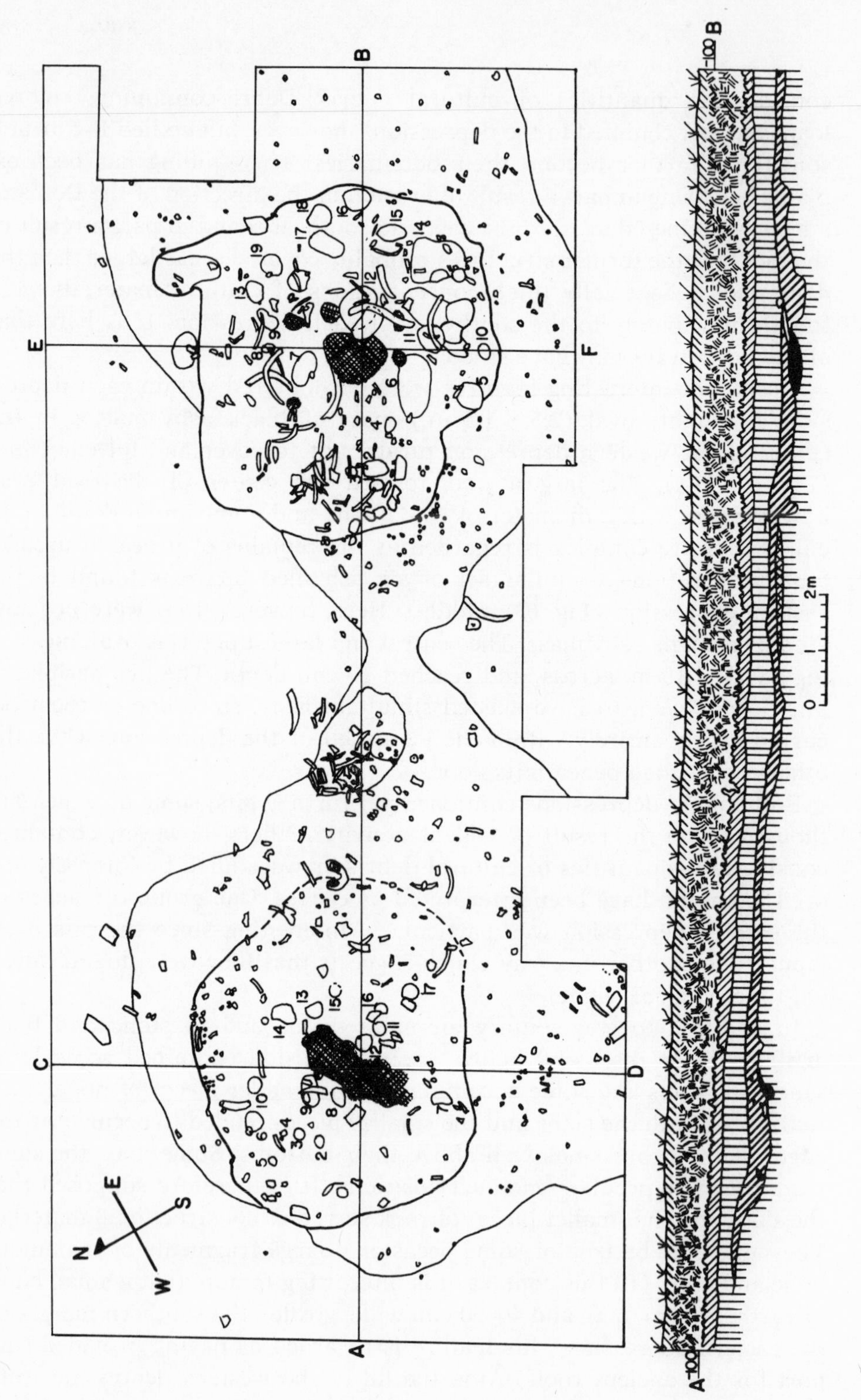
A
B
C
D
E
F
N
E
S
W
0
1
2m

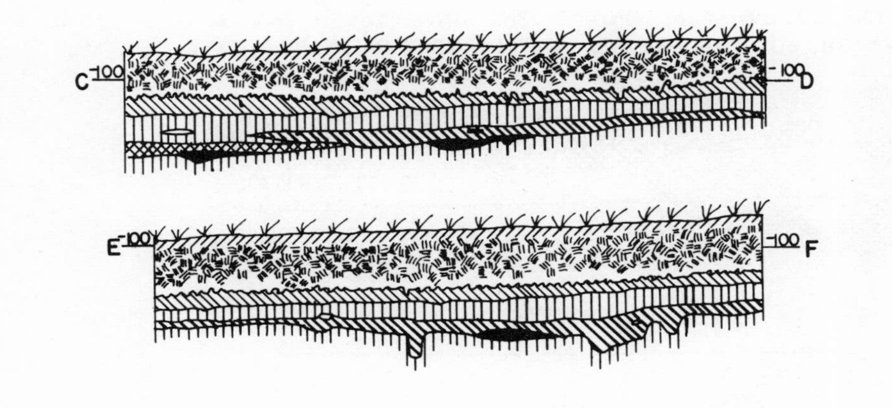

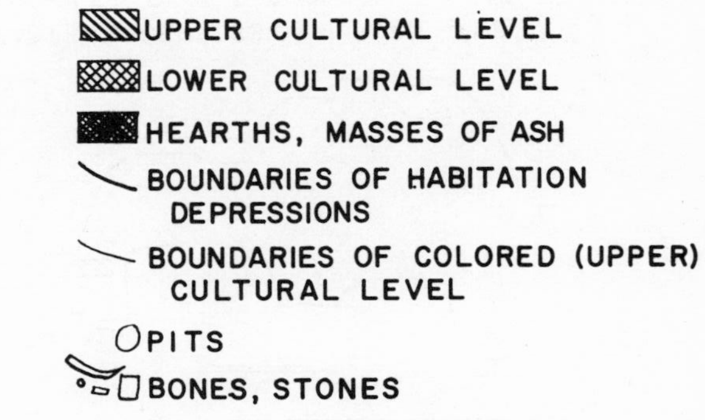

Figure 62. Plan and Profiles of Kostenki IV-Horizon 1 (redrawn after Rogachev 1955b:Figure 8).

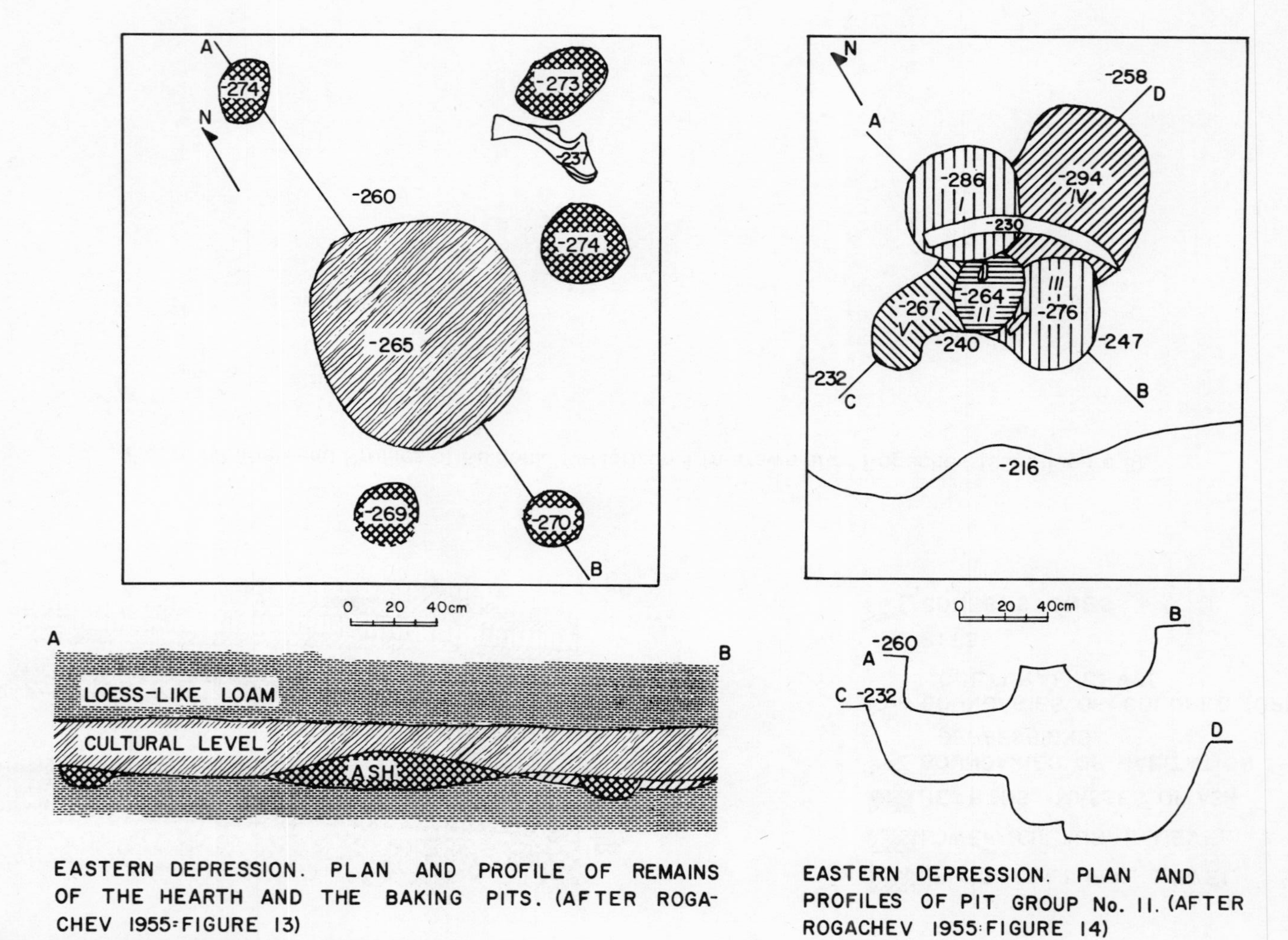

EASTERN DEPRESSION. PLAN AND PROFILE OF REMAINS OF THE HEARTH AND THE BAKING PITS. (AFTER ROGACHEV 1955:FIGURE 13)

EASTERN DEPRESSION. PLAN AND PROFILES OF PIT GROUP No. 11. (AFTER ROGACHEV 1955:FIGURE 14)

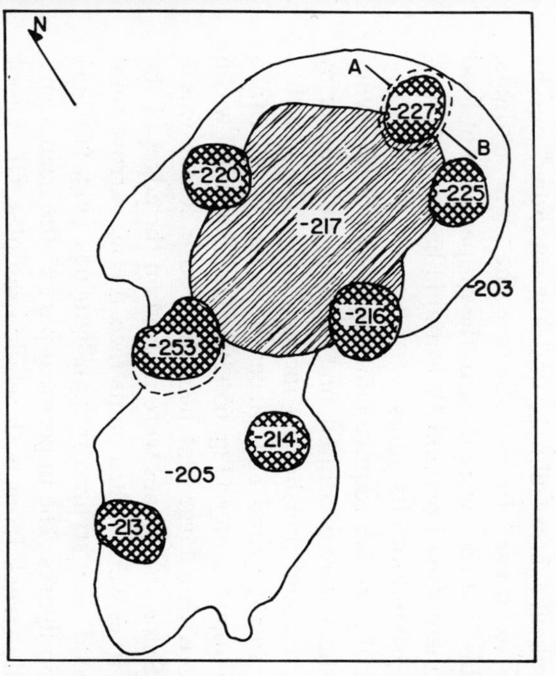

Figure 63. Hearths and Pits in the Habitation Depressions of Kostenki IV-Horizon 1 (redrawn after Rogachev 1955b:Figures 10, 13, and 14).

found two lion crania, which, it has been suggested, once rested on the roof of the building covering the depression.

The artifact assemblage of Kostenki IV-1 is presented in Table 31 (see also Figs. 64–66). The composite burin/points are considered the hallmark of the chipped-flint collection. Whole examples were shaped like willow leaves; while one end of these artifacts was retouched to a point, the other bore a dihedral burin. It has been suggested that the burin served for mounting the piece in a haft. Two of the pieces are said to bear traces of use as whittling knives (Fig. 64#1 and 2).

Perhaps even more interesting than the burin/points are the large number of ground slate artifacts. The most prominent category of these included almost completely ground lens-shaped (biconvex) discs 30–60 mm. in diameter and 5–20 mm. thick (Fig. 64#5). Virtually all the more circular examples were heavily dented near their edges. Their bulging central portions were relatively smooth. Indentations tended to concentrate on the ends of the more oval specimens. It has been suggested that the denting arose when the pieces were used as retouchers in the manufacture of flint tools. One disc was unique in having a hole through its center (Fig. 65#16). No indentations were found on this object.

Besides chipped and ground artifacts, a number of pebbles and tabular fragments of rock were discovered which displayed naturally rough or deliberately roughened surfaces (Fig. 64#6). On some examples it was possible to observe roughened areas almost entirely smoothed out by grinding. Possibly these were used to manufacture the slate artifacts. However, it is also possible that they were used in the preparation of food or in the mashing of pigment. One Kostenki IV example had a considerable amount of red ochre ground into its pores.

The bone and marl artifacts also require comment. Two of the ivory rods and two of the polishers were decorated, one rod and one polisher by punctuations, the other rod and polisher by incised lines. The "clothes fasteners" consisted of small, cylindrical pieces of bone, each with a constriction at its approximate center (Fig. 65#19). The "hairpin" was a distinctive ivory artifact with a large, flat head in whose center was a large hole (Fig. 65#20). Some short lines were incised on the edges of the head, and some very fine lines were etched on its face. A long narrow point passed away from the head. The stylized human figurines (Fig. 66#1–4) only vaguely recall human figures. The uppermost part of the head seems to have been intentionally struck from both whole examples. On one of the whole figurines, the major part of one surface of the body was nearly covered by punctuations. The stylized animal figurines (Fig. 65#1–14) likewise only vaguely recall the subjects they are supposed to portray.

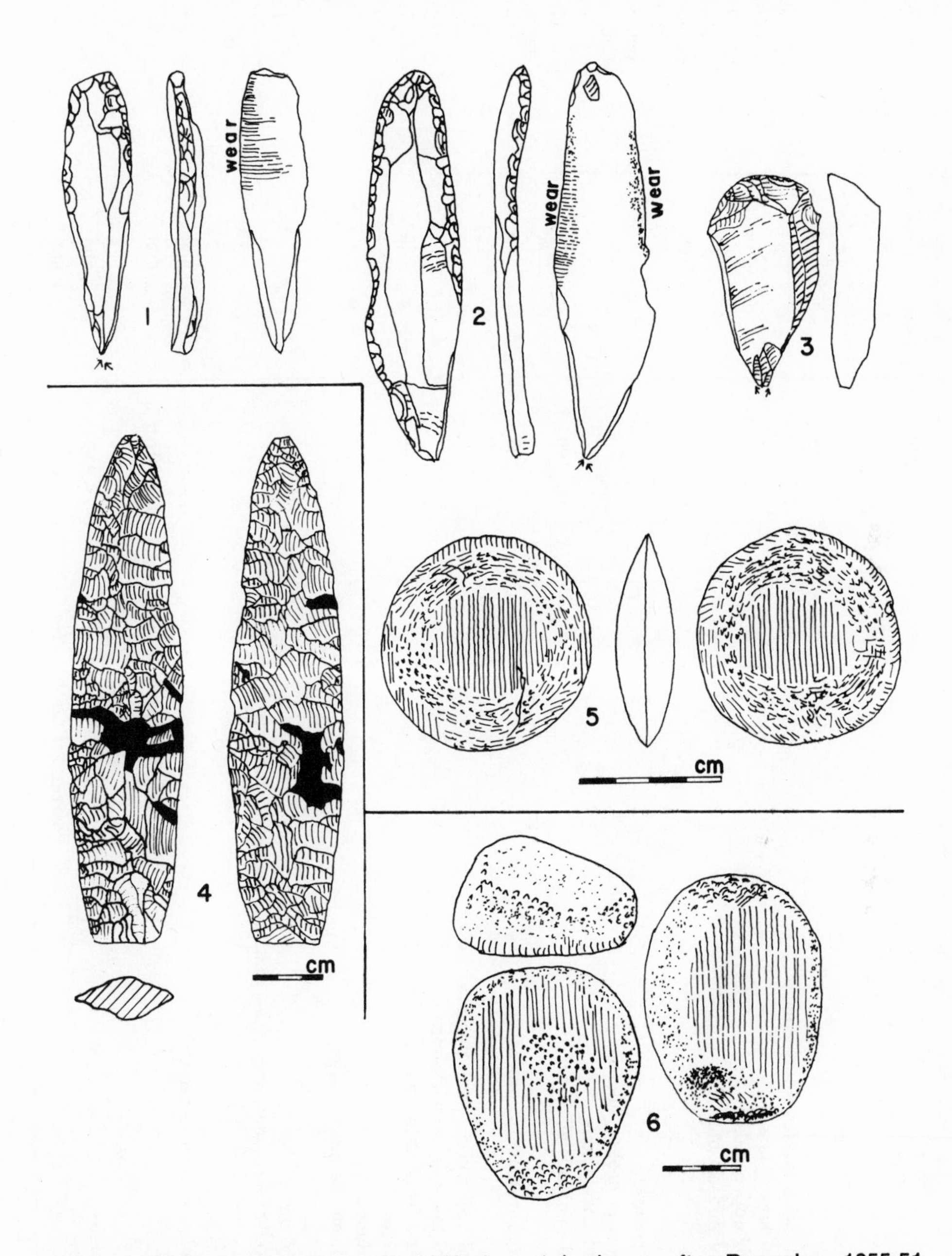

Figure 64. Artifacts from Kostenki IV-Horizon 1 (redrawn after Rogachev 1955:51, 52, 53, 60, and 69).

TABLE 31. Typological Composition of the Artifact Inventory of Kostenki IV-Horizon 1 (Compiled from Information in Rogachev 1955:37ff.)

Artifacts	*Western depression*	*Eastern depression*	*Total*
FLINT			
Backed bladelets and points	242	162	404
Whole	(38)	(41)	(79)
Almost whole with broken upper end			(60)
Fragments of lower ends			(106)
Fragments of upper ends			(94)
Fragments of midsections			(154)
Burins	ca. 270	ca. 169	ca. 439
Dihedral	(76)	(73)	(149)
Double dihedral			(ca. 20)
On the corners of broken blades			(ca. 50)
On retouched truncations			(18)
Multifaceted (= bladelet cores?)	(ca. 100)	(ca. 79)	(ca. 179)
Other			(some)
Burin/points and fragments thereof	103	88	191
Whole	(23)	(12)	(35)
Fragments of upper ends (with points)			(74)
Fragments of lower ends (with burins)			(21)
End-scrapers and fragments thereof	42	34	76
On whole blades			(38)
On broken blades			(14)
With retouch on the lateral edges			(6)
Double			(1)
End-scraper/burins			(11)
Bifacially worked knife blades/projectile points and fragments thereof[a]			4
Sidescrapers			> 10
Bifaces (hand axes)			3
Flakes and blades with some retouch	ca. 350	ca. 300	ca. 650
TOTAL retouched pieces	ca. 1,007	ca. 753	ca. 1,750
Cores	47	45	92
Unretouched pieces	ca. 6,950	ca. 5,700	ca. 12,650
TOTAL artifactual flint	ca. 8,000	ca. 6,500	ca. 14,500

QUARTZITE			
Burins			6
Leaf-shaped points and fragments thereof			5
Whole			(2)
Fragments of bases (with burins)			(3)
End-scrapers			at least 2
Side-scrapers			13
Flakes with retouch			8
Blades with retouch	29	12	41
TOTAL retouched pieces	29	12	ca. 75
Cores			6
Hammerstones			1
TOTAL artifactual quartzite	729	ca. 600	ca. 1,329
SLATE			
Ground, lens-shaped discs and fragments thereof	31	23	54
Whole	(24)	(9)	(33)
Fragments	(7)	(14)	(21)
Roughouts of discs with some traces of grinding	31	11	42
Flakes with some traces of grinding			several doz.
Bars with traces of grinding			8
Axelike artifacts with both flaking and grinding			3
Indescript fragments with traces of grinding	19	12	31
TOTAL of objects with traces of grinding	162	78	240
TOTAL of artifactual slate	730	ca. 400	ca. 1,130
VARIA (STONE)			
Pebbles with pitted ends and dented flatter surfaces (= grinding stones)			43
Fragments of quartzite and sandstone slabs (= grinding stones)			37

[a] The most distinctive of these was a 20 cm. long, bifacially worked, bilaterally symmetrical piece (Fig. 64#4) with traces of wear on its pointed end and on adjacent sections. A second example was weakly shouldered. The remaining two examples were fragments of bifacially worked pieces.

TABLE 31. (*Continued*)

Artifacts	*Western depression*	*Eastern depression*	*Total*
BONE			
Fragmentary ivory rods	9	6	15
Awls and fragments thereof	15	9	24
Whole			(9)
Fragments of sharp ends			(4)
Fragments of basal ends			(2)
Fragments of midsections			(3)
Needlelike points	3	2	5
Polishers and fragments thereof	3	8	11
Whole	(1)	(1)	(2)
Fragments	(2)	(7)	(9)
Ivory discs	1		1
Hafts for flint tools		2	2
Clothes fasteners and fragments thereof		91	91
Whole		(41)	(41)
Fragments		(50)	(50)
Hairpin (?)		1	1
Possible stylized human figurines of ivory and probable fragments thereof			6
Whole		(2)	(2)
Fragments			(4)
Miscellaneous pieces of worked bone and tooth			ca. 10
MARL			
Anthropomorphic head			1
Sheeplike head	1		1
Stylized animal figurines	5	2	7
Pendants and fragments thereof			10
Short marl bars			14
Indescript fragments of marl artifacts			27
Lumps of marl with traces of engraving			4
Lumps of marl with traces of working	20	15	35
TOTAL pieces of artifactual marl	64	37	101

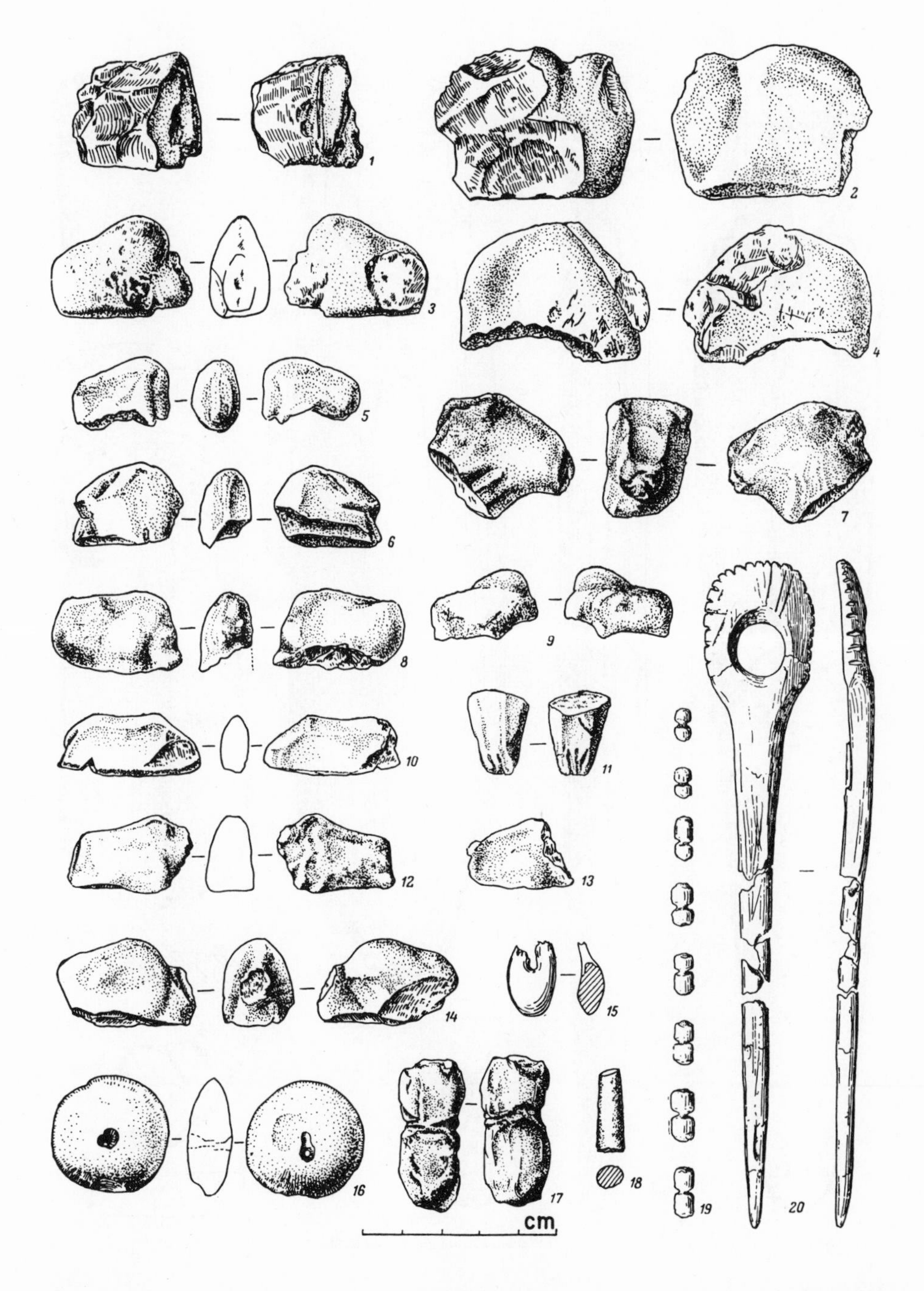

Figure 65. Various Art Objects from Kostenki IV-Horizon 1 (from Abramova 1962: Plate XX).

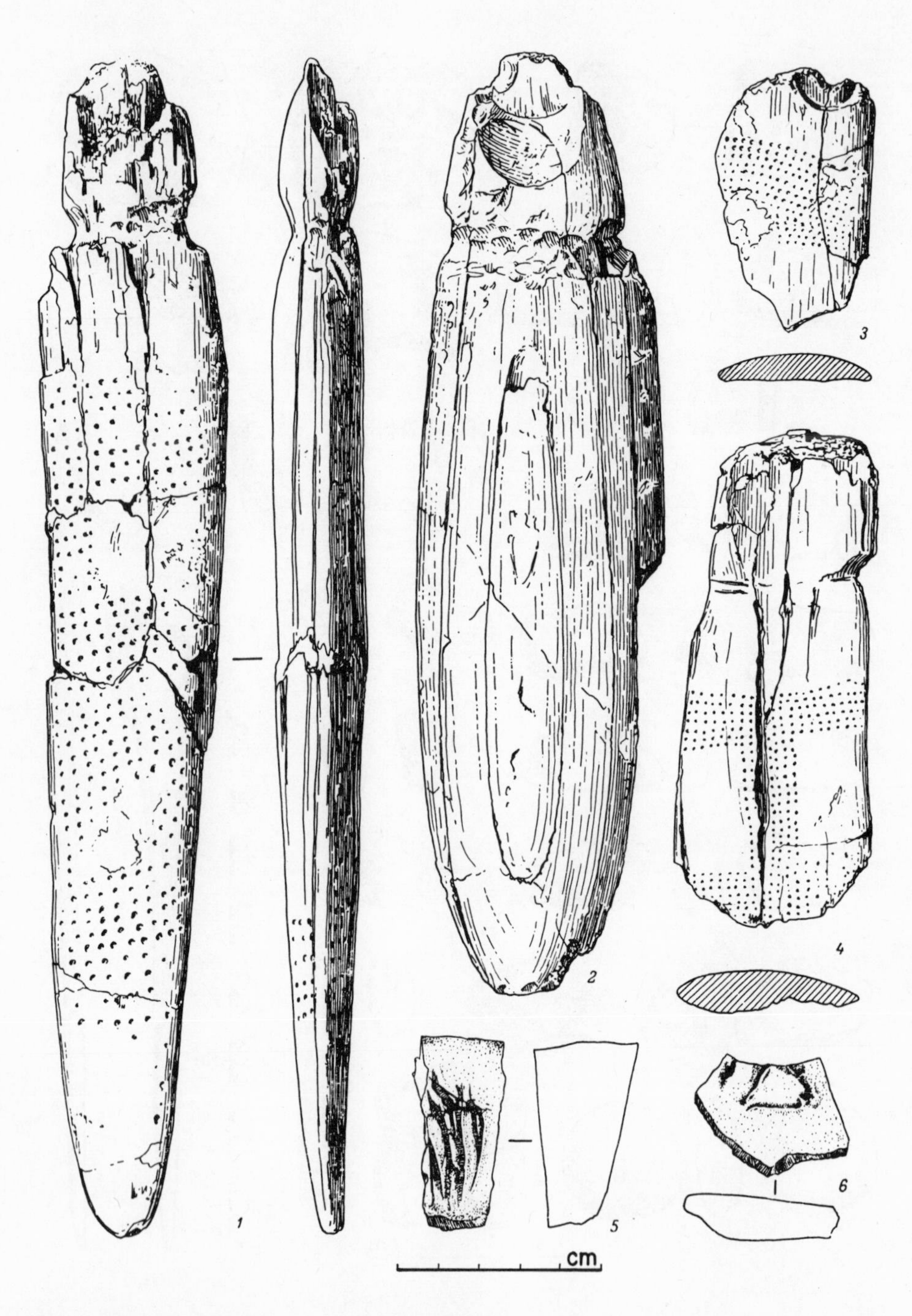

Figure 66. Anthropomorphic Figures and Fragments Thereof from Kostenki IV-Horizon 1 (from Abramova 1962:Plate XIX).

The pendants consist of small discs, each with a hole chiseled through the center.

In over-all appearance, and particularly in the burin/points and ground slate artifacts, the Kostenki IV-1 collection is unique among Kostenki-Borshevo assemblages.

Kostenki XIX and Kostenki III

The excavations of Kostenki XIX exposed 217 sq. m. in a single, continuous excavation and 12 sq. m. in six separate test pits. The pits showed that the cultural horizon did not extend far to the north or south of the large excavation. Within this excavation cultural remains were found almost everywhere except on 10 sq. m. which had been recently disturbed by local farmers. The thickness of the cultural horizon averaged 15–20 cm., but increased perceptibly in the direction of the flow of the Don nearby (that is, from north-northwest to south-southeast). However, this may not be taken as evidence that the remains were not for the most part in situ. In particular, all the flints were completely fresh and unrolled.

Significant concentrations of materials were encountered on four sections within the large excavation. These sections have been labeled Complexes I, II, III, and IV (Fig. 67). Complex I was located in the northcentral part of the excavation. It consisted mainly of a flat, unevenly bounded accumulation of ashy matter, averaging 1–2 cm. in thickness and covering an area of about 4 sq. m. Some small fragments of burnt bones, a few small lumps of red pigment (ochre), a fragment of belemnite (= a fossil invertebrate), and twenty-nine flint artifacts were discovered within the accumulation. An interesting pit with roughly rounded outlines was found beneath its center. The pit was 60–70 cm. across, about 25 cm. deep, and had nearly vertical sides (Fig. 68). It was filled with ash, charcoal, burnt bone, large grains of red pigment, a few flints, and a number of pieces of burnt and unburnt loam. Bone ash was concentrated in a thin black layer near its bottom. Both the bottom and the walls were fired red, while the bottom was composed of a series of alternate ridges and troughs. The inevitable conclusion seems to be that the pit was a hearth. A small, narrow, crooked canal or "tail" passed out from the northwestern edge. The canal was filled with the same materials as the basic pit. Its walls were sheer, but, unlike those of the pit, were not fired red.

An experiment was conducted in order to determine what, if any, function the tail might have had. Two hearth pits were dug near the excavations in the same loam containing the cultural level. Each pit had a series of ridges and troughs on its bottom, but only one had a tail. When a fire

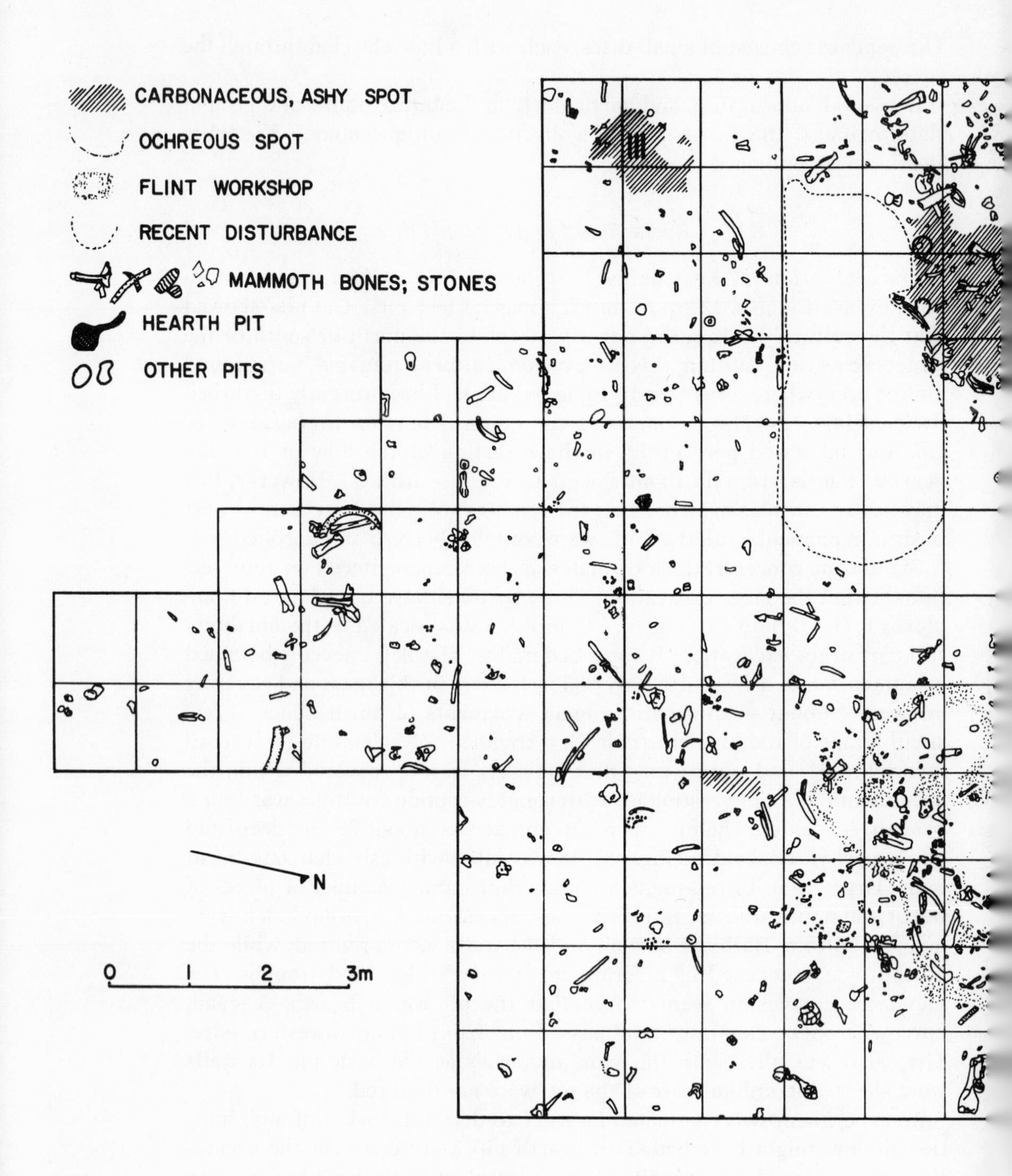
CARBONACEOUS, ASHY SPOT
OCHREOUS SPOT
FLINT WORKSHOP
RECENT DISTURBANCE
MAMMOTH BONES; STONES
HEARTH PIT
OTHER PITS
N
0
1
2
3m

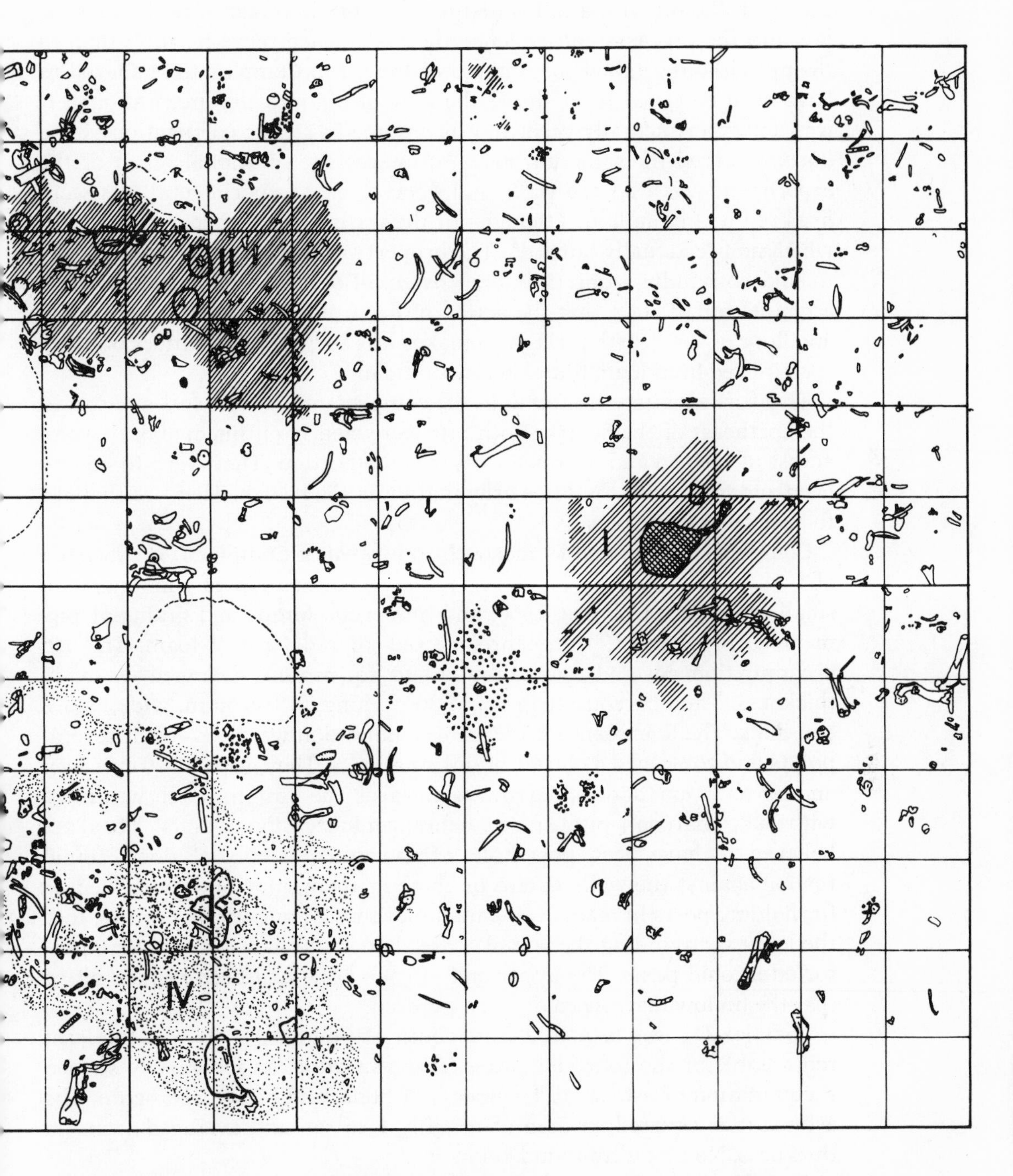

Figure 67. Plan of Kostenki XIX (redrawn after Boriskovskij 1963:Figure 103).

was lit in the pit with a tail, a distinct flow of air was observed along the tail into the pit. As a consequence the fire burned more brightly than in the pit without a tail. Thus, the tail of the pit in Complex I is believed to have been designed to facilitate the flow of air into the fire. Although it was not experimentally verified, it is assumed that the corrugation of the bottom served the same purpose. An interesting additional result of the experiment was that the walls and floor of both experimental pits were fired red within an hour (though not the walls of the experimental tail in which no fire actually burned). The property of the loam at Kostenki XIX to bake so rapidly is unique in the Kostenki-Borshevo region and certainly accounts for the fact that the action of fire was so apparent on the walls and floor of the hearth pit. It also makes less surprising a number of other spots of red-fired loam found below Complex I.

Two further pits were found in the complex, one to the west and one to the northeast of the hearth. Both pits were clearly outlined, about 20 cm. across at the top and narrower towards the bottom. They were 10–15 cm. deep and filled with the same ashy matter as the hearth. They are thought to have been post holes.

Complex II was located 4 m. south-southwest of Complex I. It consisted of two principal parts: (1) an irregular accumulation of ash, charcoal, small fragments of burnt bone, and numerous lumps and grains of pigment (ochre), and (2) an ochreous, red-colored strip of loam. The ash accumulation covered approximately 10 sq. m. and averaged 4 cm. in thickness. The ochreous strip was 1.30 m. long, 0.40–0.50 m. wide, and 2 cm. thick. The loam beneath the ash accumulation was fired red at several points and contained a cluster of five small pits. They were 10–20 cm. deep and up to 30 cm. across, narrowing towards the bottom. Each was filled with ash, charcoal, bits of red ochre, and occasional flints. They are believed to have been post holes. Unburnt fragments of bone, found resting against the walls in two or three of them, may have been wedges for holding posts in place. Some mammoth long bones driven or dug into the loam surrounding the complex are thought to have provided support for additional posts. The upper end of each bone had been broken off so that the hollow marrow cavity was exposed.

Complex III was located 2–3 m. south of Complex II. It was the least remarkable of the four complexes. It consisted of an irregularly shaped accumulation of ash, small fragments of bone, and bits of red ochre. The ashy matter covered an area of roughly 1 sq. m. and averaged 1 cm. in thickness. No pits were found below it.

Complex IV occurred 4 m. to the east of Complex II and covered an area of about 16 sq. m. In distinction from the other complexes, it

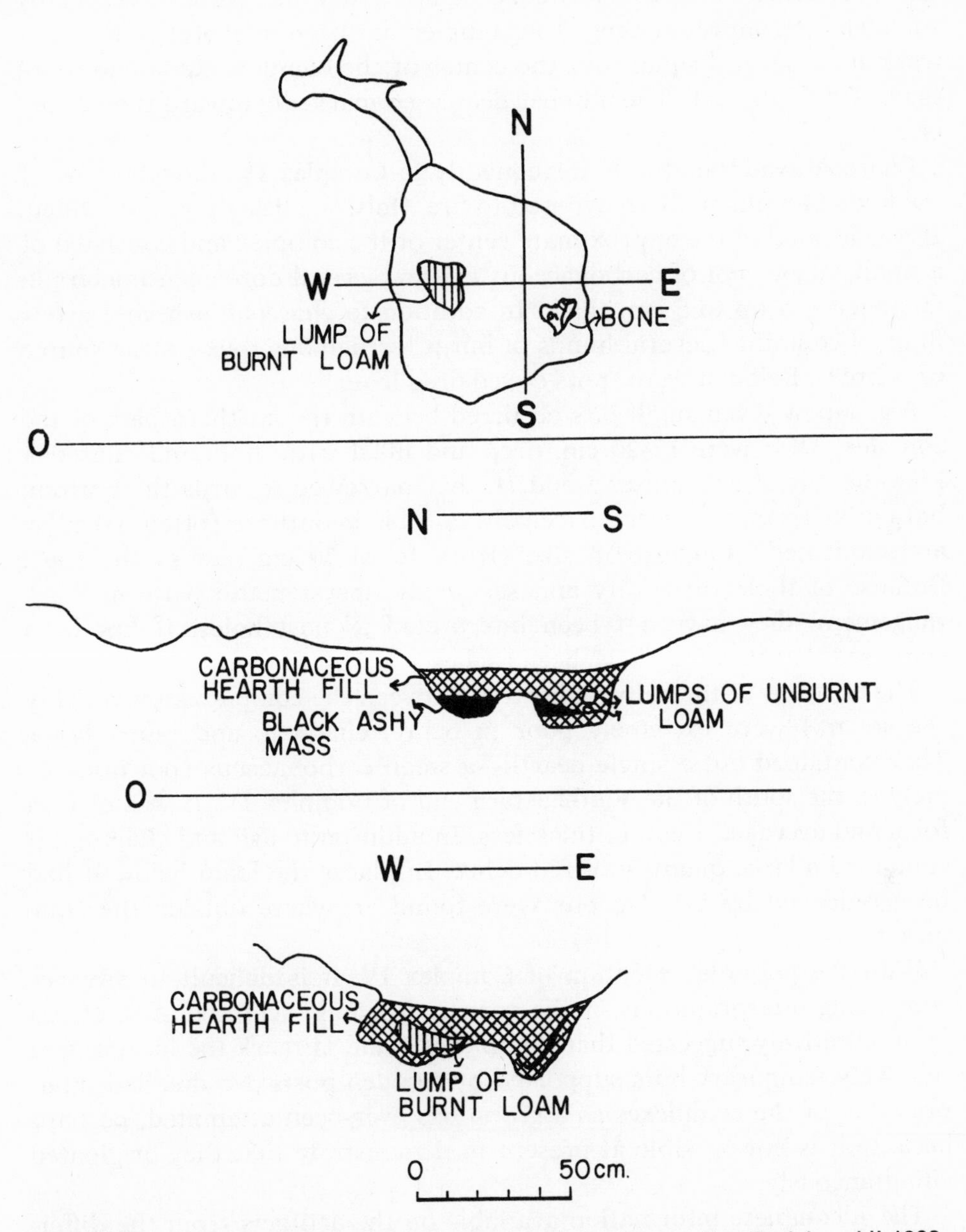

Figure 68. Hearth Pit of Kostenki XIX, Complex I (redrawn after Boriskovskij 1963: Figure 105).

consisted chiefly of a massive concentration of flint artifacts, especially small chips from retouching. The complex has been interpreted as a flint workshop. Several squares at the center of the complex contained more than 1,000 flints each. The number decreased markedly toward the peripheries.

Charcoal was found only infrequently in Complex IV, though some of the flints had plainly been exposed to fire. Only one hearth was identified. It was located in the approximate center of the complex and consisted of a small, vague spot of carbonaceous matter, several dozen centimeters in diameter and up to 5 cm. thick. In addition to charcoal, ash, and a few flints, it contained several lumps of burnt ferruginous rock (= the source of ochre?). Below it were spots of red-fired loam.

A group of seven small pits occurred beneath the northern part of the complex. They were 15–20 cm. deep and filled with flints and charcoal. Like the pits of Complexes I and II, they narrowed towards the bottom, but unlike them, they were extremely variable in outlines (often irregular and elongated) and also in size (from 10 to 50 cm. across the top). Because of their variability and seemingly unsystematic pattern of arrangement, they have not been interpreted as post holes. It has been supposed that they may have been caches.

The portions of the cultural horizon between the complexes (= roughly 186 sq. m.) were extremely poor in ochre, charcoal, and burnt bone. They contained but a single hearth—a small carbonaceous spot immediately to the south of the southeastern end of Complex IV. It was oval in form and averaged 1 cm. in thickness. In addition to ash and charcoal, it contained a large quantity of red ochre. In places the loam below it had been reddened by fire. No pits were found anywhere outside the complexes.

With the possible exception of Complex IV, it is difficult to advance convincing interpretations of the various Kostenki XIX features. It has been tentatively suggested that Complexes I and II mark the locations of relatively temporary huts supported by wooden posts. No detailed interpretation of the complexes as a group has ever been attempted, perhaps because it is not possible at present to demonstrate that they originated simultaneously.

The incomplete information available on the artifacts from the different complexes is presented in Table 32; Table 33 provides a breakdown of the assemblage from the site as a whole. The "nucleiform/macrolithic" tools (Fig. 69) are considered its distinctive feature. These tools include crude-looking artifacts, reminiscent in some cases of massive burins, in others of cores. They frequently bear traces of use in the form of stria-

TABLE 32. Stone Artifact Assemblages from the Various Complexes of Kostenki XIX (Compiled from Information in Boriskovskij 1963:125–165)

	Complexes				*Area between complexes*
	I	*II*	*III*	*IV*	
Flint not available locally	5	650	4	160	30
Locally available flint	24	350	5	ca. 16,850	970
End-scrapers	—	—	—	4	2
Splintered pieces	—	—	—	4	—
Burins	3	16	2	33	24
Nucleiform/macrolithic tools	—	2	2	6	4
Cores	5	10	1	25	10
Burin spalls	—	50	—	380	20

tions and wear polish. Such polish was also found on some of the end-scrapers, where it was confined to the dorsal surface. This kind of polish has been taken to indicate that the objects were used largely for scraping (rather than cutting, in which case wear would have been bifacial).

Only one site in the Kostenki-Borshevo region has yielded an artifact assemblage similar to that of Kostenki XIX: Kostenki III, located only 200 m. away in analogous circumstances. The artifact inventory of this site is summarized in Table 34. A comparison of this table with Table 33 shows that the assemblages of Kostenki III and XIX resemble each other not only in the abundance of burins (mostly dihedral and multifaceted) and in the presence of "nucleiform/macrolithic" tools, but also in the rarity of end-scrapers and the absence or near absence of such popular Upper Paleolithic artifact types as backed blades and points.

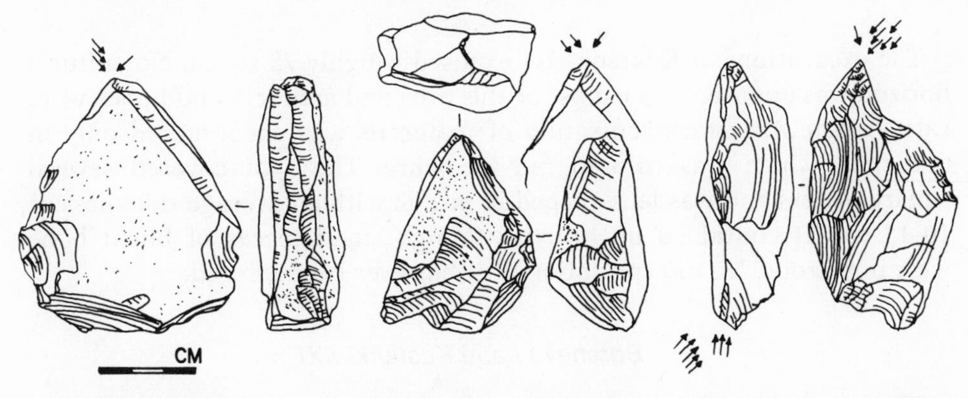

Figure 69. "Nucleiform/Macrolithic Tools" from Kostenki XIX (redrawn after Boriskovskij 1963:Figures 97 and 101).

TABLE 33. Typological Composition of the Artifact Assemblage from Kostenki XIX (Compiled from Information in Boriskovskij 1963:131ff.)

STONE ARTIFACTS	*Raw material: flint not available locally.*	*Raw material: locally available flint.*	*Total*
End-scrapers	2	4	6
Splintered pieces	4	—	4
Backed blades	2	—	2
Burins	26	52	78
On retouched truncations	—	(1)	(1)
On the corners of broken blades	(present)	(present)	(77)
Dihedral	(numerous)	(numerous)	
Nucleiform and macrolithic tools	—	ca. 15	ca. 15
Blades and flakes with continuous retouch on one or two edges			ca. 20
TOTAL retouched pieces	ca. 40	ca. 80	ca. 120
Nonretouched flakes, fragments, and lumps	ca. 614 (with chips)	ca. 17,025 (with chips)	ca. 3,430
Chips from retouching			ca. 14,250
Nonretouched blades	ca. 100	ca. 600	ca. 700
Burin spalls	ca. 90	ca. 360	ca. 450
Cores	ca. 6	ca. 45	ca. 51
TOTAL artifactual flint	ca. 850	ca. 18,250	ca. 19.000
Quartzite tools			2
TOTAL artifactual quartzite			60
BONE AND SHELL ARTIFACTS			
Awls			2
Sharpened fragments of ivory			1
Polished bone sphere			1
Fragmentary ivory point			1
Miscellaneous incised and/or polished fragments of bone			20
Perforated shells			3

The excavations at Kostenki III exposed roughly 75 sq. m. No cultural horizon was apparent over most of this area and artifacts and bones were rare. A noteworthy concentration of materials was encountered only in one spot, which was colored red by ochre. The spot covered several square meters and was lens-shaped in profile with an average thickness of 10–15 cm. It contained no hearths, though small pieces of burnt bone were numerous. No interpretation of it has ever been offered.

Borshevo I and Kostenki XXI

The principal excavations at Borshevo I were carried out in the early 1920's before thought had been given to the possibility of finding structural remnants in Pleistocene-age occupation sites. The excavations consisted of a series of pits and trenches exposing a total of about 158 sq. m. at two distinct locations, labeled Point A (= downslope) and Point B (= upslope) (Fig. 70). At both points the cultural horizon consisted of a band of loam several centimeters thick and containing variable quantities of flint artifacts, animal bones (mostly fragmentary, sometimes burnt),

TABLE 34. Typological Composition of the Artifact Assemblage from Kostenki III (Compiled from Information in Boriskovskij 1963:159–164)

	Raw material: flint not available locally	*Raw material: locally available flint*	*Total*
STONE ARTIFACTS			
End-scrapers	8	2	10
Splintered pieces	20	6	26
Burins	ca. 100	ca. 40	ca. 140
On retouched truncations			(4)
On the corners of broken blades			(2–3)
Dihedral			(ca. 133)
Nucleiform and macrolithic tools			ca. 10
TOTAL retouched pieces			ca. 186
Nonretouched flakes, fragments, lumps, and chips			ca. 1,500
Nonretouched blades			ca. 340
Burin spalls			ca. 150
Cores (mostly blade)	11	11	22
TOTAL artifactual flint	ca. 1,500	ca. 700	ca. 2,200
Artifactual quartzite (none retouched)			ca. 30
BONE ARTIFACTS			
Awls			2
Points			2
Miscellanea			1

red ochre, and charcoal. Detailed information is lacking, but it is clear that some features were encountered. For example, a concentration of ash and charcoal in one of the pits at Point A may well represent the remains of a hearth. The area immediately surrounding the concentration was particularly rich in artifacts and fragmentary bones and may mark the spot where a structure once stood. Some accumulations of mammoth bones found in excavations near this spot are thought to represent fuel reserves. Similar accumulations were also found at Point B. Unfortunately, the deposits at Point B had been disturbed not long before the excavations, and the only additional features found were the possible remains of two hearths.

The artifact inventory of Borshevo I is presented in Table 35. It is clear from the table that burins constitute the most prominent artifact type. On the great majority of burins, the spalls were removed from the upper-

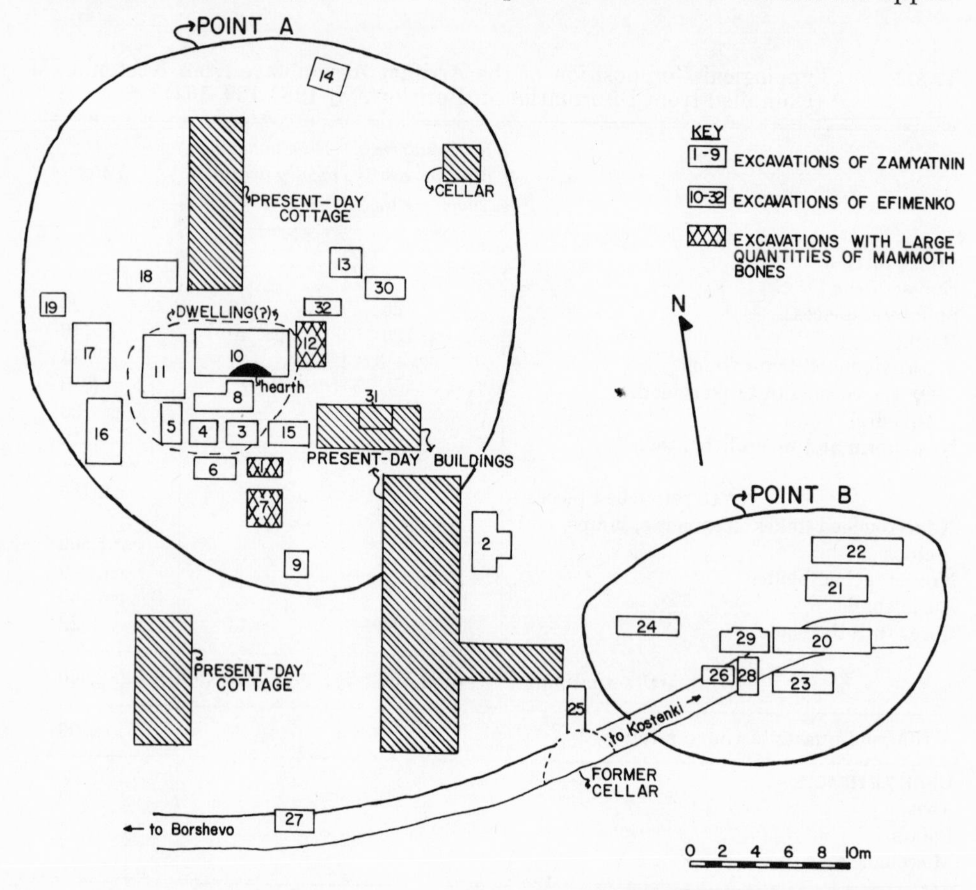

Figure 70. Plan of Borshevo I (redrawn after Vekilova 1953:Figure 10).

left-hand or lower-right-hand corner of the blank (viewed from the dorsal surface), which has led to the supposition that the users of the burins preferred one hand to the other in working with them. Among the rare, nonstone artifacts, the mother-of-pearl "beads" are particularly noteworthy since they are the only mother-of-pearl artifacts known from any Kostenki-Borshevo site.

Only one other artifact assemblage from a site in the Kostenki-Bor-

TABLE 35. Typological Composition of the Artifact Assemblages from Borshevo I and Kostenki XXI

Artifacts	*Borshevo I (compiled from information in Vekilova 1953:122–132)*	*Kostenki XXI (compiled from information in Praslov 1964)*
	Raw material: flint not locally available	Raw material: flint not locally available
STONE		
Burins	ca. 140	ca. 30
On retouched truncations	(75)	(few)
On the corners of broken blades	(23)	(few)
Dihedral	(23)	(many)
Nucleiform	(16)	?
Mixed multiple burins	(6)	?
Other	(ca. 18)	?
End-scrapers	ca. 40	ca. 26
End-scrapers on retouched blades	(25)	(many)
End-scraper/burins	8	some
Backed blades and fragments thereof	60	> 150
Whole	(19)	
Fragmentary	(41)	
Shouldered points } (= mostly partially backed blades?—RGK)	9	several (shouldered and stemmed points)
Stemmed points }	3	
Splintered pieces	2	?
Flakes and blades at least partially retouched along an edge	60–70	several
Miscellanea[a]	7	?
TOTAL retouched pieces	ca. 350	ca. 350
Unretouched flakes, lumps, and chips	ca. 4,000	several 1,000 (flakes, lumps, chips, and blades)
Unretouched blades	ca. 500	
Cores (all blade)	ca. 24	35
Burin spalls	ca. 200	several
TOTAL artifactual flint	ca. 5,070	ca. 5,500
BONE AND SHELL		
Fragmentary bone rod	1	
Horse incisor with hole bored through	1	
Flat, circular, mother-of-pearl "beads"	3	

[a] These include a variety of pieces, each with a point generally, but not always formed by retouch.

shevo region may resemble that of Borshevo I (Table 35). This is the partially described assemblage from the single cultural horizon of Kostenki XXI, also occurring in deposits covering the First Terrace. No features have been reported from Kostenki XXI.

Borshevo II-Horizons 1, 2, and 3

In several years of work at Borshevo II, 800 sq. m. were exposed, principally in two excavations located immediately on the banks of the Don (Fig. 71). Each of the three cultural horizons encountered had a different distribution (Fig. 71, top). The lowermost horizon (3) will be considered first.

Horizon 3 occurred over the entire area of the excavations. Its shoreward portion had been strongly eroded before the excavations were begun, so that an estimate of its total original extent is impossible. It can be said, however, that it stretched at least 115 m. along the Don, and 10–13 m. back from the bank.

The appearance of the horizon in profile was peculiar. Especially in the upstream excavation, where it was richest, it consisted of a discontinuous linear series of dark, wavy lenses in which cultural debris (animal bones, stone tools, and lumps of ochre) tended to concentrate. This positioning has been interpreted as indicating that the debris were not entirely in situ. However, movement from original positions cannot have been great, since the flint artifacts were generally fresh and there was no apparent size sorting of materials.

Over most of its area, the horizon was relatively poor. Notable accumulations of materials were observed at only three points (Fig. 71). The contents of the accumulations and of the area outside them are summarized in Table 36. It has been suggested that the first accumulation represents the base of an ancient structure, the second the remnants of a flint workshop, and the third a place where bone was worked.

The artifact inventory of horizon 3 is presented in Table 37. The two "mattocks" (Fig. 72) consist of sections of antler, 15.5 cm. long by 3–3.5 cm. in diameter, and 16.5 cm. long by 2.5–3 cm. in diameter respectively. One end of each is intentionally beveled to produce a chisel-like edge. The opposite end is left unworked. The surfaces of both pieces are poorly preserved, but in some places on both an incised pattern of contiguous rhombuses can be seen.

Horizon 2 occurred only in the upstream excavation. As in the case of horizon 3, its exact original extent must remain unknown since its shoreward part had been severely eroded by the Don before excavation was begun. However, supplementary test excavations demonstrated that the horizon extended roughly 24 m. along the river and at least 15–20 m. back from its banks.

Numerous discontinuities in the horizontal distribution of the horizon, its vagueness in profile, and traces of rolling on some of the flint artifacts

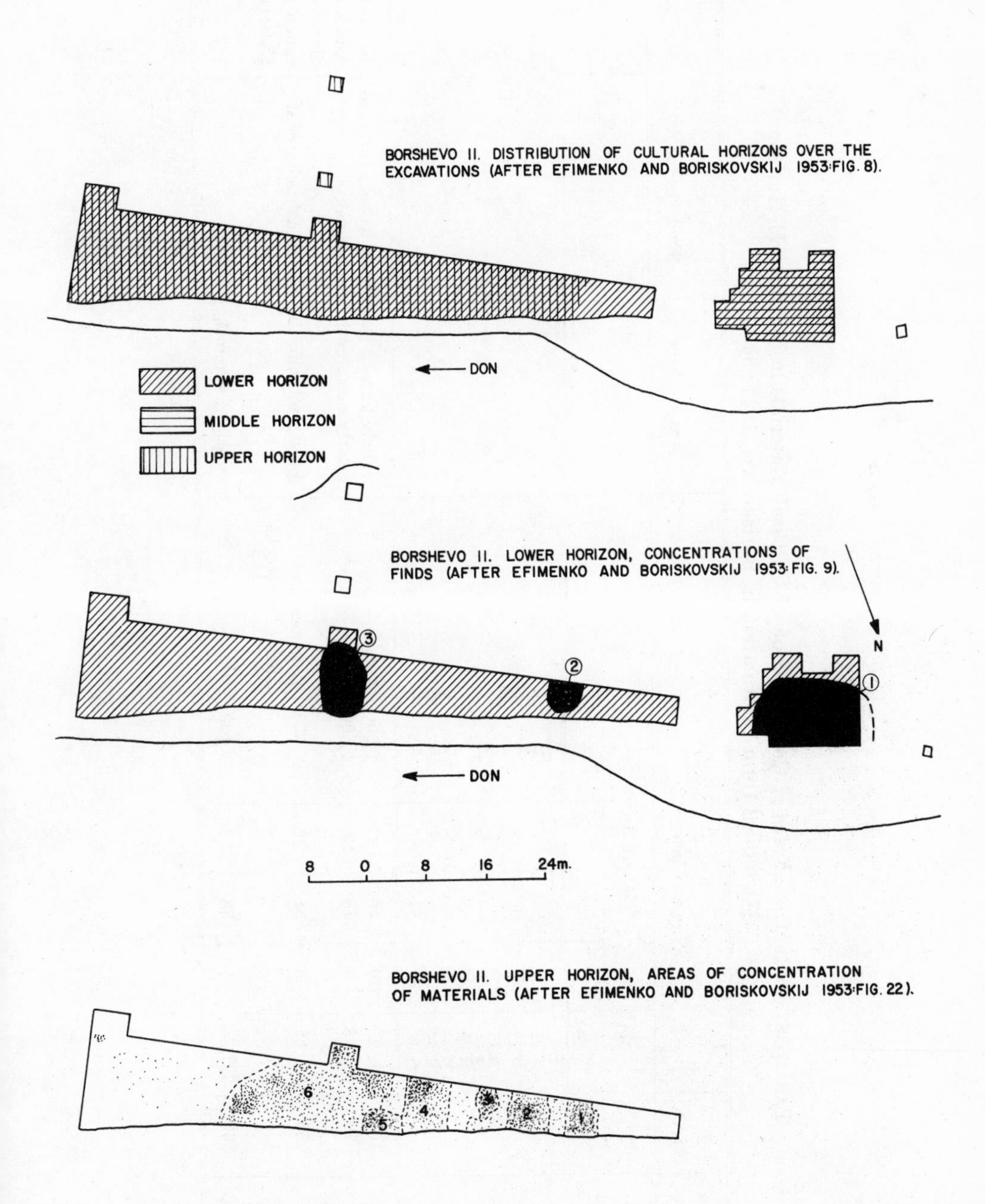

Figure 71. Horizontal Distributions of Cultural Remains in Borshevo II-Horizons 1, 2, and 3 (redrawn after Efimenko and Boriskovskij 1953:Figures 8, 9, and 22).

TABLE 36. Contents of Areas of Concentration of Cultural Materials in Borshevo II-Horizon 3 (Compiled from Information in Boriskovskij 1941: 54–57)

Area of concentration	*Sq. m.*	*Flint artifacts*					*Bone artifacts*	*Animal bone*	*Evidence for fire*	*Other*
		Percentage of flint not available locally	*Quantity*							
			End-scrapers	*Burins*	*Burin spalls*	TOTAL *flint artifacts*				
1	160	ca. 25	40	46	25	1,200	7 awls	mostly hare	ashy lenses; charcoal	ochre (pigment)
2	16	ca. 13	3	48	30	> 1,500	———	mostly mammoth	much ash	much pigment; slate retoucher
3	50	ca. 13	6	54	27	500	2 decorated antler "mattocks"	mostly mammoth	much ash; charcoal	much pigment; slate retoucher
Area outside 1, 2, and 3	500	???	5	58	13	400	———	mostly mammoth	???	???

have led to the conclusion that the materials were not entirely in situ. On the other hand, the freshness of most of the flints, and the absence of perceptible sorting by size would seem to indicate that displacement was not considerable.

Although differences were observed among squares, both in the total frequency of cultural remains and in the frequencies of different classes

Figure 72. Antler "Mattocks" from Borshevo II-Horizon 3 (redrawn after Abramova 1962:Plate XXIV).

of remains (stone artifacts, animal bones, lumps of ochre), no particularly remarkable concentrations of materials were encountered. Traces of fire were largely limited to scattered pieces of burnt bone and charcoal, although some vague carbonaceous spots were also found. It has been concluded that the horizon is the remnant of an ephemeral settlement in which no solid structures were built.

The artifact inventory of horizon 2 is presented in Table 37. Close examination showed that wear on the retouched ends of the end-scrapers was entirely restricted to the dorsal surfaces, which has led to the suggestion that these tools were used only in scraping (versus cutting, which usually leaves traces of use on both surfaces). The assemblage is said to resemble closely the one from horizon 3.

TABLE 37. Typological Composition of the Artifacts from Borshevo II-Horizons 1, 2, and 3
(Compiled from Information in Efimenko and Boriskovskij 1953:64–74, 79–92, and Boriskovskij 1941:41–54)

Artifacts	Horizons: *3*	Horizons: *2*	Horizons: *1*
	Raw material: ca. 80% flint not available locally; ca. 19% locally available flint; and ca. 1% locally available quartzite.	Raw material: ca. 80% flint not available locally; much locally available quartzite.	Raw material: ca. 98% flint not available locally; ca. 2% locally available flint and quartzite.
STONE			
End-scrapers	ca. 54	ca. 40	ca. 130
Circular and double		(some)	(25)
On fragments of blades	(most)	(most)	(95)
On whole blades		(some)	(10)
End-scraper/burins	some	some	ca. 10
Burins	ca. 206	ca. 70	ca. 80
On retouched truncations	(135)	(ca. 40)	(30)
On the corners of broken blades	(30)	(ca. 15) [bracketed with Dihedral]	(30)
Dihedral	(25)		(20)
Nucleiform	(10)	(ca. 15)	
Other	(some)		
Backed points	35 [bracketed with Backed blades]	ca. 20 [bracketed with Backed blades]	ca. 15
Backed blades			ca. 15
Truncated blades	15		ca. 7
Blades with continuous retouch along one or both edges		ca. 30	ca. 70
Varia	ca. 15[a]	3[b]	
TOTAL retouched pieces	ca. 325	ca. 160	ca. 320
Unretouched flakes, lumps, and chips	ca. 2,600	several 1,000	ca. 3,600
Unretouched blades and fragments thereof	ca. 680	several 100	ca. 1,030
Burin spalls	95	ca. 30	several doz.
Cores	21	ca. 60	ca. 25
TOTAL artifactual flint	ca. 3,600	several 1,000	ca. 5,000

Tabular pieces of slate with surface indentations (= retouchers?)	some	some	
BONE AND SHELL			
Awls	7		
Unfinished needles	1		
Randomly incised fragments of bone	several		
Modified and/or decorated ivory blades	3	1	
Mattocks	2		
Bone beads			some
Shell pendants	several	several	several

[a] Several objects resembling splintered pieces, some tools resembling side-scrapers, and some nucleiform pieces with retouch.
[b] Crudely worked bifacial pieces, one of flint and two of quartzite.

Horizon 1 was found only in the downstream excavation. As in the lower-lying levels, the original extent of the horizon was impossible to determine since the part immediately adjacent to the river had been seriously eroded before the first excavations were undertaken. However, test pits established that it extended roughly 70 m. along the river and at least 35 m. back from the banks.

The materials of the horizon are thought to have been in situ. Not only were the flints entirely fresh, but also the various kinds of debris were not sorted by size and some groups of animal bones occurred in anatomical order. Six major accumulations of material were found (Fig. 71, bottom). Each was separated from the others by an area relatively poor in finds. Further, each was unique in size, outlines, richness, and composition. For example, the first and second accumulations were differentiated from the remainder by the relative rarity of bone versus flint and ochre (occurring in lumps). The sixth and largest (ca. 180 sq. m. as against 10 sq. m. for the third and smallest) was the only one which included a hearth. The hearth, 1 m. in diameter and 1–2 cm., was a thick ashy mass with reddened loam beneath. In the other accumulations, evidence of fire was restricted to burnt bone. No interpretation of the accumulations has been offered. They are not thought to represent the remains of structures.

The discovery of features and cultural materials was not restricted entirely to the accumulations—in particular, the relatively poor area immediately downstream of the sixth accumulation provided a grouping of four wolf and two horse jaws at one point, and at another, an arrangement of large tabular pieces of soft stone closely associated with a small number of horse bones and two small ashy masses (Fig. 73).

The artifact inventory of horizon 1 is presented in Table 37. As in the case of horizon 2, wear (polish) on the end-scrapers was found most frequently on the dorsal surface of the retouched end and is assumed to indicate that the tools were used primarily for scraping as opposed to cutting. The assemblage is said to be closely similar to those from horizons 2 and 3. All three horizons are believed to be derived from a single cultural tradition.

Streletskaya I and Rudkino

The remaining First Terrace sites were either very poor or remain undescribed. Streletskaya I provided few flints and some mammoth bones from a badly eroded cultural level. Rudkino, the northernmost site in the region, has supplied some animal bones and a few flint blades, all undescribed.

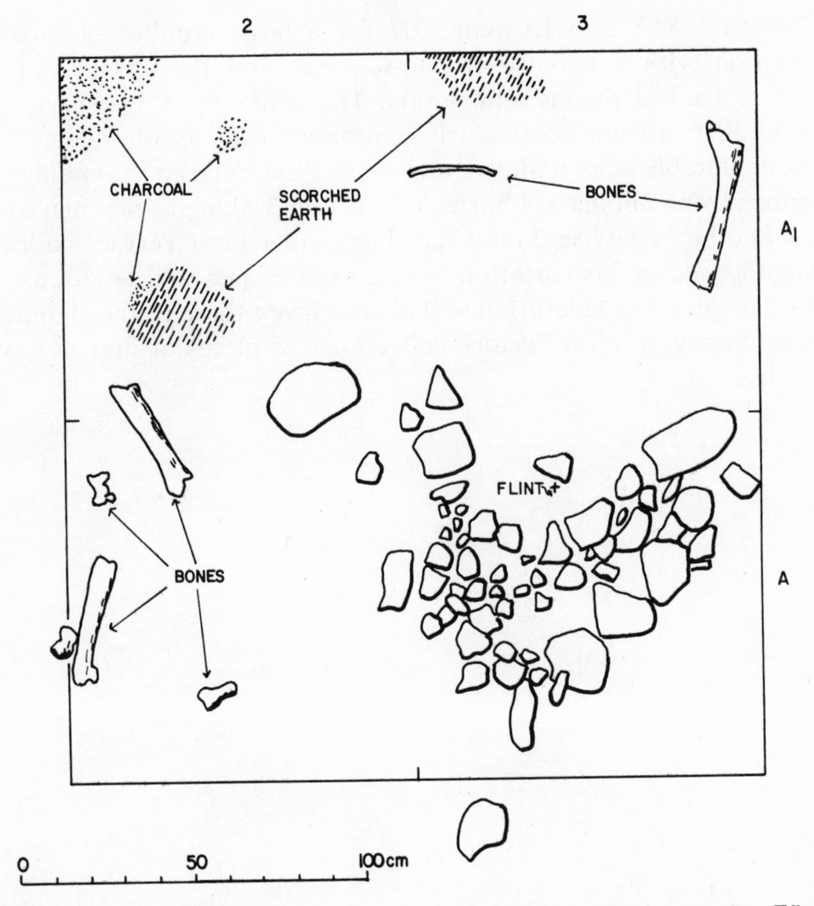

Figure 73. Pattern of Stone Slabs in Borshevo II-Horizon 1 (redrawn after Efimenko and Boriskovskij 1953:Figure 28).

Summary and Conclusion

The information presented in this chapter demonstrates that some of the First Terrace sites contain features no less striking than those found in some Second Terrace sites. The long depressions of Kostenki IV-2 and the round depressions of Kostenki IV-1 are especially remarkable. Though less spectacular, the hearth pit with a tail at Kostenki XIX is as noteworthy in giving us some insight into the technical ingenuity of Late Pleistocene man.

As in the other stratigraphic units, variety is the rule among artifact assemblages from First Terrace sites. For example, Kostenki IV-2 is known for an abundance of backed blades and points; Kostenki IV-1 for burin/points, ground slate artifacts, and a rich bone and marl inventory;

and Kostenki XIX and Kostenki III for a large number of burins in combination with a paucity of end-scrapers and the absence or near absence of backed blades and points. The artifacts of Borshevo I and Kostenki XXI are not particularly distinctive for any one element and exhibit no notable similarities to any other First Terrace assemblage. The collections from Borshevo I-horizons 1, 2, and 3, though they may resemble one another, likewise do not recall any other First Terrace collection. The significance of this variation among assemblages will be discussed in the next chapter. Consideration will also be given there to the significance of the discovery, in First Terrace collections, of pieces of flint not available locally.

chapter 11. Summary and Conclusions

The Meaning of the Diversity among the Kostenki-Borshevo Sites

No aspect of the Kostenki-Borshevo sites is more striking than their diversity. Within each of the four stratigraphic units considered in the previous chapters, sites differed much more frequently than they resembled one another. The differences were both in artifact assemblages and in features. Soviet investigators have generally concluded that the differences imply that many different tribes, each with its own culture, visited the Kostenki-Borshevo region during the time interval represented by each stratigraphic unit. Alternatively, it is possible that the differences arose when people of the same culture occupied different sites in different seasons or in different phases of their activity cycle. From a theoretical point of view, two sites would seem more likely to have been occupied by people of the same culture if the differences in their contents were mostly quantitative, that is, if they contained roughly the same types of artifacts, but in different quantities. On the other hand, two sites would seem more likely to have been occupied by people of different cultures if their contents exhibited major qualitative differences, that is, if one contained several types not present in the other and vice versa. It should be apparent from the data which were presented earlier that most of the differences among the Kostenki-Borshevo sites were qualitative. Thus, it seems probable that the interpretation put forth by Soviet investigators is substantially correct. However, it would be unwise to assert it too strongly at present, partly because generalizations about the implications of quantitative versus qualitative differences are not ironclad.[1]

A further problem in the interpretation of differences among Kostenki-Borshevo sites derives from the fact that the artifact assemblages from them have never been examined according to a single consistent and explicitly stated typology. It is conceivable that some of the apparent qualitative differences would disappear if this kind of examination were made. Finally, for as definitive an evaluation as possible of the significance of differences, it would be important to have complete quantitative information on every assemblage. A rapid perusal of the tables presented in the previous four chapters shows that so far this information is available for only a handful.

In addition to the diversity apparent within each stratigraphic unit, a comparison of them also shows that there are almost no assemblages in one unit which closely resemble assemblages in another. Soviet scholars have generally taken this diversity to indicate that there was virtually no cultural continuity in the Late Würm of the Kostenki-Borshevo region, that is, that bearers of the earlier cultures were not directly ancestral to bearers of any of the later ones. This interpretation is clearly unwarranted, however, since it assumes a clear understanding of both the rate and nature of change through time in artifact assemblages. These matters are very poorly understood at present, and there is no theoretical or empirical reason to suppose that a very long time is necessary for pronounced change to take place. Indeed, the evidence from Kostenki could just as likely imply rapid cultural change as a complete lack of cultural continuity.

Regardless of whether the late Würm of the Kostenki-Borshevo region

[1] Qualitative differences among features, especially among dwelling remnants, might be particularly misleading, because there is good reason to suppose that people of the same culture might have built quite different structures depending on the season, the likely length of stay, and other factors.

witnessed the constant and fairly frequent replacement of one people by another or merely rapid change within the cultures of a very few peoples, the rarity of pairs or groups of similar sites should come as no surprise. The reason is that the number of known sites (ca. 40 well-documented cultural horizons) is very small relative to the time span from which they were derived (15,000 years would be a conservative estimate).

Kostenki-Borshevo and the Replacement of the Mousterian by the Upper Paleolithic

Consideration of the Mousterian/Upper Paleolithic replacement in the light of evidence from the Kostenki-Borshevo region is complicated by the total lack of Mousterian sites in the vicinity. It is not yet clear whether Mousterian peoples never occupied the area or whether their sites are unknown because the earlier Würm deposits which would contain them are rare. In the absence of undoubted Mousterian sites, it is still relevant to point out that three of the earliest Upper Paleolithic sites, Kostenki I-5, Kostenki XII-3, and Streletskaya II, are Mousterian-like in containing a high proportion of flake artifacts. This has led Soviet investigators (in particular A. N. Rogachev) to suggest that these sites may be transitional between the Mousterian and the later Upper Paleolithic. This suggestion presents several problems, however. First is the point made earlier that there are Upper Paleolithic sites in Kostenki which seem to be just as old as the supposed transitional ones, but which completely lack any Mousterian elements (the outstanding example is Kostenki XVII-2). Second is the question of whether the presence of a high proportion of flake tools necessarily implies relationship to the Mousterian. Tel'manskaya-1 is also characterized by a considerable number of flake artifacts, but it immediately overlies a horizon which contains as few of these artifacts as any level at Kostenki. Further, a variety of evidence suggests that Tel'manskaya-1 must date from the terminal part of the Würm, and thus it is quite unlikely to have any direct connection with the Mousterian. Finally, there is the problem that the available geological evidence indicates that even the earliest Upper Paleolithic sites in the Kostenki-Borshevo region are somewhat later than the earliest Upper Paleolithic sites elsewhere. If this fact is true, there would be good reason to suppose that none of the Kostenki-Borshevo sites are transitional. Added support of the idea that the oldest Upper Paleolithic sites at Kostenki are not far removed from the Mousterian is lent by the fact that they are relatively poor in bone artifacts, art objects, and spectacular features. In reply to these conclusions, it may be noted that they are older and thus perhaps less well preserved, and also that they have been less extensively excavated than the later sites. Further, it is conceivable that the environmental circumstances under which the earlier sites were occupied allowed only ephemeral settlements, while in later times, perhaps with a decrease in forestation and a consequent increase in game, more permanent and durable settlements came into being. In any case, spectacular features likely to represent the remains of structures are now known from Mousterian sites, and there is no reason to suppose their gradual development during the Upper Paleolithic.

The Subsistence Base of the Kostenki-Borshevo Peoples

The numerous animal bones found in the cultural levels furnish direct evidence for subsistence. They provide no reason to suppose that subsistence changed markedly throughout the entire time interval (late Würm) from which we have sites, except perhaps at the very end (Borshevo II-1?), when it is likely that many of the large Pleistocene mammals were becoming rare or had even disappeared from the region.

As in most other Upper Paleolithic sites, the animals most abundantly represented in Kostenki-Borshevo cultural levels are large herbivores, in particular mammoth and horse. This is in contrast to the southern part of European Russia, where bison tends to predominate in Upper Paleolithic sites, and also to the far western part of the country, where reindeer and horse are most prominent. Wild cattle of any kind are very rare in the Kostenki sites and reindeer are not especially abundant. Since the prominence of horse and mammoth at Kostenki and of other animals elsewhere crosscuts both time and culture, it probably reflects natural differences in the extents to which the various animals were present in different areas in the late Würm.

In addition to the bones of large herbivores, most Upper Paleolithic sites contain remains of carnivores. At Kostenki, bones of wolves and foxes are by far the most frequent. While it is possible that the meat of these animals was eaten, it seems especially likely they were caught for their pelts. Further, perforated carnivore teeth seem to have been popular decorative items. Remains of hare are also known from most of the Kostenki-Borshevo sites, and again it seems probable that the animals were especially valued for their skins (at Kostenki IV-2, where hare bones were extraordinarily numerous, they were often found in pits wherein tanning possibly took place). Finally, rodent bones have been reported from a number of sites, and while it cannot be ruled out that some of the animals represented may have been eaten, it seems most likely that the majority of them died natural deaths in burrows dug after the sites were occupied. Substantiation for this conclusion may be seen in the frequent occurrence of rodent remains in anatomical order. In some sites, it is apparent that the preexcavation damage done by rodent tunneling was substantial, though very few details have been published on this.

It is a curious fact that remains of creatures other than mammals have only very rarely been recovered in Kostenki-Borshevo sites. Bird bones are known from only a few sites and are nowhere very frequent. Fish bones are even scarcer, only one example having been found (a vertebra of pike from Kostenki II). This paucity is particularly surprising in view of the proximity of the Don. At least on present evidence it seems fair to conclude that the ancient inhabitants did little fishing and fowling. The kinds of excavations which turned up thousands of tiny flint retouch chips would certainly have uncovered small bones if they had been there.

The absence of fish and bird bones may indicate that the various sites were inhabited mainly in winter when most game birds would have been much farther south and fishing in the frozen river would have been impossible. In the warmer months of the year, the people may have moved out onto the herbaceous uplands (interfluves) where great herds of herbivorous mammals probably grazed. No sites are presently known on the uplands, which may reflect the ephemeral nature of summer camps, inhabited only as long as the oft-moving game remained within striking distance. (It may also reflect the relative rarity of natural sections through the covering deposits on the uplands.) Possibly, the meat obtained in summer was dried to help provide subsistence in the leaner winter months, when shelter was taken in the wooded river valleys.

It is important to mention the possibility, perhaps even probability, that wild vegetable foods formed an important part of the diet of the Kostenki-Borshevo peoples (as well as of the Upper Paleolithic peoples elsewhere). With the exception of charcoal from hearths, macroremains of plants have not yet been found in any of the sites, and it is not even known what edible species might have been present. However, it is now recognized that tiny charred seeds may be preserved for extraordinarily long periods, though they are likely to go unnoticed in the most careful excavations unless special isolation procedures are utilized. The adoption of these procedures in the Kostenki-Borshevo region might yield surprising and highly valuable information.

Technology in the Kostenki-Borshevo Upper Paleolithic

The technology of the ancient inhabitants of Kostenki involved a variety of things which rarely or never fossilize—for example, wooden implements and communal hunting techniques. At the same time it included a number of items which we can infer directly from what has been found in the ground. First, there is housing. The ruins of dwellings in Kostenki-Borshevo sites are remarkable not only for their number, but for their variety. They vary in size and shape and particularly in what of them is preserved: in some cases, a large depression, in others a considerable accumulation of nearly intact mammoth bones (constructional material?), and in yet others no more than a roundish or oval area in which cultural materials are heavily concentrated. Although in one or two instances an attempt has been made to reconstruct an entire former structure, evidence for a complete reconstruction is not yet available from any site. However, it is reasonable to suppose that the frameworks of the structures were built of wood and/or bone and that they were covered with hides and/or earth. Most of the structures apparently contained fireplaces and pits for storage and cooking. Evidence for broadly similar dwellings has been found at numerous open-air, Upper Paleolithic sites in various parts of Europe.[2]

One of the most important elements in Upper Paleolithic technology, as evidenced at Kostenki and elsewhere, was fire. Besides providing warmth, light, protection from predators, and important aid in the preparation of food, fire was probably used in the manufacture of artifacts. It is known that the tips of wooden spears may be hardened by calculated exposure to fire, and recently it has been learned that flint may be made more suitable for some kinds of working (especially for pressure flaking) by careful preheating. (Knapping is done after the flint has been allowed to cool again.) Fire may also have been used by the ancient Kostenki people to obtain (from iron ore) the red, ochreous pigment of which they seem to have been so fond.

By far the most abundant evidence for technology in Upper Paleolithic sites, including those at Kostenki and Borshevo, consists of the numerous stone and bone artifacts which have been recovered. The large variety of types and subtypes of artifacts found at most sites may itself be taken as

[2] Clearly, the popular notion that Pleistocene man depended exclusively upon caves for shelter should be abandoned. Even in areas where caves are plentiful, such as southwestern France, recent investigations have disclosed structural remnants at a number of open-air, Upper Paleolithic sites.

an index of technological complexity. Although it is difficult to ascertain beyond doubt the functions of most of the types, it is nonetheless possible to make some general statements which have a high probability of being correct.

First, it is evident that a number of the artifacts must represent weapons. Some of the stone and bone points may well have served to arm throwing or thrusting spears. Although there is no direct evidence for the bow and arrow, many of the small backed and truncated elements found in such sites as Anosovka II-2, Kostenki IV-1, and Borshevo II-1, would have been quite suitable for insertion into wooden shafts to make composite arrows. However, these same pieces could have been placed in wooden or bone handles for a variety of other purposes as well.

A large number of different kinds of tools was probably used in the processing of animal remains. Most of the Kostenki sites contained a sizeable quantity of unretouched flakes and blades which are more than sharp enough to have cut flesh and skin in butchering. Frequently the edges of these blades and flakes are chipped or worn in a way which definitely indicates that they were used. Among retouched pieces which may have been cutting implements are the shouldered points of Kostenki I-1 and the leaf-shaped points of Tel'manskaya-1. Strong wear on many of these points makes it appear unlikely that they were used to arm projectiles, in spite of their form. The scraping of skins and bone may have been accomplished by the numerous side-scrapers, end-scrapers, and/or retouched blades found in most sites. On several occasions, the wear on end-scrapers turned out to be confined to one (the dorsal) surface, suggesting that they were indeed scrapers (as opposed to cutting tools).

In addition to stone artifacts, various bone objects appear likely to have been used in processing animal remains, particularly in preparing skins. One important, recurring class of bone tools has even been labeled "hide burnishers." Bone awls, and perhaps also stone borers, were probably used to punch holes in hides to manufacture the clothing and other leather items which the Kostenki-Borshevo people undoubtedly possessed. The borers may also have been used to drill holes in bone objects and in teeth and shells for pendants and beads.

The same kinds of tools which were used to process animal remains may have served to work wood and bone. Thus it is easy to imagine some of the unretouched blades and flakes as hafted whittling knives, while side-scrapers and end-scrapers may have been used to finish wooden and bone objects. One class of tools which has especially often been linked to bone working is the class of burins; and in view of the success of some modern investigators in using these tools to make bone artifacts, the linkage is likely a meaningful one. At the same time, it is possible that burins sometimes had other functions. For example, burination on some composite tools (as on the burin/points of Kostenki IV-2) may have been no more than a device to facilitate hafting.

The use of bone by the ancient inhabitants of Kostenki deserves independent discussion as one of the main indices of their technological ingenuity. Like Upper Paleolithic peoples elsewhere, the late Würm occupants of Kostenki manufactured an extraordinary variety of bone artifacts, including (in addition to those already mentioned) possible mattocks or hoes (for digging pits?), "clothes fasteners," "hairpins," and a large number of objects whose functions remain enigmatic. They also apparently employed bone in the construction of dwellings. And their use of it as fuel seems established by the abundance of charred bone fragments in sites like Kostenki I-1, in which charred wood was completely absent. At some sites, special stores of bone have been found which may have been fuel reserves. One use to which bone may *not* have been put by the ancient Kostenki-Borshevo people is the manufacture of fishing gear. Bone harpoons, well known in Upper Paleolithic sites elsewhere, are totally unknown at Kostenki. This fact accords well with the absence of fish bones in Kostenki sites.

Group Size and Duration of Settlement in the Kostenki-Borshevo Upper Paleolithic

Even more important than the architectural details of the ancient Kostenki buildings is the question of how long they were inhabited and how many people occupied them. Both these questions may be answered at present only in a very general way. The very occurrence of structural remains and the large quantity of cultural debris coming from many of the sites suggest strongly that they were inhabited for more than just a few days; but it is impossible to say whether we should think in terms of several weeks, several months, or even several years, perhaps with seasonal interruptions. A similar problem confronts us in trying to estimate the sizes of the groups which occupied the sites. If the interpretation of the features in Kostenki I-1 and Kostenki IV-2 as "long houses" is correct, then we might guess that it would have taken several families to build and inhabit them. At other sites we might postulate a social group composed of several families on the basis of the great number of large animals represented. Presumably the hunting of such animals required the cooperation of several adult males. But it is impossible to say whether several families should be interpreted as 50, 100, or 150 individuals. Possibly the size of the cohabiting group varied significantly from culture to culture and within a single culture from season to season.

Much of what has just been said bears directly on the important question of the hunting effectiveness of Upper Paleolithic peoples. It has often been said that the abundance of game and a relatively advanced technology placed these peoples among the most prosperous hunters the world has ever known. Indeed, their sites are far more numerous than those of any of their predecessors, and this appears likely to reflect more than just younger age and superior preservation. Although some sites contain the remains of what would seem to be an extraordinarily large number of individual animals (for example, more than 30 mammoths at Kostenki II), this fact alone cannot be taken as an index of hunting efficiency because of the glaring lack of concrete information on how long the sites were occupied and how many people occupied them. Only when these crucial questions are answered will we be able to assess satisfactorily the hunting prowess of Upper Paleolithic peoples.

In the absence of concrete data, it is nonetheless interesting to speculate briefly on the length of time some of the Kostenki-Borshevo sites may have been inhabited. This may be done following a procedure suggested by Grahame Clark in his classic report on the early post-Pleistocene (Maglemosian) site of Star Carr (Yorkshire). The first step in this procedure is to calculate roughly the total amount of calories available in the meat of animals represented in a site. This figure is then divided by the number of calories needed daily by a human group of arbitrary size and composition. The result is the length of time the animal flesh could have supported the human group—an estimate of the maximum amount of time they could have spent at the site. The present writer undertook calculations for the sites of Tel'manskaya-1, Kostenki IV-2 (southern "long house"), Kostenki II, and Borshevo II-1—the only Kostenki-Borshevo sites for which figures are available on the minimum number of animals represented by remains. The results of the calculations are presented in Table 38.

In examining the table, it is necessary to keep in mind a series of very important qualifications. Several of these concern the calculation of the number of animal calories represented at each site. First, although accounts of historically observed primitives allow us to suppose the Kostenki-Borshevo peoples may have had techniques for preserving meat (smoking and drying), it is still likely that portions of many animals spoiled before they could be eaten. Neglect of this fact would obviously tend to bias upwards the estimates of available calories. Second, it is pos-

TABLE 38. Estimates of Maximum Duration of Occupation of Various Kostenki Sites by a Group of 50 People Requiring 114,000 Calories/Day*

	Average body weight (kg.)	*Edible body weight (kg.)*	*Calories/ 100 g.*	*Total calories per species and per site*			
				Tel'manskaya-1	*Kostenki II*	*Kostenki IV-2*	*Borshevo II-1*
Woolly mammoth	4,540	2,724	200	16,344,000	163,440,000	20,724,000	—
Woolly rhinoceros	3,663	2,179	175	—	3,813,600	3,813,600	—
Wild horse	454	272	115	313,260	—	939,780	2,506,080
Wild cattle (bison?)	1,362	817	204	1,667,088	—	—	1,667,088
Red deer	181	109	124	—	—	108,960	—
Moose	681	407	100	—	—	—	408,600
Reindeer	148	89	100	88,500	X	88,500	354,000
Saiga antelope	25	15	100	—	—	14,982	—
Cave lion	227	136	100	136,200	X	408,600	—
Wolverine	16	10	100	—	—	9,988	—
Bear	227	136	200	—	X	272,400	—
Red fox	5	3	100	—	X	2,724	—
Arctic fox	5	3	100	16,344	X	—	—
Wolf	50	30	100	149,820	X	84,892	59,928
Hare	4	2	107	15,253	X	47,938	4,358
				18,721,465	> 177,253,600	26,521,364	5,000,054
Maximum number of days occupied				164 (5.5 mos.)	> 1,470 (ca. 4 yrs.)	233 (7.8 mos.)	43

* Data on body weights principally from Burton (1962). (Weights of extinct animals were estimated from those of their nearest living relatives.) Data on caloric values of meat from Madariaga (1962) and von Stokar (1958/59). Data on numbers of animals for calculations from Tables 11, 14, 21, and 29. The X's under Kostenki II indicate the presence of various animals in unspecified quantities. Thus it was impossible to compute the caloric values of their meat.

sible that many of the animals whose bones occur in the sites were not eaten at all, but rather were killed for their skins, tendons, bones, and so forth. An argument against the serious bias this possibility may introduce is that observations of modern primitives have shown that they seldom waste any utilizable parts of an animal, regardless of why they killed it. Further, the kinds of animals—particularly carnivores—which it is reasonable to suppose were sought chiefly for materials other than their meat are generally too few and/or too small to affect seriously the calorie estimates for any of the Kostenki-Borshevo sites. The additional objection that not all of every animal is edible is more easily dealt with. In preparing Table 38, the average live weight of each animal was multiplied by .60 to provide an estimate of edible weight. Since primitive hunters are often very resourceful at utilizing the remains of animals, this figure should be regarded as conservative: the ancient Kostenki peoples were probably capable of ingesting more than 60 per cent of most animals. The final qualification to consider is that data are unavailable on the caloric value of the flesh of many animals. Wherever data could not be obtained, the figure of 100 calories/100 grams was used. This figure again is conservative: it is the absolute minimum caloric content of any kind of scientifically tested meat.

The number of calories needed daily by a human group was derived as follows: Because 50 individuals seems to be a common group size in many hunting and gathering societies for which we have historical observations, this figure was chosen for calculation here. The composition of the group was set arbitrarily at 10 adult males, 10 adult females, and 30 children. At present a moderately active adult male requires about 3,000 calories a day, a female 2,400, and a child 2,000. For a group of 50 composed as stated the total daily requirement would then be 114,000 calories. However, it is likely that the Kostenki-Borshevo people were more than moderately active. This possibility plus the fact that they lived under relatively cold climatic conditions could have increased substantially the number of calories they needed. If 114,000 calories/day is a serious underestimate, then the number of days which it is supposed each site could have been occupied would be too great. On the other hand, it is important to realize that a sizeable amount of each group's diet may have come from plants, and, moreover, that there may have been animals eaten whose bones are not present for us to see. These factors would increase the number of calories available and thus perhaps make the estimates of occupation time more reasonable. It is possible to speculate endlessly on whether the various figures employed in the calculations are underestimates or overestimates. The important point to be emphasized is that the results of the calculations are to be regarded as no more than suggestive; in no sense are they conclusive.

In addition to the absolute figures of Table 38, the relative magnitudes may have some significance. Thus the fact that Borshevo II-1 contains far fewer potential calories "on the hoof" than the other sites may mean that it was occupied at or near the end of the Pleistocene, when climatic and vegetational conditions were changing and game was less plentiful. Certainly some explanation is required for why a site so extensively excavated should contain so little animal bone. It is in the context of comparisons that Table 39 becomes relevant. This table contains figures like those in Table 38, but for three Mousterian sites, two caves (Starosel'e and Kiik-Koba) in the Crimea and an open-air site (Il'skaya) in the steppes just to the north of the Caucasus. Comparing Table 39 to Table 38, it is immediately apparent that the Mousterian sites cannot be meaningfully distinguished from the Upper Paleolithic ones by using the caloric data presented. Further, the Starosel'e and Il'skaya data demonstrate that Upper Paleolithic sites cannot be distinguished from Mousterian ones because they sometimes contain a marked preponderance of one kind of animal. In fact, it has not yet proven possible in any part of Europe to differentiate Upper Paleolithic from Mousterian hunting behavior on the basis of differences in the bone contents of occupation sites.

Location of Sites

A glance at Map 2 (p. 28) will show that the Kostenki-Borshevo sites are almost invariably found on promontories formed by the confluence of two ravines or of a ravine and the valley of the Don. Since the ravine slopes are not and probably never were very steep, it seems unlikely that the promontories were chosen for defensive purposes. More reasonable is the suggestion that they offered good drainage. It is also interesting that the Kostenki-Borshevo region taken as a whole, roughly 10–12 km. long and about 3 km. wide, seems to have been a highly desirable location for settlement. Intensive reconnaissance for several dozen kilometers up and down the Don and away from its banks has disclosed deposits of the Late Würm age, but no additional sites. The particular attractions which the region may have offered are not entirely apparent, though the considerable extent of topographic dissection with numerous promontories for settlement might well have been a factor. The high degree of dissection might also have presented excellent opportunities for obtaining game which came down to the river for water.

TABLE 39. Estimates of Maximum Duration of Occupation of Some Mousterian Sites by a Group of 50 People Requiring 114,000 Calories/Day*

	Kiik-Koba-Horizon IV		*Starosel'e*		*Il'skaya (Zamyatnin excavations)*	
	Number of animals	*Total calories*	*Number of animals*	*Total calories*	*Number of animals*	*Total calories*
Woolly mammoth	3	16,344,000	8	43,584,000	3	16,344,000
Woolly rhinoceros	1	3,813,600	4	15,254,000	—	—
Wild horse	6	1,879,560	16	5,012,160	3	939,780
Wild ass	2	501,110	287	71,917,895	2	501,170
Wild cattle (bison?)	1	1,667,088	9	15,003,792	30	257,800
Wild sheep	1	86,487	—	—	—	—
Saiga antelope	5	75,000	14	210,000	—	—
Giant deer	8	1,525,400	2	281,400	1	190,680
Red deer	1	108,960	7	1,951,100	3	326,880
Reindeer	1	80,500	5	402,500	—	—
Wild boar	1	228,720	1	228,720	1	228,720
Wolf	1	29,964	6	180,000	2	59,928
Red fox	2	5,448	5	13,620	—	—
Arctic fox	3	8,172	3	8,172	—	—
Steppe fox	5	13,620	—	—	—	—
Bear	1	272,400	1	272,400	1	272,400
Cave hyena	1	27,240	5	136,200	4	108,960
Hare	—	—	4	8,716	—	—
	43	26,667,309	361	154,479,430	50	19,230,558
Maximum number of days occupied	234 (7.8 mos.)		1,355 (45 mos.)		169 (5.6 mos.)	

* Data on numbers of animals from Klein (1966b). See notes to Table 38.

Ideology in the Kostenki-Borshevo Upper Paleolithic

A glimpse into the ideology of the ancient Kostenki-Borshevo people is provided by their disposal of the dead and by their art. Four deliberate burials are known from the region. In each case, some kind of burial ritual seems implied. In at least one instance (Gorodtsovskaya), the deceased was accompanied by a quantity of grave goods. Perhaps nearly as interesting as the presence of burials in some sites is their absence in others, particularly in some of the more extensively excavated ones (for example, Kostenki I-1, Tel'manskaya-1, and Kostenki IV-1 and 2). The implication may be that at least some of the ancient Kostenki people were in the habit of disposing of the dead away from what seem to have been living sites. Once disposed of, the remains of the dead do not seem to have been brought back, since even isolated human bones are virtually unknown in any of the sites.

The Upper Paleolithic in general and the Kostenki-Borshevo region in particular have proven extraordinarily rich in art objects and ornaments. While there seems little doubt that the artifacts in question are properly labeled in a general sense, their specific significance remains completely indeterminate. One assumption which it does seem fair to make is that the Kostenki-Borshevo peoples, also like modern primitives, did not practice art for art's sake. All the known pieces of art probably had some relatively broad cultural significance—as religious objects, status symbols, and the like. The extraordinarily large amount of red ochre found in many of the Kostenki-Borshevo sites (and elsewhere) has frequently been interpreted as evidence of considerable interest in body painting, or at least in the coloring of art objects. The possibility should not be ruled out, however, that it had some more practical utility, perhaps in the processing of skins.

Flint, and the External Relationships of the Kostenki-Borshevo Sites

Basically two kinds of raw material were used for stone-tool manufacture by the ancient inhabitants of the Kostenki-Borshevo region: brown and yellow flint, which still occurs locally in pebble form along the banks of the Don and in slope deposits, and black flint, which at present does not occur naturally in the vicinity. Sometimes locally available quartzite was also used, but never to the same extent as flint. Experiments have demonstrated that it is easier to make artifacts from black flint than from brown or yellow. The conclusion has therefore been reached that the black flint was deliberately imported. Of course, it can be argued that the absence of natural lodes of black flint in the area today does not preclude their presence in the Late Pleistocene. This argument, however, is challenged by facts regarding the kinds of black-flint artifacts found in the sites. Cores of black flint are disproportionately rare; in any given site the ratio of them to all black-flint pieces is usually considerably smaller than the ratio of colored-flint cores to all colored-flint pieces. On the other hand, retouched objects of black flint are disproportionately frequent; the ratio of them to all black-flint pieces is generally much higher than the corresponding ratio in the colored-flint category. And black flint waste tends to consist mostly of small chips from retouching rather than of larger flakes from the preparation of cores. In sum, it is clear that the primary working of black flint was done much less frequently at the sites than was the primary working of colored flint. The black flint seems to have reached the sites largely in the form of blanks ready to be turned into tools, rather than in the form of nodules or cores. The most likely explanation for this is that it was necessary to bring the black flint from a considerable distance. It was therefore most economic to do the primary working at the source.

Considerable survey work has been done in an effort to locate places in the general environs of Kostenki where black flint may be found today. The closest area occurs 130–150 km. to the south-southwest in the valleys of the Valuj and Oskol Rivers (Map 4). Not only are there natural lodes of high-quality black flint in these valleys, but reconnaissance in them has uncovered a number of workshop sites where Stone Age man preliminarily dressed flint before carrying it away. Most of these workshops occur directly on the surface and therefore it is impossible to date them. But there is no reason to suppose that some of them could not be derived from the activities of the ancient inhabitants of the Kostenki-Borshevo region. At the same time, it must be noted that petrographic analysis has shown that only some of the Kostenki black flint is likely to have come from the Valuj-Oskol valleys. The remainder may well have come from sources as much as 270–300 km. from Kostenki. How flint was moved over such great distances is not clear. It may have been traded from group to group, it may have been obtained by parties sent out for the purpose of securing flint. Or perhaps the flint lodes were found at one of the stops on a yearly migratory cycle. In any case, other Late Pleistocene instances in which flint seems to have been moved several hundred kilometers are known from Romania and Czechoslovakia. Further evidence for the importation of goods over considerable distances into the Kostenki-Bor-

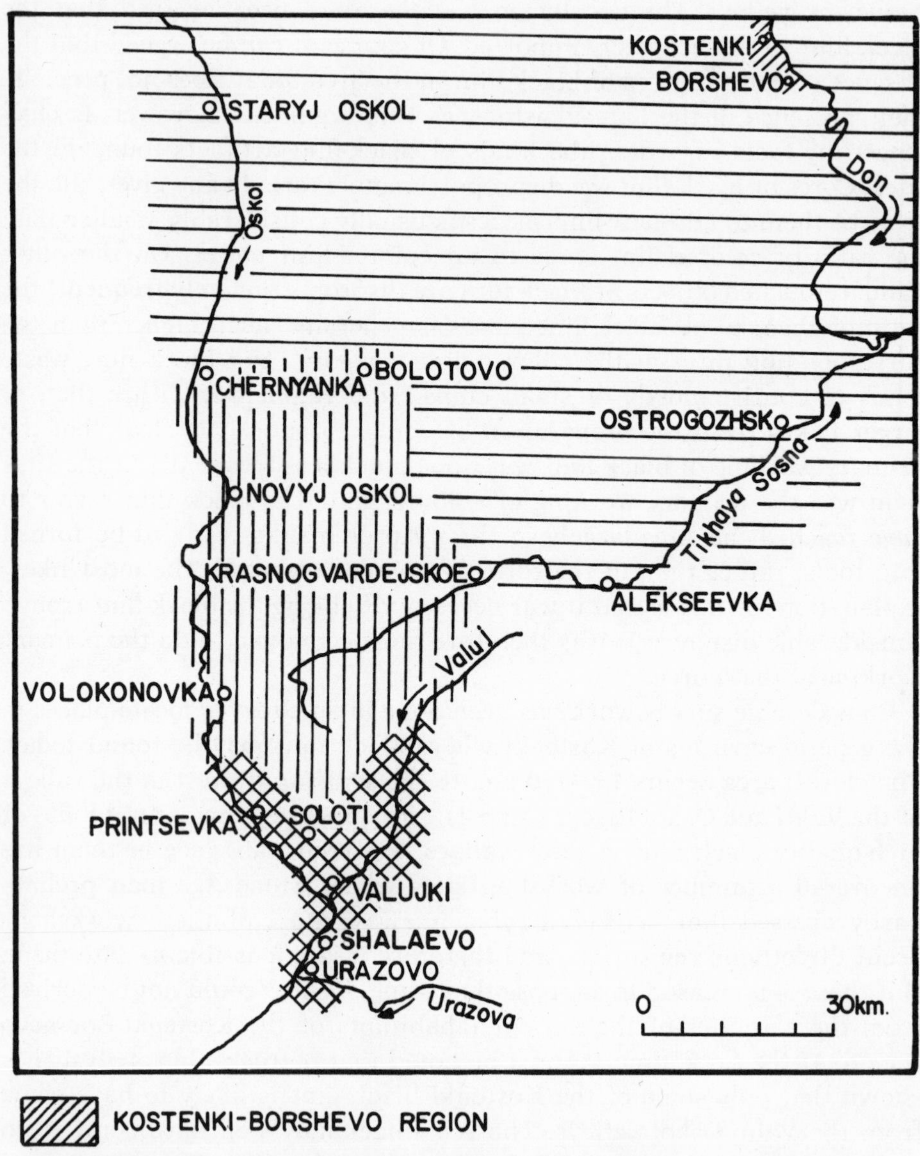

Map 4. Distribution of Different Varieties of Flint to the Southwest of Kostenki (redrawn after Boriskovskij 1963:Figure 119).

shevo region may be seen in the occurrence of fossil Black Sea shells in Kostenki I-3.

The possibility that flint and shells in the Kostenki-Borshevo area were derived from localities several tens or hundreds of kilometers distant raises the question of the evidence for relationships between the Kostenki-Borshevo sites and ones outside the region. At the moment such evidence is meager. The only Kostenki-Borshevo site which belongs beyond doubt to a culture represented elsewhere is Kostenki I-1. The resemblances between the artifact assemblage and features of this site and those from Avdeevo, 210 km. to the northwest, are striking. At present it is impossible to determine whether the two sites lie within an area which for a time at least was occupied entirely by the culture they represent, or whether one site is earlier than the other and eastward or westward movement is perhaps indicated.

In their assessment of the external affinities of the Kostenki-Borshevo sites, many Soviet investigators have been influenced by the *a priori* assumption that cultural development progressed along the same lines everywhere during the Upper Paleolithic. They have thus turned to the classic area for the study of the Upper Paleolithic, Southwestern France, and have sought to apply the names of its well-known Upper Paleolithic cultures (the Aurignacian, Solutrean, and Magdalenian) to the various Kostenki-Borshevo assemblages. It cannot be emphasized too strongly that this practice is completely unwarranted and functions only to obscure the pronounced originality of these assemblages. Rather than proving that the Upper Paleolithic cultures which have long been recognized in France were once spread over the whole of Europe, the Kostenki-Borshevo materials may be regarded as substantiating the contrary notion that one of the principal characteristics of the Upper Paleolithic was considerable variation in space.

It is safe to conclude that the late Würm occupants of the Kostenki-Borshevo region were successful hunters of big game. It is apparent that they used not only the meat of the animals they hunted, but also the skins and the bones (the latter for the manufacture of artifacts and also perhaps for construction and for fuel). They built structures and carried on many of their activities within them. The spectacular nature and size of some of the structural remnants suggest that some settlements at least were relatively permanent and included a fairly large number of people. Cultural activity was not restricted to a limited geographical area, but either through trade or actual movement, was extended over distances of several tens or even hundreds of kilometers. Evidence for what might be called spiritual life is apparent in the practice of burying the dead and in the presence of numerous art objects. All these cultural characteristics may be found in the Upper Paleolithic of other parts of Europe as well, but they are nowhere more clearly expressed than in the Kostenki-Borshevo region. It is this clarity plus the evidence for a distinctive cultural evolution in the Late Würm of the Don Valley which has made the Kostenki-Borshevo sites such a worthwhile object of study.

APPENDIX

TABLE A-1. The Chronology of Important Events in the History of Investigation of the Kostenki-Borshevo Sites

1879	Discovery and excavation of Level 1 of Kostenki I (I. S. Polyakov).
1881	Excavation of Level 1 of Kostenki I (A. I. Kel'siev).
1905	Discovery and excavation of Borshevo I (A. A. Spitsyn).
1915	Excavation of Level 1 of Kostenki I (S. A. Krukowski).
1922	Excavation of Level 1 of Kostenki I (S. N. Zamyatnin); excavation of Borshevo I (Zamyatnin); discovery of Borshevo II (P. A. Nikitin and S. N. Zamyatnin).
1923	Excavation of Level 1 of Kostenki I (P. P. Efimenko); discovery and excavation of Kostenki II (Efimenko and Zamyatnin); discovery of Kostenki III (Efimenko); excavation of Borshevo I (Efimenko and Zamyatnin); excavation of Borshevo II (Efimenko); discovery of Borshevo III (Efimenko).
1925	Excavation of Borshevo I (Efimenko); excavation of Borshevo II (Efimenko).
1926	Excavation of Level 1 of Kostenki I (Efimenko).
1927	Excavation of Kostenki II (Zamyatnin); excavation of Kostenki III (Zamyatnin); discovery and excavation of Kostenki IV (Zamyatnin); discovery of Streletskaya I (Zamyatnin).

TABLE A-1. (*Continued*)

1928	Excavation of Kostenki III (Efimenko); excavation of Kostenki IV (Zamyatnin); discovery of Kostenki V (Efimenko); discovery of Markina gora (= Kostenki XIV) (Efimenko); excavation of Streletskaya I (Efimenko).
1929	Excavation of Borshevo II (Efimenko).
1931	Excavation of Level 1 of Kostenki I (Efimenko).
1932	Excavation of Level 1 of Kostenki I (Efimenko).
1933	Excavation of Level 1 of Kostenki I (Efimenko).
1934	Excavation of Level 1 of Kostenki I (Efimenko); discovery of Kostenki X (= Anosovka I) (Efimenko).
1936	Excavation of Level 1 of Kostenki I (Efimenko); discovery of Tel'manskaya (= Kostenki VIII) (A. N. Rogachev); excavation of Borshevo II (P. I. Boriskovskij); excavation of Borshevo III (Efimenko).
1937	Excavation of Kostenki IV (Rogachev); excavation of Tel'manskaya (Efimenko); discovery of Kostenki IX (Efimenko); excavation of Streletskaya I (Rogachev).
1938	Excavation of Level 1 and establishment of Level 5 of Kostenki I (Rogachev); Excavation of Kostenki IV (Rogachev).
1948	Discovery and excavation of Levels 2, 3, and 4 of Kostenki I (Rogachev); discovery of Kostenki XIII (Rogachev).
1949	Excavation of Kostenki V (Rogachev); excavation of Tel'manskaya (Rogachev); discovery of Kostenki XII (Rogachev); excavation of Kostenki XIII (Rogachev); discovery of Rudkino (Rogachev).
1950	Discovery of Kostenki VII (Rogachev); excavation of Tel'manskaya (Rogachev); excavation of Kostenki XII.
1951	Excavation of various levels of Kostenki I (Rogachev); excavation of Kostenki VII (Rogachev); excavation of Kostenki X (Rogachev); discovery of Anosovka II (= Kostenki XI) (Rogachev); excavation of Kostenki XII (Rogachev); discovery of Gorodtsovskaya (= Kostenki XV) (Rogachev); discovery of Kostenki XVI (Rogachev).
1952	Discovery and excavation of Streletskaya II (= Kostenki VI) (Rogachev); excavation of Tel'manskaya (Rogachev); excavation of Kostenki XII (Rogachev); excavation of Gorodtsovskaya (Rogachev).
1953	Excavation of various levels of Kostenki I (Rogachev); excavation of Kostenki II (Boriskovskij); excavation of Kostenki VI (Rogachev); excavation of Kostenki VII (Rogachev); excavation of Anosovka I (Boriskovskij); excavation of Kostenki XII (Rogachev); discovery of Kostenki XVII (Boriskovskij); discovery of Kostenki XVIII (Rogachev).
1954	Excavation of Kostenki XII (Rogachev); excavation of Markina gora (Rogachev); excavation of Kostenki XVI (Rogachev and L. M. Tarasov).
1955	Excavation of Kostenki II (Boriskovskij); excavation of Kostenki XVII (Boriskovskij); excavation of Borshevo I (Rogachev).
1956	Excavation of Kostenki II (Boriskovskij); excavation of Anosovka II (Rogachev); discovery and excavation of Kostenki XIX (Boriskovskij); discovery of Kostenki XXI (N. D. Praslov).
1957	Excavation of Kostenki XIX (Boriskovskij); excavation of Kostenki XXI (Praslov).
1958	Excavation of Kostenki XIII (Bud'ko and Rogachev); excavation of Kostenki XXI (Praslov).
1960	Excavation of Anosovka II (Rogachev).
1961	Excavation of Anosovka II (Rogachev).
1965	Excavation of Anosovka II (Rogachev).

TABLE A-2. Comparison of Profiles through Deposits of the Second Terrace at Kostenki XVII (Don Valley) and at Kostenki XIV (Pokrovskij Ravine)

Kostenki XVII (from Velichko 1963:207–209)		*Kostenki XIV (from Velichko 1963:211–214)*	
	Depth from surface		*Depth from surface*
(1) Dark-grey, friable, porous loam (= "A" horizon of a chernozem) with blocky structure and containing occasional small fragments of chalk (up to 0.5 cm. across). Traces of crotowines (rodent tunnels) apparent. Color lighter below. Small tongues of sediment project into the lower-lying bed, the contact with which is wavy.	0.0–1.1 m.	(1) Humic horizon (= "A" horizon of soil).	0.0–1.1 m.
(2) Light-grey-brown, dense, porous, calcified loam (= "B" horizon of a chernozem) with vague, whitish, calcareous spots and numerous small, randomly distributed fragments of chalk (0.03–0.05 cm. across). Contact with lower-lying bed wavy.	1.1–1.8	(2) Light-grey-brown, porous loam with occasional fragments of chalk 0.3–0.5 cm. across. Color darkens with depth.	1.1–1.5m.
(3) Very light-grey-brown, dense, porous, calcified loam packed with calcareous particles and containing separate accumulations and lenses of poorly rounded chalk fragments (0.5–0.8 cm. across) as well as whitish, interdigitating, highly calcareous seams and lenses.	1.8–2.8 m.	(3) Porous, friable, light-grey-brown loam, saturated with calcareous particles. Poorly expressed tongues of light-colored loam up to 8 cm. long pass from "3" into "4" below.	1.5–1.6 m.
		(4) Porous, grey-brown loam containing a very large number of fragments of chalk, sometimes occurring in wavy lenses.	1.6–1.9 m.
		(5) Dense, porous, grey-brown loam (contains cultural horizon 1).	1.9–2.25 m.
(4) The "upper humic bed," comprised of loam containing three markedly humic strata "a," "b," and "c," separated by a weakly humic stratum (between "a" and "b") and a nonhumic stratum (between "b" and "c"). The humic layers in turn are made up of ragged, wavy lenses of loam (1–5 cm. thick) varying in humus content and in intensity of coloration. Moderately rounded chalk fragments are occasionally found in the bed. (The upper cultural horizon occurs in humic stratum "b" at a depth of 3.1–3.2 m. from the surface.)	2.8–3.6 m.	(6–9) The "upper humic bed," represented by bands and lenses of humic loam confined to three horizons separated by bands of nonhumic brown-grey and pale-yellow loam and of chalk pebbles. (Cultural level 2 was found in the middle of the "upper humic bed," level 3 at its base.)	2.25–4.00 m.

Kostenki XVII (from Velichko 1963:207–209)		*Kostenki XIV (from Velichko 1963:211–214)*	
	Depth from surface		*Depth from surface*
(5–6) Grey-brown, porous, moderately dense loam, laminated, especially in its lower part. Vague, wavy bands of darker, more friable loam are present, as are lenses (2–4 cm. thick) of moderately rounded chalk fragments (from 0.3–0.5 to 1–1.5 cm. across).	3.6–4.9 m.	(10) Dark-yellow-grey, porous loam with occasional rounded fragments of chalk 0.2–0.5 cm. across. Thin lenses of volcanic ash (1.0–1.5 cm. thick; 7–8 cm. long) occur in the body of the loam.	4.00–4.30 m.
(7) Grey-green volcanic ash (small particles of volcanic glass) present in a thin wavy stratum, sometimes broken up into separate lenses. Admixture of fine-grained sand.	4.9–4.95 m.		
(8) Grey-brown, moderately dense, porous loam, laminated. Sands of darker loam (2-3 cm. thick) are present as well as bands and lenses (3–4 cm. thick) of well-rounded chalk fragments (1–1.5 cm. across).	4.95–5.7 m.		
(9) Pale-grey, porous, slightly calcified loam with vague lenses of darker loam and moderately rounded fragments of chalk (0.5–0.6 cm. across). Passage to lower-lying bed gradual.	5.7–6.0 m.		
(10) The "lower humic bed," generally brownish, sometimes reddish due to diffusion of ochre from the (lower) cultural horizon which occurs at the very top of the bed at a depth of 6 m. from the surface. In the upper part of the bed occur lenses and bands (1–2 cm. thick) of well-rolled chalk fragments (0.3–0.5 cm. across), while in the lower part are found irregular spots of very strongly humic loam.	6.0–6.3 m.	(11) The "lower humic bed," comprised of lenses and bands of humic and nonhumic loam and containing occasional rounded fragments of chalk 0.2–0.4 cm. across. (Cultural level 4 occurred in the upper middle part of the "lower humic bed.")	4.30–5.00 m.
Below "10," a small pit with a borehole in its floor exposed an additional 5–6 m. of deposits including principally grey-brown loams and sandy loams, nearly horizontally bedded and containing bands and lenses of moderately and well-rolled chalk fragments and, near the bottom especially, strata of yellow-green sand. Near the bottom the appearance of phosphorites and greenish-yellow glauconitic sands is taken to mark the upper surface of the Upper Cretaceous sands which underlie the Second Terrace above the floodplain of the Don.		(12) Weakly porous, light-grey loam with rounded fragments of chalk 0.4–0.5 cm. across.	5.00–5.40 m.
		(13) Brown-grey, friable, sandy loam with occasional lenses of rounded fragments of chalk 0.4–0.5 cm. across. Bottom of "13" not exposed.	5.40–(6.20) m.

TABLE A-3. Comparison of Profiles through the First Terrace at Kostenki III and Borshevo II

Kostenki III (from Lazukov 1957a: 169–170)		*Borshevo II (from Sawicki 1965: 184–188)*	
	Depth from surface		*Depth from surface*
(1–2) "A" and "B" horizons of the Holocene chernozem.	0.0–1.75 m.	(1) Alluvium of the present-day Don, nonconformably overlying bed 2.	0.0–1.0 m.
(3) Porous, grey-brown, sandy loam with calcareous concretions, particularly numerous towards the bottom; some mollusc shells near the top. (The cultural horizon occurred within "3" at a depth of 2.–2.5 m. from the surface.)	1.75–3.1 m.	(2) Highly calcareous silt with a small admixture of sand. Color in the lower part brown, in the upper part greyish with rusty red and brown spots.	1.0–3.0 m.
(4) Dark-grey-brown loam, ferruginized and containing thin layers and lenses of yellow-grey quartz sand, especially towards the bottom, where the layers, 2–3 to 5–7 cm. thick, were oriented obliquely.	3.1–5.45 m.	(3) A black buried soil consisting of approximately 23 per cent silt, 3.6 per cent sand, and 73.4 per cent vegetational detritus. Contained the uppermost cultural horizon.	3.0–3.1 m.
(5) Yellow-grey and rusty yellow quartz sand, nonlaminated, becoming loamy at the base.	5.45–5.55 m.	(4) Dense, nonlaminated, light-brown silt, containing small fragments of chalk; highly calcareous in the upper part. The middle cultural horizon occurred at the top, the lowermost cultural horizon near the bottom.	3.1–?
(6) Grey-brown sandy loam, slimy and with ferruginized bands and manganese streaks; frequent layers of light-colored quartz sand.	5.55–5.80 m.	(5) Dense, porous, highly calcareous, nonlaminated, whitish-greyish sandy loam, occurring below the present-day level of the Don.	(depth not given)
(7) Grey, sandy loam, slimy and with ferruginized bands and blue-grey streaks.	5.80–6.10 m.		
(8) Laminated, light-colored, and rusty yellow sand; contained thin strata of grey-brown loam and dark-brown sand.	6.10–6.75 m.		
(9) Horizontally laminated dark-grey bluish sandy loam, slimy, with thin layers of quartz sand near the top.	6.75–7.55 m.		

TABLE A-4. General Description of the Human Remains from Kostenki-Borshevo Sites

KOSTENKI XVII, LOWER LEVEL (Second Terrace, lower humic bed)
One left third molar.

KOSTENKI XIV, HORIZON 3 (Second Terrace, upper humic bed)
Single individual, male, age 20–25 years. Skull and postcranial skeleton both well preserved; all permanent teeth in place and slightly worn; third molars less worn than others; all cranial sutures open; length of right femur 427 mm.—height of individual estimated to have been 160 cm.

KOSTENKI XV (Second Terrace, upper humic bed)
Single individual, male(?), age 5–6 years. Preservation poor; only the available portions of the cranium and mandible have been subjected to scientific study. These included a large portion of the mandible with some teeth in place, the parietals, large portions of the occipital, the temporals, the frontal, and parts of the maxillae with teeth. Most of the face, including the nasals and molars, and all of the base of the skull were absent. Some teeth had fallen out postmortem. Available for study in the upper jaw were the deciduous molars on both sides, the deciduous canine on the right side, and both first permanent molars, apparently about to erupt at time of death. The lower jaw contained all four deciduous molars, the deciduous left canine, the root of the deciduous left lateral incisor, the first permanent molars, also on the verge of eruption, and the crowns of the permanent central incisors, still deep within the maxillae. X-ray examination of the body of the mandible revealed the germs of both second molars. X-rays of the temporals showed that the tympanic antra were smaller than usual and bounded by sclerosed bone, indicating the owner had suffered from an inflammation of the mastoid process and middle ear.

KOSTENKI II (Second Terrace, grey-brown loam above the upper humic bed)
Single individual, male, age more than 50 years. Remains poorly preserved and fragmentary. The available parts of the skull include only a portion of the right half of the occipital, a large piece of the right temporal, two large pieces of the right parietal, a very small piece of the right frontal, the entire right malar, a part of the left malar, and most of the maxillae. Intact also were the body of the mandible and a portion of its ascending ramus. Limb bones too poorly preserved for description. Length of left femur 438 mm.; height of individual estimated to have been 165 cm. Cranial sutures almost completely obliterated. All teeth of the upper jaw in place except the third molars. The right third molar seems never to have erupted. Since the bone which would have held the left third molar was not preserved, it is not certain that this tooth also failed to develop. The lower, right third molar was clearly in place and strongly worn; but the portion of the lower jaw bearing the left third molar was incompletely preserved, making it impossible to determine whether this tooth had been present or not. All the other teeth of the lower jaw were present except the right canine and right incisors, apparently lost postmortem. Virtually all the available teeth were strongly worn, but without apparent caries.

KOSTENKI XVIII (intrusive into the upper Cretaceous sands making up the base of the Third Terrace)
Single individual, male (?), age 9–11 years. Postcranial skeleton too poorly preserved for description. Skull *lacks* parts of the basioccipital, a good part of the left, and virtually all of the right temporal, a sizeable portion of the right parietal, the left half of the frontal, the lower portion of the nasals, most of the right and all of the left malar, most of the maxillae (though almost all the maxillary teeth were present), and both rami on the mandible. All four permanent incisors, both permanent canines, and both first permanent molars were present in the lower jaw; however, the permanent canines, still in the process of eruption, were displaced bucally as a result of insufficient room between the lateral incisors and the fully erupted lower first

TABLE A-4. (*Continued*)

permanent molars. The lower left second permanent molar was in the process of eruption; its right-hand counterpart was visible in the body of the mandible. The upper jaw also provided an interesting picture. Both left permanent incisors were in place. Immediately behind the left lateral incisor was the fully erupted first permanent premolar, there being no canine or any place for it. The upper left first permanent molar was in place 1.5 cm. from the first premolar. The second upper left molar was beginning to erupt. Neither upper-right incisor was preserved, and at the place where one would have been expected, the right canine was the first permanent premolar, followed by the second and then a deciduous molar and the root of the broken-off, first permanent molar.

TABLE A-5. Some Measurements on Fossil Human Crania from Kostenki Sites

	Kostenki XV (extrapolated to an adult) (Yakimov 1957)	*Kostenki II (Debets 1955)*	*Kostenki XIV (Debets 1955)*	*Kostenki XVIII (extrapolated to an adult) (Debets 1961)*
BRAIN CASE				
Maximum length of the skull	198	195	179	194
Maximum width of the skull	142	140	128	150
Minimum width of the frontal	98	—	93	—
Maximum width of the frontal	117	—	107	—
Width of the occipital	103	—	99	—
Height of the skull from basion	137	135?	129	—
Cranial index	71.7	71.8 ?	71.5	77
Cranial capacity (Kochetkova 1965)	—	ca. 1500 cc.	1160–1170 cc.	—
FACIAL SKELETON				
Malar diameter	140	145	132	148
Height of the upper face	77	64	60	64
Width of the nose	26	24	27.1	—
Height of the nose	57	47	43.1	—

TOPICAL BIBLIOGRAPHY

Chapter 1. Introduction

General on the Pleistocene—Butzer (1964: Chapter 2); Emiliani et al. (1968); Flint (1965). General on Pleistocene prehistory—Howell (1965). On the earlier phases of Pleistocene prehistory in the USSR—Klein (1966a).

Chapter 2. The Cultural Remains of Pleistocene Man

On techniques of manufacturing stone tools—Bordes (1947). On Acheulean and Mousterian artifact types—Bordes (1961). On Upper Paleolithic artifact types—Sonneville-Bordes and Perrot (1954, 1955, 1965a,b). On statistical typology—Sackett (1966). On bone artifacts and the uses of Pleistocene-age artifacts—Semenov (1964).

Chapter 3. The History of Investigation of the Kostenki-Borshevo Sites

General—Beregovaya (1960:45–58); Rogachev (1957:9–14).

Chapter 4. The Geology of the Kostenki-Borshevo Sites

On sedimentological and geomorphological terms—Butzer (1964). On the geology of the Kostenki-Borshevo sites—Boriskovskij (1957); Grishchenko (1939, 1950, 1951, 1961); Gromov (1948: Chapter IV); Lazukov (1954, 1957a, 1957b, 1961); Moskvitin (1961); Rogachev (1957, 1961a,b); Sawicki (1965); Velichko (1961a,b,c; 1963). On radiocarbon dating—Butzer (1964:29–34). On radiocarbon dates from Kostenki-Borshevo sites—Cherdyntsev et al. (1965); Klein (1967); Rogachev (1966). On Würm Glacial stratigraphy and chronology—in the Netherlands and Denmark, van der Hammen et al. (1967); in Central Europe, Fink (1962). On geological dating of the Kostenki-Borshevo sites—Ivanova (1965:146–148; 1966:55–56).

Chapter 5. The Environment of Pleistocene Man in the Kostenki-Borshevo Region

General on the forest-steppe zone—Berg (1950:68–89); Mirov (1951:125–133). On pollen analysis—Butzer (1964: Chapter 16). On pollen data from Kostenki-Borshevo sites—on Kostenki I, Grichuk (1961:147–148); Grishchenko (1950:84–86); Lazukov (1957b:87–90); on Kostenki XV, Lazukov (1957b:90); on Kostenki XVII, Fedorova (1963); Velichko (1963:119); on Kostenki XIX, Velichko and Fedorova (1961); on Borshevo II, Sawicki (1965:186). On charcoal from Kostenki-Borshevo sites—Gromov (1948:307), Lazukov (1957b:91). On European Pleistocene Molluscan faunas—Ložek (1965). On molluscan fauna from Kostenki-Borshevo sites—Gromov (1948:207); Sawicki (1965:184–187). On the modern molluscan fauna of the USSR—Likhachev and Rammel'meier (1952). On European Pleistocene mammals—Thenius (1962). On the mammalian fauna from the Kostenki-Borshevo sites—general, Lazukov (1957b). On modern mammalian fauna in the USSR—Bobrinskij et al. (1944); Bobrinskij (1967). On general late Pleistocene environment in midlatitude Europe—Butzer (1964:Chapter 18); Frenzel (1959–1960).

Chapter 6. Human Remains from the Kostenki-Borshevo Sites

On Kostenki II—Debets (1955:45–48); Gerasimov (1964:152–154); Kochetkova (1965). On Kostenki XIV—Debets (1955:43–48); Gerasimov (1964:122–126), Kochetkova (1965). On Kostenki XV—Yakimov

(1957). On Kostenki XVII—Boriskovskij (1963:85). On Kostenki XVIII —Debets (1961).

Chapter 7. Sites in the Lower Humic Bed on the Second Terrace

On Kostenki I-Horizon 5—Rogachev (1950:69–74, 1953a:50–52, 1953b:11–12, 1957:36–41). On Streletskaya II(= Kostenki VI)—Rogachev (1957:97–106). On Kostenki XII-Horizon 3—Rogachev (1957:61–72). On Anosovka II(= Kostenki XI)-Horizon 5—Rogachev (1962b, 1966). On Sungir' cultural contents—Sukachev, Gromov, and Bader (1966). On Sungir' radiocarbon dates—Cherdyntsev et al. (1964:319); Klein (1967). On Polivanov Yar—Passek (1950). On Kostenki XVII-Horizon 2—Abramova (1962:27); Boriskovskij (1957:182–188, 1961a:422–426, 1963:80–124); Semenov (1964:77). On Tel'manskaya(= Kostenki VIII)-Horizon 4—Rogachev (1953c:155–156, 1957:58–60). On Markina gora(= Kostenki XIV)-Horizon 4—Rogachev (1957:85). On Kostenki V-Horizon 3—Rogachev (1951:28, 1957:93–96). On Kostenki XII-Horizon 2—Beregovaya (1960:49).

Chapter 8. Sites in the Upper Humic Bed on the Second Terrace

On Markina gora(= Kostenki XIV)-Horizon 3—Rogachev (1955a; 1957:81–85). On Tel'manskaya(= Kostenki VIII)-Horizon 3—Rogachev (1957c, 1957:56–58). On Gorodtsovskaya(= Kostenki XV)—Rogachev (1955a:30–31, 1957:106–118); Yakimov (1957:500–503). On Kostenki XII-Horizon 1B—Rogachev (1957:66). On Tel'manskaya(= Kostenki VIII)-Horizon 2—Litovchenko (1966); Rogachev (1953c:151–154, 1957:47–56). On Kostenki XVII-Horizon 1—Boriskovskij (1963:80–124). On Kostenki XVI—Tarasov (1961). On Markina gora(= Kostenki XIV)-Horizon 2—Abramova (1962:26–27); Rogachev (1955a, 1957:77–81). On Kostenki XII-1A—Rogachev (1957:61–66). On Anosovka II(= Kostenki XI)-Horizon 4—Rogachev (1961c). On Kostenki VII—Rogachev (1957:66–70). On Kostenki I-Horizon 4—Rogachev (1950:68–69, 1953a:50, 1953b:11, 1957:35).

Chapter 9. Sites Overlying the Upper Humic Bed on the Second Terrace

On Kostenki I-Horizon 3—Rogachev (1950:68, 1953a:46–50, 1953b:8–11, 1957:30–34). On Syuren' I—Klein (1965), Vekilova (1957). On Kostenki I-Horizon 2—Rogachev (1950:67–68, 1953a:44, 46, 1953b:5, 7, 8, 1957:27, 29, 30). On Kostenki I-Horizon 1—Abramova (1962:9–23, 1966:188–194); Bibikov (1959:259); Efimenko (1931a, 1931b, 1934a, 1934b:96–102, 1936, 1937, 1949, 1953:420–432, 1958); Grigor'ev (1967); Kel'siev (1882); Polyakov (1880:9–43); Rogachev (1950, 1953a,

1953b, 1957:19–27). On Kostenki V-Horizon 1—Efimenko (1953:422); Rogachev (1951:28, 1957:93–96). On Kostenki XIII—Bud'ko (1960); Rogachev (1957:16). On Avdeevo—Gvozdover (1953, 1961); Rogachev (1953d). On Tel'manskaya(= Kostenki VIII)-Horizon 1—Boriskovskij (1958:5); Efimenko (1940, 1953:314–317, 323–328); Efimenko and Boriskovskij (1957); Rogachev (1957:42–47). On Kostenki V-Horizon 2—Rogachev (1957:93–96). On Nietoperzowa Cave—Chmielewski (1965). On Kostenki II—Alpysbaev (1957, 1958, 1959); Boriskovskij (1955, 1956a, 1959b, 1963:7–79); Efimenko (1953:536); Zamyatnin (1929). On Anosovka II(= Kostenki XI)-Horizons 1 through 3—Rogachev (1953a:14–15, 1957:96–97, 1961c, 1962a,b, 1966). On Markina gora(= Kostenki XIV)-Horizon 1—Rogachev (1957:75–77). On Kostenki IX—Beregovaya (1960:50). On Anosovka I(= Kostenki X)—Beregovaya (1960:52). On Kostenki XVIII—Rogachev (1955a:31–32, 1957:15–16).

Chapter 10. Sites on the First Terrace

On Kostenki IV-Horizon 2—Efimenko (1953:484–485); Rogachev (1940a, 1940b, 1952, 1955b:89–151, 1957:91–93). On Kostenki IV-Horizon 1—Abramova (1961, 1962:23–26, 1966:194); Rogachev (1940a,b, 1955b:19–88, 1957:86–91); Semenov (1964:66, 98, 109). On Kostenki XIX—Boriskovskij (1959a, 1961a,b, 1963:125–165); Grigor'eva (1963). On Kostenki III—Boriskovskij (1963:157–165); Efimenko (1953:533–536). On Borshevo I—Efimenko (1953:315–317, 449–451); Vekilova (1953); Velichko (1961c:217). On Borshevo II-Horizons 1, 2, 3—Abramova (1962:27–28); Boriskovskij (1940, 1941); Efimenko (1953:319, 555–559, 612–614); Efimenko and Boriskovskij (1953). On Streletskaya I—Beregovaya (1960:53); Rogachev (1957:17). On Rudkino—Beregovaya (1960:45); Rogachev (1957:15). On Kostenki XXI—Boriskovskij (1963:125); Sawicki (1965:176–183).

Chapter 11. Summary and Conclusions

General on similarities and differences among the Kostenki-Borshevo sites—Rogachev (1957:119ff., 1961a). On the Mousterian/Upper Paleolithic changeover in the Kostenki-Borshevo region—Rogachev (1957:121, 123). On structural features in Mousterian sites—Chernysh (1965). On Stone Age diet, calories, etc.—Clark (1954); Madariaga (1962); Stokar (1958/59). On the Mousterian of European Russia—Klein (1966b). On heat treatment of flint—Crabtree and Butler (1964). On the isolation of charred seeds in sediments—Struever (1968). On Kostenki-Borshevo flint—Boriskovskij (1961e; 1963:166–191). On the general features of Upper Paleolithic culture—Sonneville-Bordes (1963).

REFERENCES CITED

Abbreviations

AN = Akademiya nauk (Academy of Sciences)
BKICP = Byulleten' Komissii po izucheniyu chetvertichnogo perioda (Bulletin of the Commission for Quaternary Research)
KSIA = Kratkie soobshcheniya Instituta arkheologii (Brief Communications of the Institute of Archeology)
KSIIMK = Kratkie soobshcheniya Instituta istorii material'noj kul'tury (Brief Communications of the Institute of the History of Material Culture)
MIA = Materialy i issledovaniya po arkheologii SSSR (Materials and Researches on the Archeology of the USSR)
MVSICP = Materialy vsesoyuznogo soveshchaniya po izucheniyu chetvertichnogo perioda (Materials of the All-Union Conference on Quaternary Research)
SA = Sovetskaya arkheologiya (Soviet Archeology)

SE = Sovetskaya etnografiya (Soviet Ethnography)
SPPVTE = Stratigraphiya i periodizatsiya paleolita Vostochnoj i Tsentral'noj Evropy (The Stratigraphy and Periodization of the Paleolithic of Central and Eastern Europe). Moscow, Nauka.
TKICP = Trudy Komissii po izucheniya chetvertichnogo perioda (Transactions of the Commission for Quaternary Research).

ABRAMOVA, Z. A.
1961 Animal Portrayals from the Paleolithic Site of Aleksandrovka (in Russian). *KSIA* 82:97–103.
1962 *Paleolithic Art on the Territory of the USSR* (in Russian). Moscow-Leningrad, AN SSSR.
1966 *Depictions of Man in the Paleolithic Art of Eurasia* (in Russian). Moscow-Leningrad, Nauka.

ALPYSBAEV, KH. A.
1957 The Flint Inventory of the Upper Paleolithic Settlement of Kostenki II (in Russian). *Izvestiya AN Kazakhskoj SSR,* seriya istorii, ekonomiki, filosofii i prava, 2(5) (Alma-Ata).
1958 The Paleolithic Dwelling at Kostenki II: Archeological and Ethnographic Parallels to It (in Russian). *Vestnik Akademii nauk Kazakhskoj SSR* 14(5):95–105.
1959 Some Results of the Study of Flint Tools (in Russian). *KSIIMK* 76:10–16.

BEREGOVAYA, N. A.
1960 Paleolithic Localities of the USSR (in Russian). *MIA* 181.

BERG, L. S.
1950 *Natural Regions of the USSR* (Translated from the Russian by Olga Adler Titelbaum). New York, The Macmillan Co.

BIBIKOV, S. N.
1959 Review of Efimenko (1958). *SA*(4):258–261.

BLOKHINA, N. G.
1964 The Analysis of Charcoal from Paleolithic Sites at Kostenki (in Russian). *KSIA* 97:64–65.

BOBRINSKIJ, N. A.
1967 *The Animal World and Nature of the USSR* (in Russian). Moscow, Nauka.

BOBRINSKIJ, N. A., B. A. KUZNETSOV, and A. P. KUZYAKIN
1944 *Index of the Mammals of the USSR* (in Russian). Moscow, Sovetskaya Nauka.

BORDES, F.
1947 Étude comparative des différentes techniques de taille du silex et des roches dures. *L'Anthropologie* 51:1–29.

1961 *Typologie du Paléolithique ancien et moyen.* Bordeaux, Publications de l'Institut de Préhistoire de l'Université de Bordeaux, Memoire No. 1.

BORISKOVSKIJ, P. I.

1940 Excavations of the Second Borshevo Upper Paleolithic Site in 1936 (in Russian). *SA* V:281–294.

1941 The Paleolithic Site of Borshevo II (Lower Cultural Level) (in Russian). *MIA* 2:37–60.

1955 Excavations of the Paleolithic Dwelling and Burial at the Site of Kostenki II in 1953 (in Russian). *SE* (1):39–42.

1956a Excavations of the Paleolithic Dwelling and Burial at Kostenki II in 1952 (in Russian). *SA* XXV:173–188.

1956b Belemnites in the Old Stone Age (in Russian). *Priroda* (11):113–114.

1957 Some Problems of the Development of the Upper Paleolithic Culture of the Russian Plain (in Russian). *MIA* 59:174–190.

1958 The Study of Paleolithic Dwellings in the Soviet Union (in Russian). *SA* (1):3–19.

1959a Excavations of the Paleolithic Site of Valukinskij (Kostenki XIX) in 1956 (in Russian). *KSIA* 73:57–63.

1959b Die jungpaläolithische Si^dlung mit dem Begrabnis eines Cromagnonmenschen in Kostjenki II am Don (UdSSR). *Anthropozoikum* 8:17–22.

1961a Some Paleolithic Settlements of Kostenki (Kostenki XVII and Valukinskij's Site) and Their Significance for the Periodization of the Upper Paleolithic of the Russian Plain (in Russian). *MVSICP* I:422–427.

1961b New Excavations of the Paleolithic Site of Valukinskij (Kostenki XIX) (in Russian). *KSIA* 84:30–31.

1961c Some Disputed Questions of the Periodization of the Upper Paleolithic of the Russian Plain (in Russian). *TKICP* 18:46–49.

1961d Statement in *TKICP* 18:187–189.

1961e Flint Workshops in the Vicinity of Valujki on the Oskol River (in Russian). *KSIA* 82:104–111.

1963 Essays on the Paleolithic of the Don Basin (in Russian). *MIA* 121.

BORISKOVSKIJ, P. I., and N. D. PRASLOV

1964 *The Paleolithic of the Dnepr Basin and the Priazov'e* (in Russian). Moscow-Leningrad, Academy of Sciences of the USSR.

BUD'KO, V. D.

1960 The Kel'sievskaya Site—A New Site of the Kostenki-Avdeevo Culture (in White Russian). *Vestsy Akademii navuk Belaruskaj SSR,* seriya gramadskykh navuk, 1:81–92.

BUTZER, K. W.

1964 *Environment and Archeology: An Introduction to Pleistocene Geography.* Chicago, Aldine.

CHERDYNTSEV, V. V., V. A. ALEKSEEV, N. V. KIND, V. S. FOROVA, and L. D. SULERZHITSKIJ

1964 Radiocarbon Dates of the Laboratory of the Geological Institute (GIN) AN SSSR (in Russian). *Geokhimiya* (4):315–324.

CHERDYNTSEV, V. V., V. A. ALEKSEEV, N. V. KIND, V. S. FOROVA, F. S. ZAVEL'SKIJ, L. D. SULERZHITSKIJ, and I. V. CHURIKOVA

1965 Radiocarbon Dates of the Laboratory of the Geological Institute (GIN) AN SSSR (in Russian). *Geokhimiya* (12):1410–1422.

CHERNYSH, A. P.

1965 The Lower and Middle Paleolithic of the Pridnestrov'e (in Russian). *TKICP* 25.

CHMIELEWSKI, W.

1965 Upper Paleolithic Cultures in Poland (in Russian). *SPPVTE,* pp. 15–23.

CLARK, J. G. D.

1954 *Excavations at Star Carr: an Early Mesolithic Site at Seamer, near Scarborough, Yorkshire.* Cambridge, Cambridge University Press.

CRABTREE, D. E., and B. R. BUTLER

1964 Notes on Experiments in Flint Knapping of Silica Minerals. *Tebiwa* 7(1):1–6.

DEBETS, G. F.

1955 Paleoanthropological Finds at Kostenki (in Russian). *SE* (1):43–53.

1961 The Skull from the Upper Paleolithic Burial in Pokrovskij Ravine (Kostenki XVIII) (in Russian). *KSIA* 82:120–127.

EFIMENKO, P. P.

1931a The Significance of Woman in the Aurignacian Epoch (in Russian). *Izvestiya Gosudarstvennoj Akademii istorii material'noj kul'tury* 11(3–4).

1931b Kostenki I (in Russian) (Results of the 1931 Expedition). *Soobshcheniya Gosudarstvennoj Akademii istorii material'noj kultury* (11–12):58–60.

1934a Results of Research at Kostenki (August–October 1933) (in Russian). *Problemy istorii dokapitalisticheskikh obshchestv Gosudarstvennoj Akademii istorii material'noj kultury* (4):64.

1934b Paleolithic Sites of the Eastern European Plain (in Russian). *Trudy II mezhdunarodnoj konferentsii Assotsiatsii po izucheniyu chetvertichnogo perioda Evropy* V:88–113.

1936 Some Results of the Study of Fossil Man in the USSR (1932–1935) (in Russian). *Materialy po chetvertichnomy periodu SSSR,* pp. 111–120.

1937 Excavations of a Paleolithic Site at Kostenki in 1934 (in Russian). *Trudy Sovestskoj sektsii Mezdunarodnoj assotsiatsii po izucheniyu chetvertichnogo perioda (INQUA)* (1): 265–271.

1940 A New Paleolithic Site at Kostenki (in Russian). *BKICP* 6–7: 46–48.

1949 From the Materials of the Paleolithic Settlement of Kostenki I, Dug-out A (in Russian). *SA* I: 113–126.

1953 *Prehistoric Society* (in Russian). Kiev, AN Ukrainskoj SSR.

1958 *Kostenki I* (in Russian). Moscow-Leningrad, AN SSSR.

EFIMENKO, P. P., and P. I. BORISKOVSKIJ

1953 The Paleolithic Site of Borshevo II (in Russian). *MIA* 39: 56–110.

1957 The Tel'manskaya Paleolithic Settlement (1937 Excavations) (in Russian). *MIA* 59: 191–234.

EMILIANI, C., et al.

1968 The Pleistocene Epoch and the Evolution of Man (with critiques). *Current Anthropology* 9(1): 27–47.

FEDOROVA, R. F.

1963 Natural Conditions in the Period of Habitation of Upper Paleolithic Man in the Region of the Village of Kostenki of Voronezh *Oblast'* (according to the Data of Spore-Pollen Analysis of the Deposits of the Site of Spitsyn—Kostenki XVII) (in Russian). Pp. 220–229 in Boriskovskij (1963).

FINK, J.

1962 Die Gliederung des Jungpleistozäns in Österreich. *Mitt. Geol. Ges. Wien* 54: 1–25.

FLINT, R. F.

1965 The Pliocene-Pleistocene Boundary. *GSA Special Paper* No. 84, pp. 497–533 (New York, Geological Society of America, Inc.).

FRENZEL, B.

1959/60 Die Vegetations- und Landschaftzonen Nord-Eurasiens während der letzten Eiszeit und während der postglazialen Wärmezeit. *Abhl. Akad. Wiss. Lit.* (Mainz), *Math.-Naturw.,* Kl. (1959), Nr. 13; (1960), Nr. 6.

GERASIMOV, M. M.

1964 *People of the Stone Age* (in Russian). Moscow, Nauka.

GRICHUK, V. P.

1961 The Geological Age of Archeological Sites Dated by Paleobotanical Materials (in Russian). *TKICP* 18: 146–156.

Grigor'ev, G. P.
1967 A New Reconstruction of the Above-Ground Dwelling of Kostenki I. *Current Anthropology* 8(4):344–349.

Grigor'eva, G. V.
1963 The Functional Determination of Tools from the Valukinskij Site (Kostenki XIX) (in Russian). *MIA* 121:192–200.

Grishchenko, M. N.
1939 Neogene and Quaternary Terraces of the Don (in Russian). *Byulleten' Moskovskogo obshchestva ispytatelej prirody*, nov. ser., XLVII, otd. geolog., XVII (6).
1950 The Paleogeography of the Kostenki-Borshevo Region in the Epoch of the Upper Paleolithic (in Russian). *KSIIMK* 31:75–88.
1951 An Attempt at the Geological Comparison of the Upper Paleolithic Sites of Avdeevo on the Sejm and Kostenki I (Polyakov's Site) on the Don (in Russian). *BKICP* 18:87–89.
1961 Statement in *TKICP* 18:210–213.

Gromov, V. I.
1948 The Paleontological and Archeological Basis of the Stratigraphy of the Continental Deposits of the Quaternary Period on the Territory of the USSR (in Russian). *Trudy Instituta geologicheskikh nauk AN SSSR*, Vyp. 64, geologicheskaya seriya, No. 17.

Gvozdover, M. D.
1953 The Working of Bone and the Bone Artifacts of the Avdeevo Site (in Russian). *MIA* 39:192–226.
1961 Specific Features of the Flint Inventory of the Avdeevo Paleolithic Site (in Russian). *KSIA* 82:112–119.

Hammen, T. van der, G. C. Maarleveld, J. C. Vogel, and W. H. Zagwijn
1967 Stratigraphy, Climatic Succession and Radiocarbon Dating of the Last Glacial in the Netherlands. *Geologie en Mijnbouw* 46(3):79–95.

Howell, F. Clark, and the Editors of Life
1964 *Early Man*. New York, Time, Inc.

Ivanova, I. K.
1965 *The Geological Age of Fossil Man* (in Russian). Moscow, Nauka.
1966 The Stratigraphy of the Upper Pleistocene of Central and Eastern Europe according to the Study of Loesses (in Russian). *Verkhnij Plejstotsen*, pp. 32–65. Moscow, Nauka.

Kel'siev, A. I.
1882 Paleolithic "Kitchen Debris" in the Village of Kostenki (in Russian). *Trudy Moskovskogo arkheologicheskogo obshchestva* 9(2) 154–179.

KLEIN, R. G.
1965 The Middle Paleolithic of the Crimea. *Arctic Anthropology* 3(1): 34–68.
1966a Chellean and Acheulean on the Territory of the Soviet Union: A Critical Review of the Evidence as Presented in the Literature. *American Anthropologist* 68(2,2):1–45.
1966b The Mousterian of European Russia. Unpublished Ph.D. Dissertation, University of Chicago.
1967 Radiocarbon Dates on Occupation Sites of Pleistocene Age in the USSR. *Arctic Anthropology* 4(2):223–226.

KOCHETKOVA, V. I.
1965 The Cranial Capacity of the Paleolithic Man from the Site of Markina gora (in Russian). *Voprosy antropologii* 20:99–101.

LAZUKOV, G. I.
1954 The Geological-Geomorphological Characterization of the Kostenki-Borshevo Region and Natural Conditions at the Time of Habitation of Upper Paleolithic Man (in Russian). *Materialy po paleogeografii* I:89–148.
1957a The Geology of the Sites of the Kostenki-Borshevo Region (in Russian). *MIA* 59:135–173.
1957b Natural Conditions during the Upper Paleolithic in the Kostenki-Borshevo Region (in Russian). *SA* (3):84–104.
1961 The Relative Age of Sites of the Kostenki-Borshevo Region (according to Geological-Geomorphological Data) (in Russian). *MVSICP* I:405–414.

LIKHACHEV, I. M., and E. S. RAMMEL'MEIER
1952 *Terrestrial Molluscs of the Fauna of the USSR*. Translated from the Russian by Dr. Y. Lengy and Z. Krauthamer of the Israel Program for Scientific Translations. Zoologicheskij Instituta AN SSSR.

LITOVCHENKO, L. M.
1966 The Group of Dwellings of the Second Cultural Level of the Tel'manskaya Site (in Russian). *Voprosy istorii i arkheologii,* otdelenie obshchestvennykh nauk AN Byelorusskoj SSR, pp. 298–305.

LOŽEK, V.
1965 Das Problem der Lössbildung und die Lössmollusken. *Eiszeitalter und Gegenwart* 16:61–75.

MADARIAGA, B.
1962 Analisis paleontologico de la fauna terrestre y marina de la Cueva de la Chora. *Excavaciones arqueologicas en España* 26:51–74.

MIROV, N. T.
1951 *Geography of Russia*. New York, John Wiley and Sons, Inc.

MOSKVITIN, A. I.
1961 Statement in *TKICP* 18:218–222.
PASSEK, T. S.
1950 Tripol'e Settlements on the Dnestr (in Rusian). *KSIIMK* 32:40–57.
POLYAKOV, I. S.
1880 An Anthropological Journey into Central and Eastern Russia (in Russian). *Zapiski Akademii nauk* (St. Petersburg) 37(1):1–81.
PRASLOV, N. D.
1964 The Gmelin Site at Kostenki (in Russian). *KSIA* 97:59–63.
ROGACHEV, A. N.
1940a The Aleksandrovka Paleolithic Site (Kostenki IV) (in Russian). *BKICP* 6–7:48–50.
1940b The Paleolithic Settlement of Kostenki IV (in Russian). *KSIIMK* 4:36–41.
1950 The Lower Horizon of Cultural Remains of Kostenki I (in Russian). *KSIIMK* 31:64–74.
1951 The Lower Level of Cultural Remains of the Tel'manskaya Site at Kostenki (in Russian). *KSIIMK* 37:23–29.
1952 Remains of a Prehistoric Dwelling of Upper Paleolithic Time Near the Village of Kostenki on the Don (in Russian). *SA* XVI:100–119.
1953a New Data on the Stratigraphy of the Upper Paleolithic of the Eastern European Plain (in Russian). *MIA* 39:39–55.
1953b Excavations of Kostenki I (in Russian). *KSIIMK* 51:3–15.
1953c Some Problems of the Chronology of the Upper Paleolithic (in Russian). *SA* 17:149–160.
1953d Investigation of the Remains of a Prehistoric Settlement of Upper Paleolithic Time Near the Village of Avdeevo on the Sejm in 1949 (in Russian). *MIA* 39:137–191.
1955a A Burial of the Old Stone Age at the Site of Kostenki XIV (Markina gora) (in Russian). *SE* (1):29–38.
1955b The Aleksandrovka Settlement of the Old Stone Age Near the Village of Kostenki on the Don (in Russian). *MIA* 45.
1957 The Multilevel Sites of the Kostenki-Borshevo Region on the Don and the Problem of the Development of Culture in the Upper Paleolithic Epoch on the Russian Plain (in Russian). *MIA* 59:9–134.
1961a The Relative Antiquity of the Upper Paleolithic Sites of the Central Russian Upland (in Russian). *MVSICP* I:397–404.
1961b Statement in *TKICP* 18:194–197.
1961c Anosovka II—A New Multilevel Site at Kostenki (in Russian). *KSIA* 82:86–96.
1962a The Anosovka-Mezin Type of Paleolithic Dwellings on the Russian Plain (in Russian). *KSIA* 92:12–17.

1962b Schematic Sculptures of Animals from Kostenki (Anosovka II) (in Russian). Pp. 78–80 in Abramova (1962).

1966 Excavations of the Paleolithic at Kostenki (in Russian). *Arkheologicheskie otkrytiya 1965 goda* (ed. B. A. Rybakov), pp. 40–42. Moscow, Nauka.

SACKETT, J. R.

1966 Quantitative Analysis of Upper Paleolithic Stone Tools. *American Anthropologist* 68(2,2):356–394.

SAWICKI, L.

1965 Problems of the Stratigraphy and Geological Age of the Paleolithic Sites of Kostenki and Borshevo (in Russian). *SPPVTE*, pp. 166–199.

SEMENOV, S. A.

1964 *Prehistoric Technology* (translated from the Russian by M. W. Thompson). New York, Barnes and Noble.

SONNEVILLE-BORDES, D. DE

1963 Upper Paleolithic Cultures in Western Europe. *Science* 142:347–355.

SONNEVILLE-BORDES, D. DE, and J. PERROT

1954, 1955, 1956a, 1956b Lexique typologique du Paléolithique supérieur. Outillage lithique. *Bulletin de la Société préhistorique française* 51:327–335; 52:76–79; 53:408–412; 53:547–560.

STOKAR, WALTER VON

1958/59 Über die Ernährung in der Eiszeit. *Quartär* 10/11:59–62.

STRUEVER, S.

1968 Flotation Techniques for the Recovery of Small-Scale Archeological Remains. *American Antiquity* 33(3):353–362.

SUKACHEV, V. N., V. I. GROMOV, and O. N. BADER

1966 The Sungir' Upper Paleolithic Site (in Russian). *Trudy geologicheskogo Instituta AN SSSR* 162.

TARASOV, L. M.

1961 The Uglyanskaya Paleolithic Site (Kostenki XVI) (in Russian). *KSIA* 85:38–47.

THENIUS, E.

1962 Die Grosssäugetiere des Pleistozäns von Mitteleuropa. *Zeitschrift für Säugetierkunde* 27:65–83.

VEKILOVA, E. A.

1953 The Paleolithic Site of Borshevo I (in Russian). *MIA* 39:111–136.

1957 The Site of Syuren' I and Its Place among the Paleolithic Sites of the Crimea and Neighboring Localities (in Russian). *MIA* 59:235–523.

VELICHKO, A. A.

1961a The Possibilities of Geological Comparison of the Regions of

Paleolithic Sites in the Basins of the Desna, Don, and on the Territory of Czechoslovakia (in Russian). *TKICP* 18:50–61.

1961b Statement in *TKICP* 18:215–218.

1961c *The Geological Age of the Upper Paleolithic of the Central Regions of the Russian Plain* (in Russian). Moscow, AN SSSR.

1963 Spitsyn's Site (Kostenki XVII) and Its Significance for the Solution of Basic Questions of the Geology of the Kostenki-Borshevo Region (in Russian). *MIA* 121:201–219.

VELICHKO, A. A., and R. V. FEDOROVA

1961 The Conditions of Occurrence of the Paleolithic Site of Valukinskij (Kostenki XVII) (in Russian). *KSIA* 84:32–37.

YAKIMOV, V. P.

1957 The Upper Paleolithic Child from the Burial at the Gorodtsovskaya Site at Kostenki (in Russian). *Sbornik Muzeya antropologii i etnografii* 17:500–529.

ZAMYATNIN, S. N.

1929 Expedition for the Study of Paleolithic Cultures in 1927 (in Russian). *Soobshcheniya Gosudarstvennoj Akademii istorii material'noj kul'tury* II:209–214.

INDEX

Abramova, Z. A., 241, 242
Acheulean "culture," 23
Aleksandrovka (= Aleksandrovskaya)
(*see* Kostenki IV)
Alleroed Interstadial, 47, 49, 59
Alluvial deposits (defined), 34
Alpysbaev, Kh. A., 242
Amersfoort Interstadial, 47
Anosovka I (= Kostenki X), 161
Anosovka II (= Kostenki XI)
horizon 1A
artifact inventory, 158
features, 153, 157
horizon 1B, 161
horizon 2
artifact inventory, 159–160
features, 159
Anosovka II (*continued*)
horizon 3
artifact inventory, 159
features, 158
horizon 4, 107–108
horizon 5, 76
"Anvil" (defined), 9
Artifacts
bone, types, 21–22
functions, 18, 20
general definition, 8
stone, types, 8–20
Aurignacian "culture," 229
Avdeevo, 140–141, 229
Awls (bone)
definition, 21

Awls (*continued*)
  occurrence in sites, 79, 83, 97, 106, 107, 116, 123, 144, 154, 168, 179, 190, 200, 201, 206, 209

Backed blade (*see* Blade, backed)
Backed bladelet, 15
Backed point (*see* Point, backed)
Bader, O. N., 241
Baton de commandement, 122
"Beads " (*see* "Pendants")
Beregovaya, N. A., 240, 241, 242
Berg, L. S., 240
Bibikov, S. N., 120, 241
Biface (= "hand-axe"), defined, 18
Biryuchij log (*see* Kostenki IX)
Blade
  backed (defined), 13
  with continuous retouch along one or both edges (defined), 13
  denticulate (defined), 17
  general (defined), 15
  notched, 17
Bladelet, backed (defined), 15
Blank (defined), 13n
Bobrinskij, N. A., 238
Boelling Interstadial, 47, 49, 59
Bordes, F., 9, 11, 13, 18n, 239
Borer (defined), 17
Boriskovskij, P. I., 30, 102, 150, 232, 240, 241, 242
Borshevo I (= Kuznetsov log)
  artifact inventory, 202–203
  discovery, 30
  features, 201–202
Borshevo II
  charcoal, 59
  geology, 45, 234
  horizon 1, 208–209, 210
  horizon 2, 204, 207–209
  horizon 3, 204, 206–209
  pollen, 59
Borshevo III (= Vishunov log), 161
Broerup Interstadial, 47
Bruin, C. de, 29
Bud'ko, V. D., 232, 242
Bulb of percussion (defined), 9
Burials (*see* Graves)
Burin
  on the corner of a broken blade, 14
  dihedral, 14
  flat, 15
  general definition, 14
  on a lateral truncation, 14
  mixed multiple, 15
  multifaceted, 14
  multiple, 15
  on a retouched truncation, 14
  types (defined), 14–15
Burin spall (defined), 14
Butler, B. R., 242
Butt (of a flake) (defined), 9
Butzer, K. W., 239, 240

Caucasus Mountains, late Pleistocene volcanic activity, 38, 41
Central Russian Upland, 36
"Chalk" (defined), 38
Châtelperron Point (*see* Point, backed)
Cherdyntsev, V. V., 240, 241
Chernozem (soil), 38
Chernysh, A. P., 242
Chmielewski, W., 242
Chopper (defined), 18
Chopping-tool (defined), 18
Clark, J. G. D. (Grahame), 221, 242
Colluvial deposits (= colluvium)
  definition, 34
  occurrence in the Kostenki-Borshevo Region, 38–39
Composite tools (defined), 18
Core (= nucleus) (defined), 9
Core-tools (defined), 18
Cortex (defined), 9
Crabtree, D. E., 242
Cretaceous Period, 38n
Cro-Magnon peoples, xxii
Cultural horizon (or level) (defined), 26

Debets, G. F., 238, 239
Denekamp Interstadial, 47
Denticulate (defined), 13
Denticulate blade (*see* Blade, denticulate)
Dnepr (= Riss) Glaciation, 38

Dnepr/Valdaj (= Eem) Interglacial, 38
Devonian Period, 38n
Dorsal surface (of a flake) (defined), 9
"Dwelling ruins" (*see* "House ruins")

Efimenko, P. P., 30, 114, 118, 120, 121, 141, 231, 232, 241, 242
Emiliani, C., 239
End-scraper, 13
Ergen' deposits, 38

Features (defined), 7–8
Fedorova, R. F., 59, 240
Figurines (= statuettes)
  animal (occurrence in sites), 139–140, 161, 186, 190
  general definition, 21
  human (occurrence in sites), 129, 139, 153, 154, 186, 190
Fink, J., 240
Flake (defined), 9
Flint, R. F., 239
Font-Yves point (*see* Point, backed)
Frenzel, B., 240

Gagarino, 30
Gerasimov, M. M., 240
Glinishche (*see* Kostenki III)
Gmelin, S. G., 29
Gmelinskaya (*see* Kostenki XXI)
Gontsy, 29
Gorodtsovskaya (= Kostenki XV = Gushchinskaya)
  artifact inventory, 97–98
  features, 92–96
  human remains, 236
  pollen, 58
Graves (= burials)
  Gorodtsovskaya, 94, 96
  Kostenki II, 150–151
  Kostenki XVIII, 164
  Markina Gora-3, 90
Gravette point (*see* Point, backed)
Grichuk, V. P., 240
Grigor'ev, G. P., 121, 241
Grigor'eva, G. V., 242
Grinding stones (defined), 20
Grishchenko, M. N., 30, 240
Gromov, V. I., 240
Ground stone artifacts
  definition, 20
  occurrence in sites, 186
Gushchinskaya (*see* Gorodtsovskaya)
Gvozdover, M. D., 242

Hammen, T. van der, 240
Hammerstone (defined), 9
"Hand-axe," 18
"Headbands," 123, 126, 128
Hengelo Interstadial, 47
Hide burnisher (*see* Polishers)
Holocene, 2
Hominidae, 1, 4
Homo sapiens, 71
  neanderthalensis (= Neanderthal man), 71, 72
  sapiens, 24, 71, 72
"House ruins"
  Anosovka II-1A, 153, 157
  Anosovka II-2, 159
  Borshevo I, 201–202
  Gorodtsovskaya, 92
  Kostenki I-1, 114–121
  Kostenki I-3, 112
  Kostenki I-5, 76
  Kostenki II, 146, 150
  Kostenki IV-1, 180, 181–186
  Kostenki IV-2, 170, 171–177
  Mousterian, 216
  Tel'manskaya-1, 141–143
  Tel'manskaya-2, 99, 101
  Tel'manskaya-3, 91
Howell, F. C., 237
Human remains
  Gorodtsovskaya, 236
  Kostenki II, 236
  Kostenki XVII-2, 236
  Kostenki XVIII, 236–237
  Markina Gora-3, 236
"Humic beds" (occurrence in Kostenki-Borshevo), 41

Il'skaya, 224–225
Ivanova, I. K., 240

Karacharovo, 29
Kel'siev, A. I., 231, 241
Kel'sievskaya (*see* Kostenki XIII)

Kiik-Koba, 224–225
"Kitchen debris" (defined), 21
Klein, R. G., 239, 240, 241, 242
Kochetkova, V. I., 240
Kostenki I (= Polyakov's site)
  horizon 1
    artifact inventory, 122–140
    features, 114–121
  horizon 2, 112, 116
  horizon 3
    artifact inventory, 113
    features, 112
  horizon 4, 108
  horizon 5
    artifact inventory, 79
    features, 76
  pollen, 58
Kostenki II (= Zamyatninskaya)
  artifact inventory, 153–155
  features, 146, 150–151, 153
  human remains, 236
Kostenki III (= Glinishche)
  artifact inventory, 199–201
  geology, 235
Kostenki IV (= Aleksandrovka = Aleksandrovskaya)
  horizon 1
    artifact inventory, 186–193
    features, 180, 181–186
  horizon 2
    artifact inventory, 175–179
    features, 170, 171–177
Kostenki V
  geology, 42–45
  horizon 1, 140
  horizon 2, 145
  horizon 3, 84
Kostenki VI (*see* Streletskaya II)
Kostenki VII (= Kostenki XII-1C = Sal'kovskaya), 108
Kostenki VIII (*see* Tel'manskaya)
Kostenki IX (= Biryuchij log), 161
Kostenki X (*see* Anosovka I)
Kostenki XI (*see* Anosovka II)
Kostenki XII (= Volkovskaya = Kvasovskaya)
  horizon 1A, 107
  horizon 1B, 97–98
  horizon 1C (*see* Kostenki VII)
Kostenki XII (*continued*)
  horizon 2, 84
  horizon 3, 79
Kostenki XIII (= Kel'sievskaya)
  artifact inventory, 123–124
  features, 139
Kostenki XIV (*see* Markina Gora)
Kostenki XV (*see* Gorodtsovskaya)
Kostenki XVI (= Uglyanskaya = Uglyanka)
  artifact inventory, 106
  features, 102, 104
Kostenki XVII (= Spitsynskaya)
  geology, 233–234
  horizon 1
    artifact inventory, 104
    features, 102
  horizon 2
    artifact inventory, 82–84
    features, 81
    human remains, 236
  pollen, 58–59
Kostenki XVIII (= Pokrovskij log = Vorontsovskoe)
  features, 164–165
  human remains, 236–237
Kostenki XIX (= Valukinskij's site)
  artifact inventory, 198–200
  features, 193–198
  pollen, 59
Kostenki XXI (= Gmelinskaya), 203
Kostenki-Avdeevo "culture," 140
Kostenki-Borshevo Region
  Late Pleistocene environment (summary), 70
  locations of sites, 25–26, 224
  modern setting, 51–52
  Upper Paleolithic
    duration of occupation, 215
    group size, 220–224
    ideology, 226
    subsistence, 216–217
Kostenki-Borshevo sites
  diversity in contents, 213–215
  external relationships, 229
  geological age, 47–49
  geology, 36–45
  history of discovery, 26–31, 232
  human remains, 72–74, 236–237

Kostenki-Borshevo sites (*continued*)
locations, 25–26, 224
mammalian remains, 65–69
molluscan remains, 62–65
non-locally available flint, 85, 108, 164, 212, 227–229
pollen data, 53–54
radiocarbon dates, 46
Kostenki knives
definition, 17
occurrence in sites, 120
Kostenki points, 121–122, 140–141
Kostenki-Streletskaya "Culture" (= Kostenki-Sungir' "culture"), xxxiii, 76, 81, 85, 107, 108, 158
Kostenki-Sungir' "culture" (*see* Kostenki-Streletskaya "culture")
Kostensk (= Kostenki), 29
Krukowski, S. A., 231
Kuznetsov log (*see* Borshevo I)

Lazukov, G. I., 30, 66, 240, 241
Leaf-shaped points (*see* Points, leaf-shaped)
Likachev, I. M., 240
Litovchenko, L. M., 101, 241
Loam (defined), 34
Loess (defined), 35
Ložek, V., 65, 240

Madariaga, B., 242
Maglemosian, 221
Markina Gora (= Kostenki XIV)
geology, 233–234
horizon 1, 161
horizon 2
artifact inventory, 107
features, 106
horizon 3
artifact inventory, 92
features, 89–90
human remains, 236
horizon 4, 84
"Marl" (defined), 38
"Mattocks" (bone), 122, 123, 204, 206, 209
"Medallions," 139
Middle Paleolithic (*see* Mousterian "culture")
Mikulino (= Eem) Interglacial, 38
Mirov, N. T., 238
Moraine (*see* Till)
Moskvitin, A. I., 240
Mousterian "culture," 23
bearers, 71
"house ruins," 216
replacement by Upper Paleolithic, xxi, 85, 215, 216

Neanderthal man 71, 72
Needles (bone)
definition, 21
occurrence in sites, 107, 123, 126, 209
Nietoperzowa Cave (Jerzmanowice), 145–146
Nikitin, P. A., 231
Notch (defined), 11–12
Notched blade, 17
Nucleus (= Core), 9

Occupation horizon (or level) (defined), 26
Oldowan "culture," 23

"Paddle-shaped shovels," 96–98
Particle grades (or sizes), 33–34
Passek, T. S., 241
Paudorf (= Stillfried B) Interstadial, 48, 49
"Pendants" (*includes* "Beads")
definition, 21
occurrence in sites, 83, 92, 97, 101, 116, 158, 179, 193, 200, 202–203, 209
Périgord, xxii
Perrot, J., 239
Peter the Great, 29
Pieces with double truncation (defined), 17
Pincevent, xxv
Pleistocene, 1–4
Points (types defined)
backed
Châtelperron, 15
Gravette, 15
Font-Yves, 15

Points (*continued*)
bone, 21
on a flake, 11
Kostenki, 121–122, 140–141
shouldered, 17
stemmed (= tanged), 17
Pokrovskij log (*see* Kostenki XVIII)
Polishers (bone)
definition, 21
occurrence in sites, 83, 101, 107, 116, 123, 125–126, 144, 154, 179, 190
Polivanov yar, 81
Pollen analysis, 52–53
Pollen diagram (defined), 53
Pollen spectrum (defined), 53
Polyakov, I. S., 29, 231, 241
Polyakov's Site (*see* Kostenki I)
Praslov, N. D., 232

Radiocarbon dating, 46–47
Rammel'meier, E. S., 240
Retouch (defined), 11
Rogachev, A. N., 30, 76, 81, 89, 92, 99, 121, 141, 143, 153, 171, 206, 232, 240, 242
Rudkino, 210

Sackett, J., 18n, 239
Sal'kovskaya (*see* Kostenki VII)
Sawicki, L., 38, 240, 242
Semenov, S. A., 20, 84, 121, 239, 241, 242
"Shaft-straightener" (= baton de commandement), 122
Shouldered point, 17
Side-scraper (defined), 11
Sites (types defined)
primary, 26
secondary, 26
surface, 26
Soil (defined), 35
Solifluction
defined, 35
occurrence in the Kostenki-Borshevo region, 41
Solutrean "culture," 229
Sonneville-Bordes, D. de, 18n, 239, 242
Spitsyn, A. A., 29, 231
Spitsynskaya (*see* Kostenki XVII)
Splintered (= battered) pieces (defined), 17–18
Star Carr, 221
Starosel'e, 224–225
Statuettes (*see* Figurines)
Stemmed (= tanged) points, 17
Stillfried A (soil complex), 47
Stillfried B (*see* Paudorf)
Stokar, W. von, 242
Stream terraces
definition, 36
occurrence in Kostenki-Borshevo region, 39–45
Streletskaya I, 210
Streletskaya II (= Kostenki VI), 79
Striking platform (defined), 9
Struever, S., 242
Sukachev, V. N., 241
Sungir', 81

Tambov Lowland, 36
Tarasov, L. M., 101, 102, 232, 241
Tel'manskaya (= Kostenki VIII)
horizon 1
artifact inventory, 143–145
features, 141, 143
horizon 2
artifact inventory, 101
features, 99–101
horizon 3
artifact inventory, 92
features, 91
horizon 4
artifact inventory, 84
features, 84
Thenius, E., 240
Till (= moraine)
definition, 35
occurrence in the Kostenki-Borshevo region, 38
Truncated blade or flake (*see also* Pieces with double truncation) (defined), 15

Uglyanskaya (= Uglyanka) (*see* Kostenki XVI)
Upper Paleolithic "Culture" (*see also* Kostenki-Borshevo Region, Upper Paleolithic), 23–24

Valdaj (= Würm) Glacial, xxiii, 38
Valukinskij's site (*see* Kostenki XIX)
Vekilova, E. A., 241, 242
Velichko, A. A., 30, 240, 242
Ventral surface (of a flake) (defined), 9
Vishunov log (*see* Borshevo III)
Volcanic ash (occurrence in the Kostenki-Borshevo region), 38, 41
Volkovskaya (*see* Kostenki XII-1A and 1B)
Vorontsovskoe (*see* Kostenki XVIII)

Weathering zone (*see also* Soil), 35

Yakimov, V. P., 240, 241

Zamyatnin, S. N., 30, 231, 232, 242
Zamyatninskaya (*see* Kostenki II)